Conceived, written, typeset, illustrated, and

designed by Andrew R. Gallimore. Tokyo, 2022.

Strange Worlds Press, July 2022. First edition.

ISBN: 978-1-7391101-0-9

Reality Switch Technologies.

リアリティスイッチ技術

Psychedelics as Tools for the Discovery
and Exploration of New Worlds.

Contents.

現実管理課

現実
制御学
研究所

東京

現実制御学研究所、東京

諸事万端は幻想です

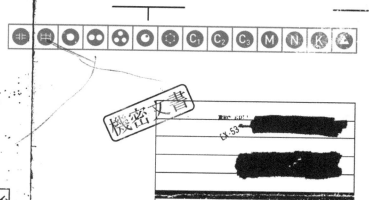

REC EPI

EX-53

<XXXXXX_3489_004_AO>

リアリティ
スイッチ

Chapter 1: Other Worlds

別世界

「ベツセカイ」

"It's a very salutary thing to realise that the rather dull universe in which most of us spend most of our time is not the only universe there is."

Aldous Huxley

現実△
制御学
研究所

2QAM5Q92

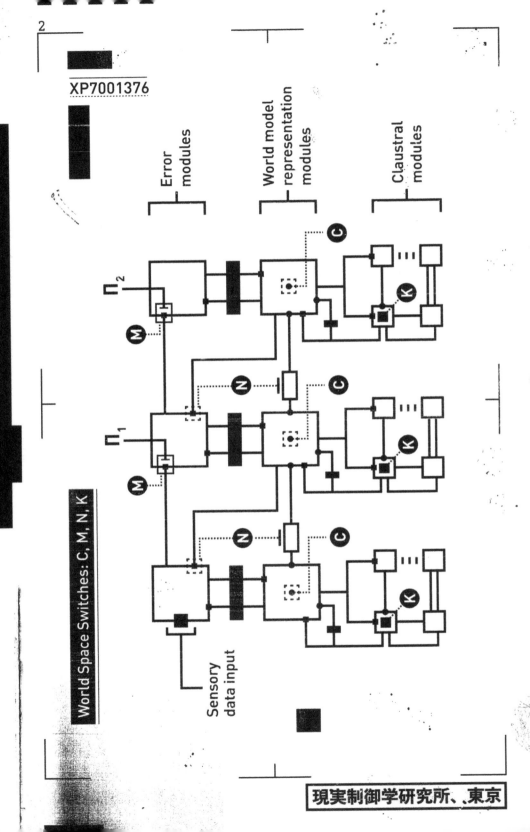

World Space Switches: C, M, N, K

Error modules

World model representation modules

Claustral modules

Π_2

Π_1

Sensory data input

現実制御学研究所、東京

From the moment you're dragged naked, bloodied, screaming from your mother's womb, and as the soft warm darkness and muffled vibrations suddenly give way to bright lights, rich colours, and a crisply popping soundscape, you find yourself sliding irreversibly into a bewilderingly strange and complex structure that will cloak and immerse you from that day forward: a world. To be born is to be thrown into a world — the irrevocably subjective and private reality within which each of us lives out each of our lives.

Indeed, the existence within a world defines one's entire life — without a subjective world within which to live, there can be no meaningful life.

Switch off the machines. ▮▮▮▮▮▮▮▮▮▮▮▮▮▮▮▮▮▮▮▮▮▮▮▮▮▮

For most, the normal waking world of cities, mountains, rivers, and rain is the only world they will ever know. But, since ancient times, humans have recognised that certain substances plucked from the environment can be used to stimulate the brain and change the nature of the subjective world. For at least 2,000 years, the Huichol people of Mexico have used the *peyote* cactus to gain access to otherwise invisible landscapes revealed in stark geometric beauty by the mescaline molecule residing within this most sacred of succulents (1). The ritual decoction, *ayahuasca*, containing the reality-switching alkaloid N,N-dimethyltryptamine (DMT), has been one of the primary conduits to the luminal realms for the indigenous tribes of Amazonia for more than 3,000 years (2). And mushrooms of the genus *Psilocybe* have played equally important roles as gateways to worlds and their inhabitants inaccessible to the mundane sober mind among the Mazatec people (1).

But despite their long history in these traditional forms of medicine and ritual, the psychedelics are a relatively recent addition to the Western pharmacopeia. The discovery of psychedelics by the Western world was first met with wonder, followed by an excited anticipation of their potential as tools for exploring the mind and treating psychological disease, and then by misinformation, suspicion, and suppression. Ignorance, misunderstanding, and fear form a dark thread through the history of psychedelics in the late 20th century. Fortunately, this thread is finally beginning to fray. Dubbed the psychedelic renaissance, modern science and medicine are again beginning to recognise the unprecedented potential of psychedelics as tools not only for exploring the nature of our mind and the workings of the human brain, but also as revolutionary treatments for a range of debilitating and life-depleting psychiatric conditions, from depression to anxiety to post-traumatic stress disorder (3). There can be little doubt that the role of these molecules in medicine will continue to expand in the coming years, ultimately becoming some of the most powerful instruments in the psychiatrist's pharmacological toolbox.

But aside from their great promise in the clinic, psychedelic molecules are tools for the discovery and exploration of new worlds. Whilst at first blush this might seem rather fanciful, the existence of alternate worlds that can be accessed using psychedelics is incontestable. The short-acting natural psychedelic, DMT, for example, reliably induces the complete replacement of the normal waking world with a bizarre, complex, apparently hyperdimensional, reality replete with a diverse panoply of seemingly intelligent beings eager to communicate with the tripper (4). The uniquely-structured salvinorin molecules, isolated exclusively from the Mexican ritual herb *Salvia divinorum*, bear a similarly striking ability to catapult the user into worlds equally bizarre and equally difficult to comprehend, let alone explain (5). Of course, it's tempting to glibly dismiss such visions as mere hallucination, as distortions of a true base reality to which we anthropocentrically assume privileged and lossless access. But this is a lazy and facile assumption. In a sense, all experienced worlds are equally real in that all experiences are real. Of course, this doesn't mean that the fearsome Reptilian Overlord encountered at the peak of a DMT trip exists anywhere outside of your experience, but within your experience it most certainly exists. Whether it continues to exist after the trip ends is another question entirely.

Whatever one chooses to believe about the ontological status of the miraculous realms to which these molecules grant access, psychedelics reveal in a most startling manner that the familiar world of daily life is but one amongst countless others available to all humans that find themselves seemingly stranded on this muddy little rock swirling through our dark little corner of the Milky Way. These worlds are not to be found on neighbouring star systems or distant galaxies reachable only by directed pulses of electromagnetic radiation or in a promised future of interstellar travel, but are ever present, right here, waiting to be discovered and explored. It's all too easy to drift through life entirely unaware of their existence. But you are in possession of an exquisite machine motionlessly buoyant in the softly circulating fluids of your skull.

A world-building machine.

Your brain is the most complex structure in the known universe, and the world-building machine *nes plus ultra*. And psychedelic molecules are the tools for tuning and operating this machine.

Despite their widely varying effects and potencies, all psychedelics are unified in altering the structure and dynamics of the experienced world. And all subjective experienced worlds are unified in their construction, being sculpted by the brain. Of course, by virtue of the sensory apparatus that funnels information from outside, the familiar world of normal waking life has an undeniable relationship to the environment. But the subjective world itself is always fabricated by the brain's world-building machinery. What DMT, and other reality-switching psychedelics, reveal is that the brain is capable of constructing worlds that bear no relationship whatsoever to the normal waking world.

Once we understand how the human brain builds, sculpts, and refines your world in normal sober waking life, an explanation for these strange alternate worlds visited under the influence of certain exogenous molecules begins to reveal itself. Beyond Huxley's "rather dull universe in which most of us spend most of our time", a vast set of reality channels is available and can be accessed by the brain with great facility once the right molecular stimulation is provided.

It is the aim of this manual, using a combination of neuroscience, pharmacology, and biochemistry, to explain how these reality channels operate and, ultimately, how we might learn to tune and operate them. We will discuss in unprecedented detail how your brain's reality channel can be rapidly and efficiently switched — at will — by an array of molecules scattered throughout the natural world and across the benches of the modern organic chemistry laboratory. The late great psychedelic guru of the first psychedelic revolution, renegade psychologist, and outright rascal Dr. Timothy Leary exhorted: "Learn to use your nervous system!" It is the aim of this book to teach you, not only how to use your nervous system, but to understand its inner workings, to take you under the hood to the switches, circuits, and wiring deep within.

The ability of psychedelic molecules to switch the brain's reality channel depends upon a complex interplay of mechanisms operating at several levels of organisation. At the most fundamental level, psychedelics interact with specific receptor proteins embedded in the membranes of neurons, the fundamental information-generating cells of the brain. These drug-receptor interactions elicit specific effects on the properties and behaviour of the neurons in which the receptors are embedded. These neuron-level effects then modulate the manner in which neurons generate and share information between themselves. Ultimately, it is these changes in the structure and flow of information through the networks of the brain that manifest as the change in the structure of the subjective world, whether it be a subtle shift or a complete switch to an entirely new reality. A number of these distinct multi-level mechanisms in the brain — the World Space Switches — have been identified, each altering the brain's model of reality in its own particular manner, activated by its own class of psychedelic molecules.

Each of the known Switches comprises not just the molecule-receptor interactions, but the entire network mechanism that ensues. And, of course, if we are to understand these Switches completely, we must seek to understand each of these organisational levels and how they relate to and interact with each other. Chapters 2 to 5 will be devoted to this end. In these foundational chapters, we will discuss the general mechanism by which the human brain constructs worlds and is able to "tune into" a particular reality channel, beginning with the normal waking world — the Consensus Reality Space.

In chapter 6, we will introduce the central concept of the World Space — the state space within which all reality channels will be found — before we begin, in chapter 7, to elucidate the underlying mechanisms of these reality channels, beginning with the basic machinery of the World Space Switch: the receptors embedded in neurons, the molecules with which they interact, and the intracellular signalling pathways they activate and modulate. We will then be ready to tackle the specific World Space Switches themselves. We will begin, in chapter 8, with arguably the most important and versatile switch — the C-Switch — which is activated by the so-called *classic psychedelics*, including tryptamines such as psilocybin and LSD, and the phenethylamine psychedelics, including mescaline, 2C-B, and a large number of related molecules. We'll begin by discussing the molecular structure and basic organic chemistry of the classic psychedelics, and how they bind and activate receptors on the neuronal membrane leading to specific biochemical events inside the neuron. We'll then discuss, in chapter 9, how these neuron-level biochemical processes lead to the characteristic effects of psychedelic drugs on global brain activity and the structure of the experienced world. In chapter 10, we will introduce two important "activation modes" of the C- Switch and how they can be used to understand the structure of the World Space.

Having developed a thorough understanding of the C-Switch, together with the requisite pharmacological, biochemical, and neurological underpinning, we'll be ready to explore the other known Switches. The M-Switch, the subject of Chapter 11, is perhaps the least utilised of all the known Switches in the modern world, and is activated by the so-called "deliriant" psychedelics, which include atropine and scopolamine from the Old World witching herb mandrake and the beautiful but lethal Deadly Nightshade.

Chapter 12 will focus on the N-Switch, activated by the purely synthetic psychedelic dissociative ketamine, as well as a range of structurally related molecules, including the infamous "peace pill", PCP. Finally, in chapter 13, we will turn our attention to the most recently discovered Switch, the world-shatteringly bizarre K-Switch, known to be activated by the extremely potent salvinorin family of molecules isolated from *Salvia divinorum*. In the final chapter, we will shift our focus from the present to the future, imagining how we might use our understanding of the brain's World Space Switches and the molecules that activate them to engineer and explore entirely new channels of reality.

Although this book will discuss the mechanism of action of psychedelic molecules in an unprecedented level of explanatory depth and detail, it is not intended as an academic work and is suitable for anyone with an interest in psychedelic drugs and their action in the brain. Although many of the concepts will undoubtedly challenge a reader unfamiliar with basic biochemistry, pharmacology, or neuroscience, anyone with a keen interest in the subject should find the book fully accessible. However, it is expected that the reader be familiar with basic concepts in biology (high-school level should be sufficient), including the structure of cells, protein structure (primary, secondary, and tertiary structure), and the function of enzymes, as well as some basic chemistry, including ions and their charges, and the idea of diffusion down concentration gradients. When discussing the molecular structure of the psychedelics and their interaction with receptor proteins, we will need to discuss some organic chemistry that is likely beyond high-school level. As such, an introductory primer on the structure of organic molecules is provided in the appendix.

リアリティ
スイッチ

<XXXXXX_3489_004_AO>

Chapter 2: The World-Building Machine

世界を作る機械

「セカイヲツクルキカイ」

"When I took my first breath, my world was born with me. When I die, my world dies with me. In other words, I wasn't born into a world that was already here before me... I bring my own world into existence, live it out, and take it with me when I die."

内山 興正
Kosho Uchiyama

現実△
制御学
研究所

2DHM5X6MTIHTUAI969QC

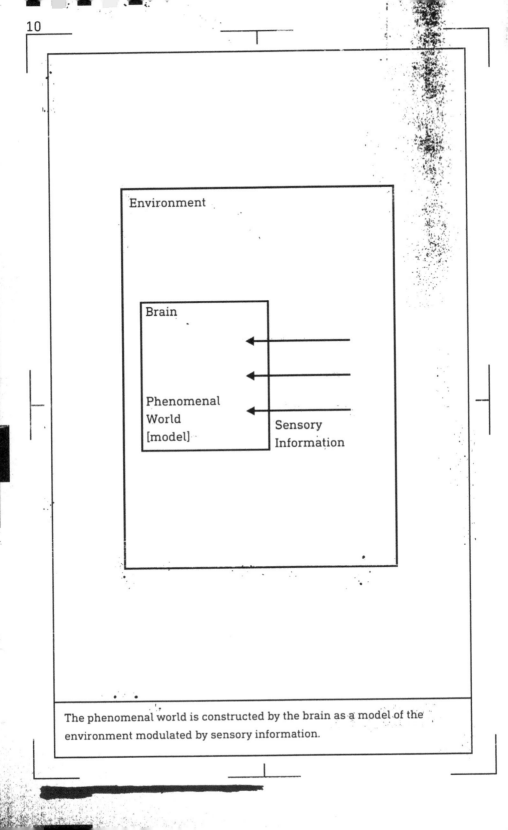

The phenomenal world is constructed by the brain as a model of the environment modulated by sensory information.

Before we begin, take a moment and look away from this book. Have a good look around. Notice the richness of the visual scene that surrounds and envelopes you — the colours, the lines, the shapes, the textures, the movement, the objects you recognise, perhaps some you don't, and the way they interact with each other, some in the distance, others close by. Perhaps you're indoors, perhaps outdoors — either way, you find yourself immersed in a world bursting with visual detail and information.

Now turn your attention to the sounds — whether you're sat in a busy cafe with people chatting and shuffling all around you, chairs scraping, coffee cups rattling; or whether you're sat alone at a desk or in bed, perhaps hearing the hum of traffic outside or music playing in the background. And, of course, there are the smells, perhaps the subtle fragrances of the room of which we we rarely take notice, a scented candle, or the pungent aroma of food being prepared in the room next door.

All of this unified, multi-sensory experience is your own personal subjective world. It feels perfectly natural and intuitive to identify this experienced world with the environment that surrounds you. But, whilst there seems to be an obvious relationship between what's going on outside your brain and the world you experience, we must be careful not to confuse the two. If you see a tiger sleeping quietly in the corner of the room, you might assume that there exists such a creature out there in the environment that you are observing. However, if you also have a high fever and a friend calmly informs you that no such tiger exists and that you must be hallucinating, then you might reasonably begin to question your senses. Whether or not there is actually a tiger in the room, the experience of the tiger in your visual field is the same. The difference lies in the relationship between that experience and the environment.

German philosopher Emmanuel Kant distinguished between the subjective experience of an object, which he termed the phenomenon, and the unknowable thing-in-itself, independent of our perceptions, which he called the noumenon (1). Your brain never has direct access to the environment, but must rely on noisy patterns of information received via the senses to construct a working model of it. The world you experience, which we will refer to as the phenomenal world (after Kant), is what that model feels like from your subjective perspective. Of course, your world doesn't seem like a model, such is the speed and adroit with which your brain constructs it. German philosopher Thomas Metzinger makes the point clearly:

> "The global model of reality constructed by our brain is updated at such great speed and with such reliability that we generally do not experience it as a model. For us, phenomenal reality is not a simulational space constructed by our brains; in a direct and experientially untranscendable manner, it is the world we live in." (2)

Throughout the course of evolution, development, and experience, your brain has learned to construct a model that allows you to navigate the environment, distinguish between predators and prey, find a mate, and generally to survive to pass on your genes to the next generation. In evolutionary parlance, this is an adaptive model. We'll refer to the normal waking phenomenal world, functioning as an adaptive model of the environment, as the *consensus world*. This is the world you might consider to be the "real" world or, perhaps even, the only "true" world. But we must avoid the unhelpful, and ultimately confusing, temptation to try and divide the contents of your phenomenal world into the "real" and the "unreal". Your phenomenal world is *always* a model and it's always built by your brain.

When you saw a tiger in the corner of the room, it's tempting to assert that the tiger was unreal. But, whether or not there was actually a tiger in the room, the tiger was part of the phenomenal world model constructed by your brain. So, in a sense, all phenomenal worlds are equally real in that they're all built by the brain. However, not all phenomenal worlds are adaptive models of the environment. So, it's more accurate to say that the "tiger" was a non-adaptive perception or model, rather than a false or unreal one. Your brain included a tiger in your world model when it was non-adaptive to do so — it's hardly helpful to be seeing large predators when no such creature is actually present in the environment. Your brain has no yardstick by which to measure the truth or reality of its world model. Even the term "hallucination" can be confusing, since it implies a clear distinction between real perceptions and unreal, hallucinated, ones. Hallucinations, generally, are better defined, as with the tiger, as non-adaptive models (3).

Throughout this book, we'll be discussing phenomenal worlds as models constructed by the brain. Whilst the relationship between the model and the environment can change, the phenomenal world is always the model. This is important to bear in mind and, in general, when we use the term "world" we'll be referring to a phenomenal world constructed by the brain. We'll generally use the term "environment" to refer to that noumenal space outside the brain from which sensory information is received, rather than plumping for confusing terms such as "the outside world".

When a psychedelic molecule finds its way into your brain, it changes the structure and dynamics of its world model. This is experienced as the psychedelic effect — the change in your phenomenal world — which might be subtle or profound. A low dose of *Psilocybe* mushrooms, for example, might elicit subtle changes in the world — objects begin to shimmer or breathe, colours appear more vivid and pop out of the surroundings, and everything appears more fluid and dynamic. A high dose of DMT, in contrast, alters the structure of the world model so dramatically that the consensus world is transformed in its entirety, and replaced by one altogether new and startlingly strange — the reality channel is switched. Between these extremes, the large range of both natural and synthetic psychedelic molecules vary in their effects, but are unified in perturbing the brain's world-building mechanisms and altering the structure and dynamics of the world model. Later, we'll see how these effects are achieved, and how they reveal a vast array of potential world models available to the brain and accessible using these molecules. But first we need to discuss exactly what this world model is built from and how it's constructed.

Despite its obvious complexity, your brain is fundamentally an information generator and it's the information generated by its activity that's used to construct the model experienced as your phenomenal world. Initially, this is likely to seem rather abstract so, in this foundational chapter, we'll discuss exactly what we mean by information, how it's generated by the brain, and how this information can be used to build that model.

Formally, information can be defined as the opposite of uncertainty. Information is what we know about something compared to what we don't. Gaining information about something reduces the uncertainty. So what exactly do we mean by uncertainty? If a friend tells me his girlfriend is pregnant, the sex of the child is, at first, uncertain — it could be a boy or a girl and, assuming the monthly scans don't reveal the presence or absence of a dangling appendage between the little foetal legs, this uncertainty will remain until he or she is welcomed into the world a few months later. At this point, the uncertainty collapses to one of the two possibilities. The same applies to a coin flip: as the coin spins in the air, whether it will land *heads* or *tails* is uncertain but, again, this uncertainty collapses to one or the other when it lands. The roll of a dice presents a similar scenario, the only difference being the number of possibilities.

Coins and dice (and the sex of newborn babies) are systems that can exist in a finite number of possible states, and we generate information when one of those states is selected from the others. The uncertainty about the possible states is reduced to a single state. A coin represents a two-state system, whereas a dice is a six-state system. When a dice stops rolling, we gain more information than we obtain from a coin flip. This should be intuitively obvious but, more formally, we can say that there's a greater reduction in uncertainty — from six possible states to one — when a dice stops rolling compared to the reduction of two states to a single state when the coin lands. And, generally, the greater the number of possible states a system can occupy, the greater the reduction in uncertainty when a single state is selected and the greater the amount of information generated. Another way of saying this is that, by selecting a single state from a finite number of possible states, all the other alternative states are *ruled out*. A coin landing heads up *rules out* a single alternative state: tails. A dice landing on a six rules out the other five possible numbers.

The *bit* is almost certainly the most well-known and utilised unit of information and is defined by the amount of information generated by a 2-state system. So, a coin can encode a single *bit* of information, as can each digit of binary code, with each digit being either a 1 or a 0. Likewise, when I learn the sex of my friends' newborn baby, I gain precisely a single bit of information. Crucially, a single digit of binary code — let's say a '1' — provides you with a single *bit* of information precisely because it rules out the single alternative digit: '0'. There are only two possible states. However, if the digit '1' is selected from the ten integers from 0 to 9, then this same digit generates more information (about 3.3 bits), since we're now selecting from ten possible states and, as such, no longer using binary code. In other words, it's of critical importance to know how many states are being ruled out when trying to quantify how much information a single state generates.

To generate large amounts of information, we either need to employ a system that can select from a large number of states, or we can combine a large number of simpler systems. Of course, this is how modern digital computers are able to rapidly generate and process vast amounts of information: by using long strings of binary digits. For example, a string of four binary digits (such as 1 0 1 1) encodes, obviously, four bits of information. However, it's important to note that the information is generated because 1-0-1-1 is a single state from all possible 4-binary-digit permutations.

It's easy to calculate the number of possible states as 2^n, where n is the number of digits in the binary string. In this case, n=4, so there are 16 possible states ($2^4=2\times2\times2\times2$). In other words, a string of four binary digits is a 16-state system encoding four bits of information:

Coin [binary]

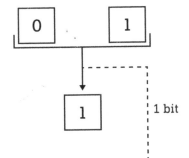

Uncertainty reduction: 2 to 1

Dice [senary]

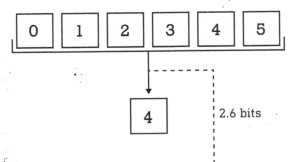

Uncertainty reduction: 6 to 1

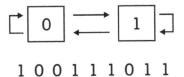

1 0 0 1 1 1 0 1 1

The binary system can exist in one of two exclusive states. When one state is selected, one bit of information is generated, which can be recorded as a sequence of binary digits representing the same amount of information.

0 0 0 0	1 0 0 0	0 1 0 0	0 0 1 0
1 0 0 0	1 1 0 0	1 0 1 0	0 0 0 1
0 1 0 0	0 1 1 0	0 1 0 1	0 0 1 1
1 1 1 0	1 1 0 1	0 1 1 1	1 1 1 1

All 16 states of a 4-digit binary string

It's usually much simpler to combine strings of 2-state systems — such as binary code — than to build and use 16-state systems if you want to encode four bits of information. You could also use four coins, or the answers to four YES/NO questions to encode the same information. And, indeed, this is why digital computers generally use bits to encode information, since strings of arbitrary length can be used to generate as much or as little information as required.

In general, any system that can select from a large number of states can generate large amounts of information. This includes the brain, which generates inordinate amounts of information by selecting from an extremely large number of possible states. Every time your brain selects a single state from its repertoire of potential states, it rules out vast numbers of alternative states and thus generates vast amounts of information. And, it is this information that manifests as your phenomenal world.

The major information-generating part of the brain is the thin outer layer known as the cerebral cortex (also known as the neocortex, but we'll refer to it simply as the cortex), a 2-4mm thick folded sheet built from about 50 billion information-generating cells — neurons — amongst over 500 billion supporting cells (4). The neurons of the cortex are heavily interconnected to form a bewilderingly complex network capable of generating colossal amounts of highly complex information. In particular, it's the cortex that's responsible for building your phenomenal world model.

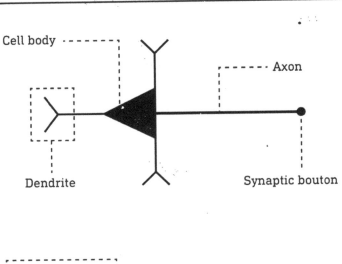

Cell body

Axon

Dendrite

Synaptic bouton

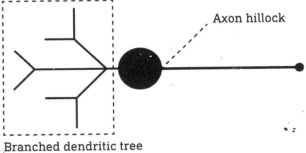

Axon hillock

Branched dendritic tree

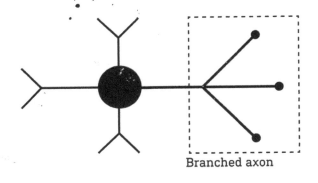

Branched axon

Neuron types can differ in the shape of their cell body, as well as the location and pattern of axonal and dendritic branching.

There are a variety of different types of neuron within the cortex, and we'll meet several of these in the chapters that follow. However, despite structural and functional differences between neuron types, all are unified by their function as information-generating cells afforded by their distinctive structure and behaviour. The *cell body* is the central hub and computational centre of the neuron, and from which varying numbers (depending on the type of neuron) of membrane protrusions — known as *dendrites* and *axons* — extend outwards. The role of the dendrites is to receive information from other neurons and transmit this information to the cell body for processing. The role of the single axon is to carry this processed information away from the cell body to be passed to other neurons. So, the overall task of a neuron is to receive information (via its dendrites), process this information (at the cell body), and then transmit the processed information to other neurons using its axon.

Information is processed by the cell body in a conceptually simple manner. Information arriving from the dendrites is summed and, based on this summation, the cell body makes a decision: remain quiet (do nothing) or fire a brief electrochemical signal called an *action potential* (or a *spike*), which travels along the axon away from the cell body and towards one or more downstream neurons. So, in effect, the cell body has reduced a potentially complex pattern of information arriving from the dendrites to a simple 2-state — *fire* or *no-fire* — system that generates a single bit of information. Firing an action potential is often likened to generating a '1' in binary code. If the neuron remains quiet — no-fire — then it generates a '0'. Although this is something of an oversimplification, it helps make it clear why an action potential carries information. We should also note that a neuron generates as much information by remaining quiet as it does by firing — in both cases the neuron is selecting one of two states and ruling out the other.

The fire/no-fire decision is the most important computation performed by a neuron and is the basis for the colossal amounts of information generated by the cortex as a whole. To understand this computation, which will be of central importance when we

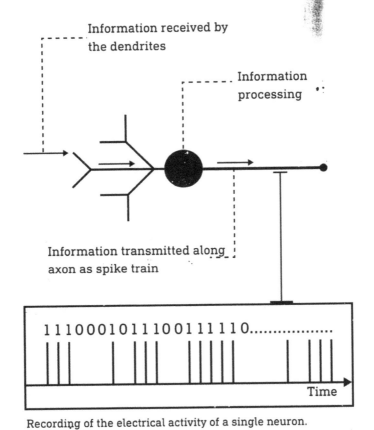

Information received by
the dendrites

Information
processing

Information transmitted along
axon as spike train

1 1 1 0 0 0 1 0 1 1 1 0 0 1 1 1 1 1 0..................

Time

Recording of the electrical activity of a single neuron.

The pattern of action potentials [spikes] encodes information in a manner analogous to a string of binary digits.

consider the mechanism of action of psychedelics, we need to consider what an action potential is and how it's generated.

As with every living cell, the neuron is bounded by a semi-permeable membrane that controls the flow of molecules between the inside and outside of the cell. However, neurons are distinct from most other cells in that they use special proteins to actively pump positively-charged sodium ions (Na^+) out of the cell and, at the same time, pump potassium ions (K^+) into the cell. The result is an excess of Na^+ outside the cell and an excess of K^+ inside the cell. Furthermore, these *sodium-potassium pumps* transport only two K^+ ions into the cell for every three Na^+ ions pumped out. The net result is an excess of positive charge on the outside of the cell or, equivalently, the inside of the cell is negatively-charged relative to the outside. This electrical charge imbalance across the membrane is referred to as the *membrane potential*. Specifically, when a neuron is quiet — not firing — its membrane potential sits at around -70 millivolts (the *resting potential*)(5).

In addition to the sodium-potassium pumps, the neuronal membrane is also host to a whole gamut of channel proteins that control the flow of specific molecules and ions across the membrane. Central to the generation of the action potential are *voltage-gated sodium channels (VGSC)* and *voltage-gated potassium channels (VGPC)*. As their name suggests, these channels can exist in an open state, in which sodium/potassium can flow through the channel across the membrane, or a closed state, in which the flow of ions is blocked — the gate is closed.

At the resting potential, both the VGSCs and the VGPCs are in the closed state. However, if the membrane potential is pushed to around -55 millivolts — the *threshold potential* — (we'll discuss later why this might happen), a conformational change in the VGSC protein causes it to rapidly switch from the closed to the open state. Since there is a large excess of sodium ions outside the cell (a concentration gradient in the inward direction), these positively-charged ions flow into the cell, carrying their positive charge with them and causing the membrane potential to shoot rapid-

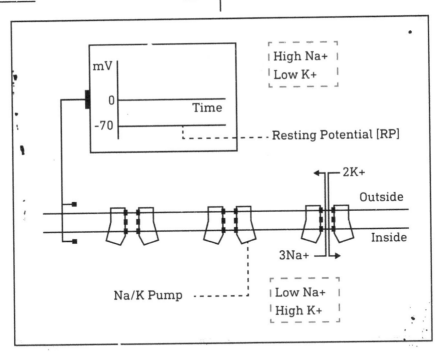

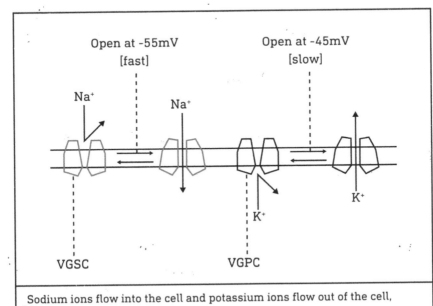

Sodium ions flow into the cell and potassium ions flow out of the cell, down their concentration gradients.

ly upwards, past zero, to around 40 millivolts, at which point the VGSCs close again. This is called *depolarisation* and is the first leg of the action potential. Similar to the VGSCs, the VGPCs also open as the membrane potential shoots upwards (at around -45mV). However, they open much more slowly and, in fact, by the time the VGPCs are fully open, the VGSCs are beginning to close again.

Once the VGSCs have closed and the VGPCs are open, potassium ions rush out of the cell (since their concentration gradient is in the opposite direction to sodium), taking their positive charge with them. This causes the membrane potential to drop back towards the resting potential, which it slightly undershoots — this is known as *hyperpolarisation* — before the VGPCs close and the sodium-potassium pumps restore the ion gradients, and the membrane potential returns to the resting potential, ready for another action potential. So, overall, an action potential is a rapid and brief reversal of the membrane potential that acts as the electrochemical signal that carries information.

An action potential is initiated at a point where the axon connects to the cell body called the *axon hillock* — once the membrane reaches the threshold potential and the VGSCs open at this location, the membrane is depolarised and an action potential is initiated. As the sodium ions flow into the cell, they tend to diffuse away from the axon hillock, carrying their positive charge and depolarising those regions of membrane adjacent to the hillock towards the threshold potential, and triggering the opening of the VGSCs. In this way, the action potential, although initiated at the axon hillock, moves rapidly along the axon towards its terminus, carrying its information away from the cell body as a propagating signal — the fundamental "bit-like" unit of information used by the brain as a whole. Sequences of these signals form spike trains that encode patterns of information in a manner comparable to the sequences of 1s and 0s used by modern digital computers (6).

So, the "decision" made by the cell body as to whether or not to fire an action potential comes down to whether or not the membrane potential at the axon hillock reaches the threshold potential: if it

Anatomy of the Action Potential.

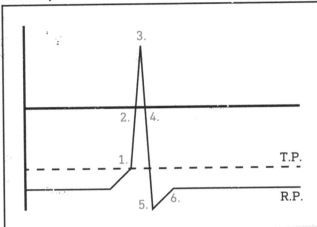

1. Initiation. Membrane potential reaches the threshold potential [T.P.] (-55mV). VGSCs open.

2. Depolarisation phase. Sodium ions flood into the cell, down their concentration gradient, rapidly depolarising the membrane.

3. Peak. VGSCs close. VGPCs open.

4. Repolarisation phase. Potassium ions flood out of the cell, rapidly repolarising the membrane.

5. Hyperpolarisation. Delayed closing of VGPCs causes the membrane potential to undershoot the resting potential.

6. Return to rest. Na/K pumps return the membrane potential to the resting potential.

現実制御学研究所、東京

fails to reach this critical potential, the neuron will remain quiet but, if the threshold is reached or surpassed, opening of the VGSCs and VGPCs ensues and an action potential is guaranteed. In this way, an action potential is an all-or-nothing affair, a digital event, a 1 or a 0. But what is the force that pushes around the membrane potential at the cell body and axon hillock? To understand this, we need to consider what happens to an action potential when it reaches the end of the axon.

Although the billions of neurons that make up the neocortex are individual cells, they don't work in isolation — they are heavily interconnected via their dendrites and axons to form a highly complex set of networks among which information — in the form of spikes — is shared, processed, and integrated (7). Once an action potential reaches the terminus of an axon, it can go no further, since action potentials cannot (usually) be passed directly from neuron to neuron. However, a small, highly structured, chemical connection — called a *synapse* — between the axon terminal and a dendrite of another neuron exists to transmit the information carried by the action potential from the *pre-synaptic neuron* to the *post-synaptic neuron*. When the action potential reaches the enlarged axon terminal — the *synaptic bouton* — a series of biochemical events initiated by an influx of calcium ions triggers the release of special molecules — *neurotransmitters* — into the *synaptic cleft*. These neurotransmitters then diffuse across the cleft and bind to special receptor proteins embedded in the post-synaptic neuronal membrane.

Dependent on the type of neurotransmitter — over 100 different types are known — and the type (or types) of receptor protein embedded in the postsynaptic membrane, a particular neurotransmitter can have a variety of effects on the postsynaptic neuron (8). But the important point is that the neurotransmitter transmits the information encoded by the action potential across the synapse, from one neuron (the presynaptic neuron) to another (the postsynaptic neuron). Note that the terms pre- and post-synaptic are used only to describe which side of a particular synaptic connection a neuron sits. The vast majority of neurons in the cortex are both

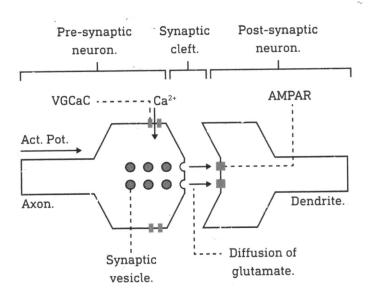

Arrival of the action potential at the synaptic bouton causes VGCaCs to open and calcium ions to flow into the neuron. This triggers the release of neurotransmitter [glutamate] from synaptic vesicles into the synaptic cleft to diffuse and bind to the AMPARs.

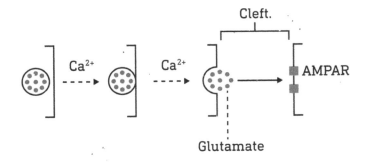

Neurotransmiitters are released into the synaptic cleft as a synaptic vesicle fuses with the pre-synaptic membrane, triggered by calcium ions.

pre- and post-synaptic neurons in that they both receive and provide connections to large numbers of other neurons.

When we introduce the classic psychedelics in chapter 8, we'll discuss in much more detail how neurotransmitters and other molecules — including psychedelics — bind and activate receptors, as well as the effects this can have on the complex signalling networks inside neurons. However, for now, we'll focus on two principal neurotransmitters, their most important receptors, and their effects on the postsynaptic cell.

Glutamate, a type of amino acid, is the brain's most important "wiring neurotransmitter", in that its main role is to provide a strong stimulating connection between the pre- and post-synaptic neuron. There are a number of aptly-named glutamate receptors embedded in neuronal membranes, and we'll meet others in later chapters, but the AMPA (don't be concerned about the origin of this name) receptor (AMPAR) is arguably the most important. Just like VGSCs, the AMPA receptor is actually a sodium ion channel (9). However, unlike the voltage-gated sodium channel, the AMPA receptor is gated not by a change in membrane potential but by the binding of glutamate: When glutamate binds to the AMPA receptor, it causes the ion channel part of the AMPAR protein to switch from a closed to an open state. Sodium ions can then flow down their concentration gradient into the dendrite and depolarise that part of the membrane. However, as soon as glutamate unbinds from the AMPA receptor, it flips back to the closed state and sodium ions are again blocked from entering the cell.

This brief opening and closing of the AMPA receptor can be observed as a brief jump in the membrane potential known as an *excitatory postsynaptic potential (EPSP)*. Although a single EPSP is unlikely to push the membrane potential to the firing threshold, via its heavily branched dendritic tree, a single neuron might receive hundreds, or even thousands, of EPSPs from other neurons. These EPSPs can travel, in a similar manner to action potentials, along the dendrite towards the cell body. The role of the cell body is then to sum — or integrate — these EPSPs and, if their sum

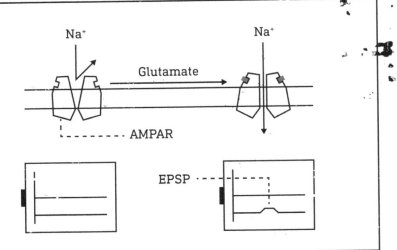

AMPARs are opened by the binding of glutamate, allowing sodium ions to flow into the neuron and briefly pushing the membrane potential towards the firing threshold.

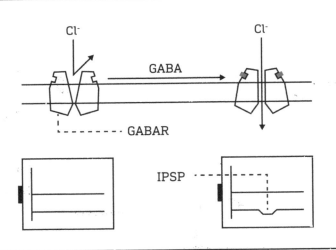

GABARs are opened by the binding of GABA, allowing chloride ions to flow into the neuron and briefly pushing the membrane potential away from the firing threshold.

pushes the membrane potential at the axon hillock to the firing threshold, then the neuron will fire. This is the basis for the cell body's computation and decision to fire or no-fire (remain quiet). The more EPSPs a neuron's dendrites receive in a certain period of time, the more likely the membrane potential at the axon hillock is to reach firing threshold. Timing is important for this integration to be successful — a single EPSP only lasts a few milliseconds before decaying, so there's only a limited window of opportunity for EPSPs to be summed.

EPSPs alone don't provide neurons with much control over the firing of action potentials and limit the computations they can perform. EPSPs are, after all, always stimulating — they always depolarise the membrane potential, nudging it towards the firing threshold. Another crucial neurotransmitter, called GABA, is used to *inhibit* neurons, nudging the membrane in the opposite direction. GABA is released by so-called *inhibitory neurons*, and binds to GABA receptors, also found on the postsynaptic membrane (10). And, like AMPA receptors, the GABA receptor is an ion channel, but is selective for the negatively-charged chloride ion (Cl⁻). As with sodium ions, neurons actively pump chloride ions out of the cell, so there's a higher concentration of chloride ions outside the cell relative to the inside. When GABA binds to the GABA receptor, the ion channel opens and chloride ions rush into the dendrite down their concentration gradient. However, since chloride ions are negatively-charged, they push the membrane potential further from the threshold potential (make it more negative). That is, they hyperpolarise the neuronal membrane. This generates an *inhibitory postsynaptic potential (IPSP)* in the dendrite. And, as with the EPSPs, these IPSPs are integrated by the cell body.

So, at any point in time, the cell body might be receiving large numbers of both EPSPs and IPSPs from the many excitatory and inhibitory neurons connected to its dendritic tree. The EPSPs are pushing the membrane potential towards the firing threshold, whilst the IPSPs are pulling it in the opposite direction. These are summed by the cell body and so, overall, whether or not a neuron fires will depend upon the balance of activity of the excitatory

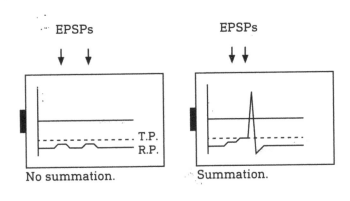

EPSPs   EPSPs

No summation.   Summation.

EPSPs decay rapidly, but can be summed if another EPSP is generated before the previous one decays completely. If the summed EPSPs push the membrane over the firing threshold, an action potential is initiated.

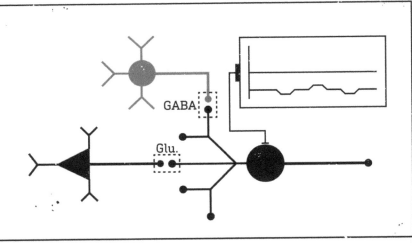

GABA

Glu.

A neuron is likely to receive both excitatory and inhibitory (red) inputs from large numbers of other neurons. These will generate EPSPs and IPSPs, nudging the membrane potential towards and away from the firing threshold.

(glutamate-releasing) and inhibitory (GABA-releasing) neurons to which it's connected. For example, a group of inhibitory (presynaptic) neurons can work together to keep a postsynaptic neuron quiet (not firing), whereas a burst of activity in a set of excitatory neurons might successfully overcome this inhibition by delivering a flurry of EPSPs in a short period of time and set the neuron off with a burst of action potentials.

The human neocortex contains around 100 trillion (100,000,000,000,000) synapses (11), together forming an unfathomably complex network of interconnected neurons. The beauty of this type of chemical connection lies in its flexibility — the strength of synaptic connections can be strengthened or weakened or switched off entirely, new synapses can be constructed and old ones deleted. There are a number of ways that a synapse can be strengthened (synaptic potentiation) or weakened (synaptic depression) to execute this control, on both the presynaptic and postsynaptic side of the synaptic cleft. For example, increasing the number of AMPA receptors in the postsynaptic membrane will, naturally, increase the number of channels through which sodium can flood into the cell in response to glutamate release, leading to a larger EPSP (12). Conversely, the synapse can be weakened by reducing the postsynaptic AMPA receptor population. Potentiation and depression can also be effected by increasing or decreasing, respectively, the amount of glutamate released from the presynaptic terminal. Using these, and other, mechanisms, it's possible for the strength of synaptic connections between neurons to be finely tuned. Much of the brain's ability to generate information, perform complex computations, and generally control the flow of information through its networks is afforded by these synapses. The sculpting of synaptic connections allows the cortex to sculpt the patterns of information it generates and, ultimately, it's this information, generated by trillions of action potentials per second and processed through the cortical networks, that manifests as your phenomenal world.

Of course, it's one thing to understand how the billions of neurons that comprise your cortex generate and share information, but how this information can actually *be* the phenomenal world that immerses you every moment of your waking life (and when you're asleep and dreaming or under the influence of a psychedelic drug) is unlikely to be obvious. To get a feel for how much information is contained in just your visual world, imagine trying to describe your field of vision with a level of detail that would allow a skilled artist to reproduce it with photographic precision. How long would it take? How many words — how much information — would you need? And, of course, your world isn't static, but changes with each passing moment — every time you move your eyes, the wind catches the leaves of the tree by the window, or your cat stretches in the corner of the room, your visual world changes, sometimes barely noticeably, sometimes dramatically. In fact, every moment of your waking life is different from the last — you never experience the same visual world twice. This richness and detail in your phenomenal world is only possible owing to your cortex's ability to generate almost inexpressibly vast amounts of highly structured information.

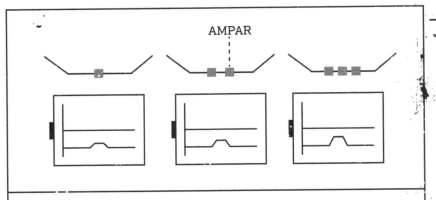

The strength of a synaptic connection can be tuned by manipulating the number of AMPARs on the postsynaptic membrane. The higher the AMPAR population, the larger the EPSP generated by activation of the synapse.

Before thinking about why certain patterns of information generated by the cortex can represent different features of the world — the colour blue or the shape of a wine bottle, for example — we'll focus first on the massive quantity of information the cortex can generate. We'll also ignore for the time being how sensory information entering the cortex from the environment affects the world model. In general, if the cortex can organise itself such that it can exist in a very large number of possible states, then it can, by definition, generate massive amounts of information by selecting from and adopting one of those states, thus ruling out all the other possibilities. And, indeed, all the information in your phenomenal world is generated, at each moment, by your brain selecting from a vast repertoire of possible states (13). Your experience of a rich, detailed, and dynamic phenomenal world, bursting with information, is precisely the movement of your cortex from state to state. But what do these states actually look like?

One of the simplest ways of creating a system that can exist in a large number of possible states, and thus generate large amounts of information, is to group together a large number of simple 2-state systems (recall the strings of binary code). The entire cortex is an extremely complex network of interconnected neurons that form a unified structure. However, the neurons aren't distributed smoothly throughout the cortex, but organised into small cylindrical networks of around 100 neurons known as mini-columns (we'll refer to them simply as 'columns'), of which there are around 100 million in the average human cortex, packed side-by-side to form a kind of mosaic (14). Each of these columns can switch between two states: when its neurons are highly active and firing action potentials amongst themselves, the column is in an active state. When its neurons are more quiet, the column is in an inactive state. Whilst this is something of an oversimplification, it illustrates how these columns can generate information, by selecting from their possible states.

So, rather than a completely unified homogenous system, the cortex is effectively 'chopped up' into around 100 million individual 2-state systems, each of which generates information by selecting from one of its states. The overall state of the cortex is thus the pattern of active/inactive states of all its columns. Assuming (and, again, simplifying) that each column is independent and can freely select from its active or inactive states, the total number of distinct states the cortex could adopt is around $2^{100,000,000}$, which is

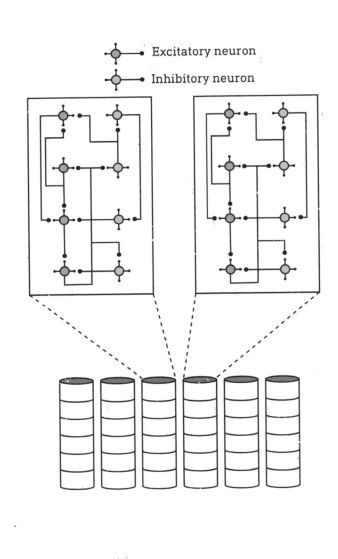

Excitatory neuron

Inhibitory neuron

Cortical columns are packed side-by-side, each containing ~100 excitatory and inhibitory neurons that form a connected network that regulates activation of the column.

a number so unimaginably massive as to be practically infinite (ask your calculator if you don't believe me). Every moment of your conscious life, your brain selects a single one of these states and generates all the information that constitutes your phenomenal world at that point in time.

But, of course, your phenomenal world doesn't feel like a mere pattern of information — colours, textures, forms, objects, movements, sounds, sensations, and smells all make up your experience of a world. In other words, your phenomenal worlds contains a wealth of different features, which the cortex must be able to represent within its overall pattern of column activation. The cortex achieves this by partitioning the columns into different column types, with each type responsible for generating a particular type of information — this is known as *functional segregation* (15). Colour information, for example, is represented using a different set of columns to those that represent lines and movement. We'll look at this in more detail in chapter 5, but for now it's sufficient to appreciate that functionally-segregated columns are responsible

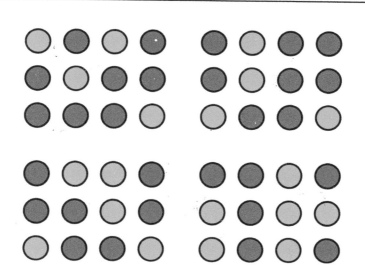

Four distinct activation patterns of 12 columns.
[Blue: Active, Grey: Inactive]

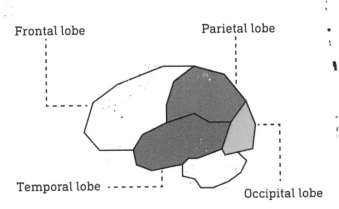

Frontal lobe

Parietal lobe

Temporal lobe

Occipital lobe

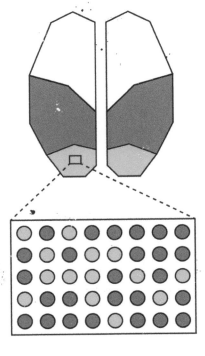

The four lobes of the cerebral cortex. At the microscopic level, the cortex is built from a mosaic of cortical columns packed side-by-side.

for representing different features of the world.

To appreciate how this works, we'll use a highly simplified and entirely unrealistic example. Also, to keep things as simple as possible, and since humans are primarily visual creatures, we'll focus only on the visual world. Each hemisphere of the human cortex is subdivided into four lobes: the frontal lobe, parietal lobe, temporal lobe, and the occipital lobe, which sits at the back of the brain. The visual cortex lies within the occipital lobe, and is composed of the large set of cortical columns responsible for representing the visual world.

Overleaf are three objects: a blue circle, a red square, and a white triangle. To represent these different objects, we can separate their distinct features — their shape and colour — and tune cortical columns to represent these features. Each object is represented by a distinct pattern of column activation or, equivalently, a distinct state selected from the 64 possible states of the six columns (2^6). Your subjective experience of the object *is* the information generated by the adoption of that particular state.

Of course, your own visual world is much much richer and more complex than simple coloured geometric shapes, but the same principle applies: All the features of your subjectively experienced world — the world in its entirety — are represented by the activation of sets of functionally-segregated cortical columns in the visual areas of the cortex, which together form a specific pattern of column activation that is experienced as your world. The selection of that particular activation pattern (state) generates information by ruling out countless other states (13). And, it is the state itself — the particular pattern of column activation — that gives that information its structure. Whether you experience, say, a dark and drizzly city street or a bright cloudless summer sky, your world is always the structured information generated by your brain.

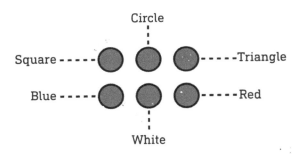

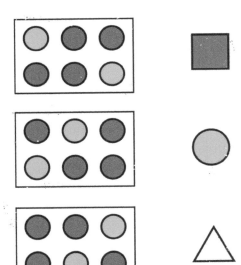

By functionally-segregating six columns to represent shape and colour, every shape-colour combination object can be represented (only 3 combinations shown). [Blue columns are active; grey columns are inactive]

INDEXED · 129

機密文書

リアリティ
スイッチ・

<XXXXXX_3489_004_AO>

Chapter 3: Consensus Reality Space I [Fundamentals]

合意的現実空間：1

「ゴウイテキゲンジツクウカン」

"If the outside world fell in ruins, one of us would be capable of building it up again, for mountain and stream, tree and leaf, root and blossom, all that is shaped by nature lies modelled in us."

Hermann Hesse

現実△
制御学
研究所

All that appears in the world is modelled in the brain.

Every moment is a unique pattern of cortical column activation, a single state of the cortex selected from a practically endless repertoire of possible states, manifesting as the richly informative and irrevocably subjective experience of a world.

Whilst your world is always built from information generated by your brain, there is quite obviously a relationship between this phenomenal world and the environment. It bears repeating:

> Your normal waking phenomenal world is a model of the environment.

Your brain evolved to construct this model to facilitate your ability to navigate and survive within the environment (1). However, there is never any direct connection between your brain and the environment — your brain relies on noisy patterns of information from the senses to guide the construction and maintenance of this model. When you descend into REM sleep at night, your brain uses the same model as during waking to construct the dream world (2). This is why, for most people and for most of the time, dreams are largely continuous with waking life with all its mundanities, down to the proportion of time watching TV or talking on the telephone (3). Your brain has evolved — learned — to construct this model of the environment and it's this model that you live out your life immersed within. In the waking state, the model is continuously informed and modulated by sensory information from the environment, whereas the dream state is disconnected from sensory information — this is why dreams can become erratic and unstable, shifting from scene to scene. But, whether awake or dreaming, the basic model constructed by the brain is the same.

Cortical columns are functionally-segregated cylindrically-organised sets of neurons tuned to generate specific types of information that, together, generate all the features of your information-rich world. In fact, your phenomenal world is this information generated by the pattern of column activation. However, as well as being extremely information-rich, your world is also unified — you don't experience fragmented worlds, each containing a single isolated object, for example. Nor, despite colour and form being represented by different sets of columns, do you experience the "redness" of a strawberry separately from its distinctive bulbous shape. These distinct features are bound together. In fact, your entire phenomenal world is bound to form a unified, indivisible, structure. This is only possible owing to the massive interconnectivity of your cortex. Rather than a mosaic of independent columns, large numbers of synapses connect columns to form a dense column network. These connections allow information to flow between columns, and the pattern of activation of individual columns forms a unified state — your unified phenomenal world (4).

A number of different types of excitatory and inhibitory connections unify the columns of the cortex and we'll be discussing synaptic connections both within and between columns. These synaptic connections are absolutely fundamental to the cortex's ability to regulate and modify its activity, perform computations, respond to sensory information, and generally maintain a stable yet dynamic and richly informative world model. Without a deep understanding of connectivity, the mechanisms underlying the effects of psychedelics on the world would forever remain a mystery. In this chapter, we'll focus on connections between columns — inter-column connections — formed by synapses connecting the neurons in one column to the neurons of others. We'll develop these ideas further in chapters 4 and 5, when we'll also need to consider intra-column connections — those between neurons in the same column — which are important in regulating the computations performed by individual columns.

There are broadly two types of inter-column connections: direct and indirect connections. Direct connections are also known as cortico-cortical connections, since they're simply the connections formed from one column in the cortex to another, without any intermediary structures. These might be short-range connections between neighbouring columns, or long distance connections between columns separated by great distances across the cortex.

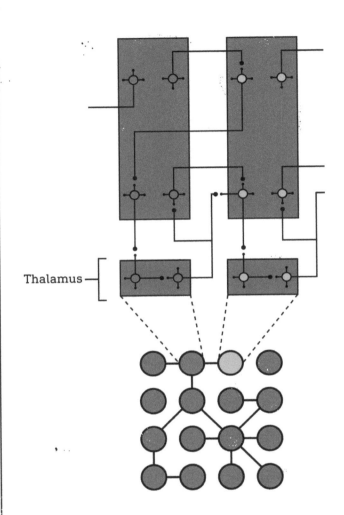

Thalamus

62-83894

Cortical columns are connected by direct column-to-column synaptic connections, as well as indirect connections via the thalamus.

The indirect connections are also known as cortico-thalamo-cortical connections, since they connect cortical columns via the thalamus, a walnut-sized (and shaped) structure sitting at the centre of the brain. The thalamus is often described as a relay station — or gate — through which all sensory information must pass on its way to the cortex (5). However, this is only one of its roles — the thalamus has also been described as a miniature map of the cortex, since every column is reciprocally connected to its own corresponding region of the thalamus (6). Neurons from each column send axons to the thalamus, where they make synaptic connections. The thalamus then sends its own axonal projections in return to the same column, forming a thalamocortical loop (7). As such, it's more accurate to refer to cortical columns as thalamocortical columns (but we'll stick with cortical columns for simplicity).

When a cortical column is activated — by sensory information from the relay areas of the thalamus, for example — this thalamocortical loop plays an important role in maintaining the activity in the column over time. Furthermore, in addition to this loop connecting back to the same column, the thalamus also sends out connections to other columns. These are the indirect connections providing another route by which columns can speak to each other, in addition to the direct cortico-cortical connections.

When you observe an object in your visual world, such as a strawberry, the columns that encode its various features — its plump round shape, its shiny texture, its characteristic red colour — are activated. Both direct and indirect connections help to unify these active columns to form a stable pattern of activity that encodes the strawberry as a whole (and is indeed experienced as the strawberry in your visual field).

Overall, your entire phenomenal world is encoded as a pattern of column activation — the cortical state we introduced in the last chapter — unified by these connections. Your world shifts and changes from moment to moment as a sequence of these cortical states, one state flowing into the next.

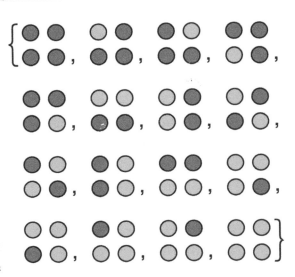

The complete state space of a set of 4 columns comprises 16 states..

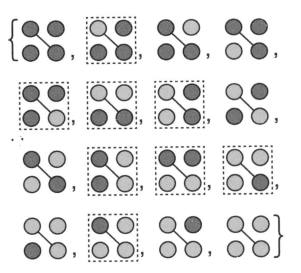

A connection between column 1 and column 3 makes them mutually activating: whenever column 1 is active, column 3 is activated (and vice versa). This contracts the state space by removing states in which either column 1 or 3 alone is active.

All possible cortical column activation patterns — all possible states — form a vast state space (for an idea as to the size of this state space, refer to 2^n calculation from the last chapter). However, only a select repertoire of states from this state space are ever selected. If the cortical columns were disconnected and entirely independent, all possible states would be equally likely. However, the vast majority wouldn't represent anything like a coherent and meaningful, let alone useful, model of the environment. Of all possible states, most would be structureless noise, much like the white noise of a detuned TV set. But, of course, your cortex glides effortlessly from state to state, each state as rich and meaningful as the last, and each experienced as an almost perfectly stable and coherent world. Your cortex has learned to select the states that represent a functional model of the environment — we'll refer to this set of states within the overall state space as the Consensus Reality Space.

By sculpting the patterns of connectivity between cortical columns, the cortex can control the flow of information between columns and the states that it tends to adopt. So, connectivity is used to define the states of the Consensus Reality Space and to ensure that the cortex remains within this space. But how does the brain learn which states represent a functional model of the environment and which do not?

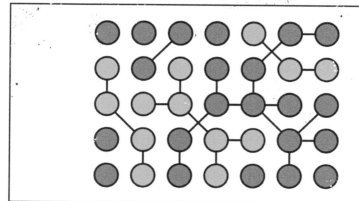

Connections between columns allow them to activate/deactivate each other, controlling the flow of information and the states adopted by the cortex.

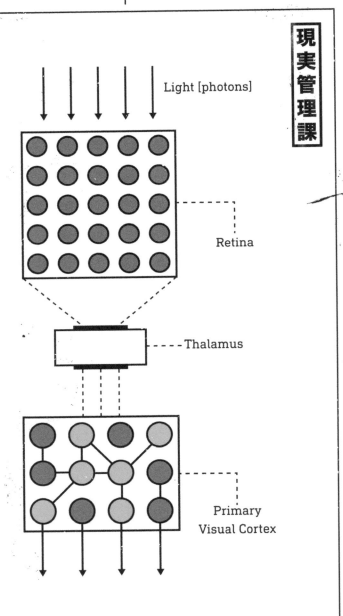

現実管理課

Light [photons]

Retina

Thalamus

Primary
Visual Cortex

Light stimulates photosensitive cells in the retina, which transmit
information, in the form of spike trains, to the visual cortex (via the
thalamus), activating cortical columns.

Sensory information is received by the cortex as patterns of action potentials from the sense organs — the retinae at the back of the eyes, the delicate vibration-sensitive bones of the inner ear, the touch receptors throughout the skin, for example. However, since we're focusing on the visual system, we'll consider only visual sensory information. We'll deepen our understanding of visual processing in chapters 4 and 5, but for now it's sufficient to be aware of the basic route by which information reaches the cortex from the eyes, and how basic visual features are encoded.

The retina at the back of each eye contains a thin layer of light-sensitive neurons. The three types of cone cells are responsible for high-acuity colour vision: The S-cones absorb only blue light; the M-cones absorb green light; and the L-cones are sensitive to red light. Under low-light conditions, the cone cells are poorly activated and another type of light-sensitive cell, the rod cells, take up the slack. These are, however, unable to distinguish between colours and have low spatial acuity. Patterns of light entering the eye from the environment stimulate the cells and trigger patterns of action potentials — the information — that propagate along a bundle of axons known as the optic tract to connect with neurons in a specialised visual relay area of the thalamus. These relay neurons, which are distinct from those involved in the indirect cortico-thalamo-cortical connections, then pass these patterns of information to an area of the visual cortex at the back of the brain, where they activate functionally segregated columns tuned to respond to particular visual features — colours, lines, movement — encoded in the patterns of action potentials (8).

The visual cortex is constructed as a hierarchy of connected areas running from the very back of the cortex towards the front, until meeting the parietal lobe over the top of the brain and the temporal lobes along each side. The primary visual cortex (V1) is the lowest area in the hierarchy and responsible for receiving the patterns of information from the retinae via the thalamus. The columns in V1 form a complete ordered map of the cells in the retinae (a retinotopic map) and thus the entire visual field. They are also tuned to respond to, and so extract, the basic — so-called low-or-

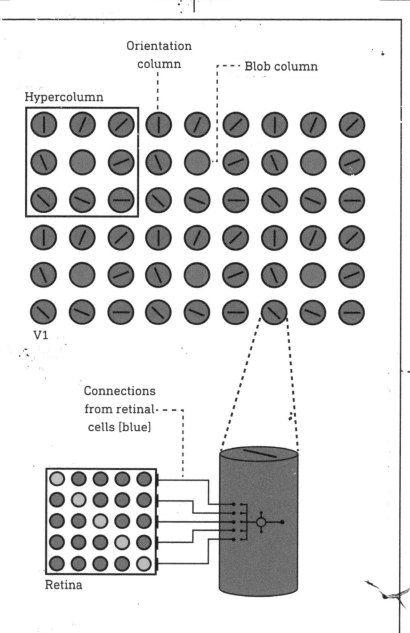

Hypercolumn

Orientation column

Blob column

V1

Connections from retinal cells [blue]

Retina

Simple orientation neurons within an orientation column are tuned to be activated by a specific line orientation by being connected to retinal cells arranged in that orientation [thalamus omitted].

der — features of the visual world encoded in these action potentials: lines and their orientation and position, as well as colour and movement (9). It is these low-order features gleaned from sensory information that the brain uses to help construct and maintain a coherent, stable and, above all, useful model of the environment.

The entire visual field is represented as a patchwork of roughly 1mm square areas of V1 cortex known as *hypercolumns*, each built from around 100 cortical columns separated into two types: *orientation columns* and colour-sensitive *blobs* (10). Each orientation column is tuned to detect lines in a particular orientation and will only be strongly activated when stimulated by lines close to that orientation. This orientation selectivity is governed by *simple orientation neurons* within the orientation column tuned to respond to a particular line orientation by virtue of their connections to the cells in the retina (ignoring the thalamus for the time being). If a set of these retinal cells arranged in a line are stimulated together, they will stimulate the simple neuron within a narrow time window, and the individual EPSPs are more likely to be summed and push the neuron over its firing threshold.

Complex orientation neurons in the same column receive connections from the simple orientation neurons and can detect movement. If a set of simple neurons are activated in quick succession (as would be the case for a moving line), the EPSPs are summed before decaying, activating the complex neuron and indicating movement of the line (11). So, a single column containing these simple and complex neurons, all tuned to the same specific line orientation, is itself tuned to represent this orientation and movement in the visual field.

Blobs are sets of columns interspersed between orientation columns, but are insensitive to line orientation and are tuned to only respond to colour. Overall, a single hypercolumn contains columns tuned to detect all possible line orientations and colours in its area of the visual field. And the entire visual field is represented by a pattern of activation of all the hypercolumns in V1, representing all the different lines and their movement and colours.

Now, imagine an entirely unrealistic primitive brain with entirely independent disconnected cortical columns. So, when a column is activated, it has no effect on the activity of any other columns. In this brain, all possible cortical states are equally likely — the cortex can move through its entire state space. Despite being primitive, this brain can still receive sensory information from the environment and, just like your brain, is constantly bombarded with an endless stream of visual information: lines, movement, and colours that activate hypercolumns. Naturally, this sensory information is not random: the environment is rife with regularities and patterns and, as such, so is the sensory information received by the senses. Of course, there is also a lot of irregularity and noise in the patterns of sensory information, and the brain's role in perception is to extract the regularities from the noise.

As patterns of sensory information are received by this primitive brain, it can learn these patterns by forming connections between columns that are regularly activated together. Imagine, for example, looking at that red square from chapter 2: the patterns of light absorbed by the retina will stimulate the particular columns tuned to the features of the square. By forming connections between these columns, the cortex can effectively learn how to model the object even in its absence or when presented with incomplete sensory information, since activation of a subset of these connected columns will tend to activate the others to form the complete representation. This learned pattern of column activation is the model of the red square you experience, whether in waking life or in a dream. In fact, it's precisely because your brain has learned how to build this model that you're able to dream about the objects and situations you experience in waking life (12). In the same manner, by continually sampling patterns of sensory information from the environment, the cortex sculpts the connections between the columns and, ultimately, learns to construct a dynamic, adaptive, and functional model of the environment in its entirety. The beauty of this model is that, once established, incomplete and noisy sensory information can be used to "fill in" the world and, as we'll explore in much more detail in the next chapter, continually *predict* the flow of sensory information into the cortex.

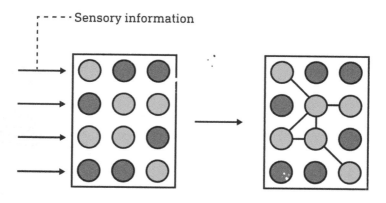

Columns activated [blue] together by a pattern of sensory information will tend to form connections.

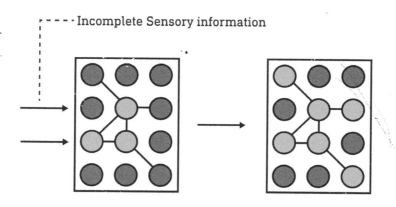

By mutual stimulation, connected columns can "complete the pattern" even with incomplete sensory information.

When we compare this "evolved brain" to the "primitive brain" we began with, the primitive brain can move freely between all possible states within the state space with equal probability. The evolved brain, in contrast, by sculpting its connectivity, has effectively selected the states that represent a functional model of the environment — it has contracted its state space to only those states within the Consensus Reality Space. This is analogous to tuning an old TV set — when first switched on, the screen is awash with nothing but fizzing white noise. Every possible pixel pattern buzzes across the screen, but none of it has any meaning — it's just noise. But, by tuning the TV to a particular frequency, a clear channel crackles into view. In a similar manner, the brain has learned to "tune into" the environment. Although the patterns of information received from the environment are dynamic and noisy, the brain has learned to distinguish between the important regularities and the random noise. The familiar objects you experience in the world are those regularities your brain has learned to detect and to model.

Once the brain has successfully learned to construct a complete model of the environment, it's natural to wonder as to the role of sensory information on a moment-by-moment basis. Firstly, it's important to note that the world model is never finished, but is updated and refined continually — from the moment you emerge from the womb until your inevitable demise, your brain is continually sampling sensory information to sculpt and refine the connectivity that defines the model. To understand the other crucial role of sensory information, it's useful to think about what happens when you dream.

As you descend into REM sleep several times each night (and assuming you remember those dreams), you're likely to be amongst the majority that find their dreams to be rather mundane continuations of their waking life, albeit perhaps coloured by particularly salient events of the day or worries that have occupied your mind for some time. There's a very good reason for this: the dream world is constructed by the brain using precisely the same model it uses to construct the waking world (13). Of course, the dream world is distinctly different to the normal waking world, which is stable and predictable. The dream world, in contrast, lacks this stability — the scene might shift seamlessly from a party in your back garden to the inside of an aircraft; the face of a family friend becomes inexplicably associated with the dripping maw of the family dog. Even during dreaming, your phenomenal world is experienced as a sequence of cortical states, one state flowing into the next. Normally, in waking life, this flow of states is guided by information from the senses. Sensory information helps to select one state from the others, from moment to moment. However, during dreaming, the brain is essentially disconnected from the environment and loses the guidance of sensory information. As a result, the flow of states becomes erratic, guided not by the patterns of sensory information, but by emotion, memories, and even random fluctuations in cortical activity. Whilst your world is always constructed by your brain, sensory information serves to constrain and regulate the flow of states with each passing moment. In the next chapter, we'll see how the model is actually *tested* against sensory information. But before discussing such model testing, we need to think a little more deeply about the interaction between the information that comprises your phenomenal world and the information flowing into the brain from the environment.

現実管理課

コピーは全て
破棄された

<XXXXXX_3489_004_AO>

リアリティ
スイッチ

Chapter 4: Consensus Reality Space II [Deep]

合意的現実空間：2

「ゴウイテキゲンジツクウカン」

"Stone crumbles.
Wood rots.
People, well, they die."

Chuck Palahniuk

現実△
制御学
研究所

Nothing is permanent but impermanence.

The world is ever changing and the task of your brain is to track these changes, to model the events and processes continuously unfolding in the environment. Building a model of the environment isn't such a difficult task, but building a model that is both stable and yet capable of rapidly updating based on a constantly changing flow of noisy sensory information is a Herculean one.

The cortex maintains a balance between order and chaos, with its dynamic responsive behaviour emerging perched on the thinnest of ledges known, suitably, as the *Edge of Chaos*. Systems that exhibit this kind of behaviour, both stable and yet dynamic and responsive to the environment, are known as *complex adaptive systems* (1). Like the brain, complex systems self-organise from large numbers of components that interact according to simple rules. It is from these interactions that the behaviour of the entire system emerges. The cortex's world model emerges from the trillions of synaptic connections between the billions of neurons from which it's constructed.

Complex systems are not merely complicated systems — an aircraft is certainly a complicated system, built from a vast number of both small and large components controlled by an array of computers powered by sophisticated software. However, the functions and behaviour of an aircraft are a product of its design, and the components must themselves be designed and brought together to construct a functioning flying machine. Complex systems, in contrast, self-organise from their components without any central controller, their behaviour emerging from their interactions. All living organisms — and, indeed, many groups of organisms — are complex systems that emerge at the Edge of Chaos. It is only in this narrow band that separates rigid order from unbridled disorder that stable but dynamic living systems can emerge. In fact, life itself is a special type of emergent behaviour of certain complex systems — those that can maintain, regenerate, and reproduce themselves over time (2). So, life is not a property of matter, but a process that emerges from its interactions.

Complex adaptive systems — including multicellular living organisms, such as ourselves — are often hierarchically constructed, with smaller complex systems embedded within a greater complex system. Every neuron in the brain is itself a complex system built from large numbers of interacting molecular components. It is from the interactions between these components that the structure, functions, and behaviours of a neuron emerges. And, of course, the cortex and its functions — such as the ability to construct a world model — emerge from the trillions of interactions between these neurons.

However, sitting at the edge of chaos is something of a precarious position — there is always the danger that a particularly sharp perturbation from outside could push the brain into the chaotic realm where any semblance of stable order is lost. The brain must strike a delicate balance between maintaining stability whilst remaining responsive to sensory information. Whilst essential, sensory information is a constant threat to this order. As it enters the brain, sensory information stimulates cortical columns and, via their connectivity, spreads to other columns. Without proper directing and processing, the spread of activity between columns might easily push the brain into a disordered state. In addition, processing information is expensive — the reseting of the membrane potential following an action potential, for example, requires energy to pump the ions back across the membrane. Refilling synaptic vesicles with neurotransmitters after synaptic transmission also has a high energy cost. So, whilst sensory information is essential for guiding the update of the world model, it cannot be allowed to enter the brain freely. Sensory information must be filtered, and only the information important for the continued fidelity of the world model should be absorbed and processed. In other words, the brain must attempt to filter out — or quench — as much sensory information as possible, whilst still allowing the important information to pass through (3).

But what is the important information?

How does the brain know which sensory information to filter out?

58

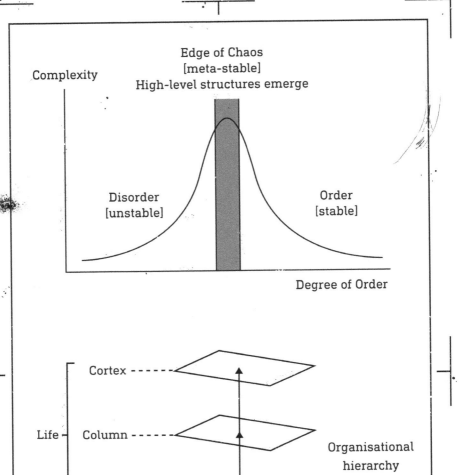

Complex systems emerge at the Edge of Chaos, perched between order and chaos. Neurons emerge from the interactions between molecular networks, columns from the interactions between neurons, and the cortex from the interactions between columns -- a hierarchically-organised complex system built from smaller complex systems.

The brain employs a conceptually simple principle to distinguish between sensory information it must absorb and process and that which it can discard:

1. The brain uses its world model to predict the sensory information it will receive in the following moment. *The brain is constantly trying to predict what will happen next, based upon what it thinks is happening now.*

2. Any sensory information that is correctly predicted is extinguished (filtered out). Only the sensory information that the brain *fails* to predict — surprising information — is absorbed and processed (4).

The rationale behind this strategy is equally simple: The accurate prediction of sensory information implies a cortex that's successfully modelling the unfolding of events in the environment, in which case, the cortex has no requirement for further sensory information. Until, that is, something that the cortex *cannot* predict — something surprising — happens. Then it needs to know about it, since unpredicted information indicates that the model is beginning to fail or is incomplete and must be updated.

The cortex continually compares its predicted sensory input with the actual sensory input and only the difference between them — a *prediction error* — is processed. It's these errors that can be used to update and correct the model.

So, the brain can reduce the amount of sensory information it must process by accurately predicting as much sensory information as possible, and so keep prediction errors to a minimum. The more accurately the cortex can model the evolution of events in the environment, the better its predictions, and the less it needs to actually absorb and process sensory information. But this is no easy task, for two main reasons.

The image below is immediately recognisable as a type of insect. Having settled your gaze on the insect, your cortex quickly settles on the most appropriate model. How much information does your cortex now require to accurately maintain the model? It has everything it needs. As long as nothing surprising occurs, the cortex is able to accurately predict the flow of sensory information from the image, and any prediction errors are minimal.

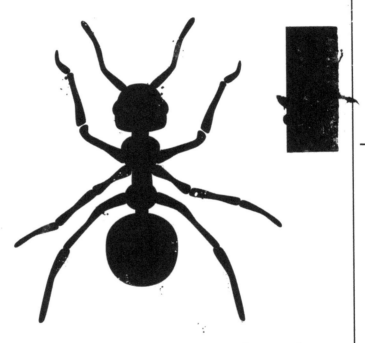

Now imagine the insect beginning to scuttle around the page. Immediately, the cortex's model of a static insect is no longer valid. The cortex fails to predict the sensory information and prediction errors rapidly begin to accumulate, forcing an update to its model — adding the appropriate movement — until the errors decline again.

1. The environment is complicated, filled with a plethora of structures and processes occurring simultaneously across the visual field. To maximise its predictive capabilities, the cortex must find the optimal way of modelling these ongoing dynamic complexities.

2. The visual system — comprising the eyes and its pathways into and through the brain — isn't a video camera, recording snapshots of the world and somehow presenting them to your conscious mind. The cortex only has indirect access to the environment via the patterns of action potentials received from the retinae via the thalamus.

Despite these difficulties, when you open your eyes you're greeted with an almost perfectly stable, meaningful, and entirely familiar world. How does your brain achieve such a remarkable feat?

As the events in the environment unfold, and as the head and eyes move, the pattern of retinal cell stimulation changes, and so does the pattern of column activation in the primary visual cortex, V1. So, when we say that the brain is trying to predict the flow of sensory information, it's this shifting pattern of column activation in V1, stimulated by sensory information, that must be predicted. And it's the model of the environment constructed by the cortex that must be optimised to maximise the accuracy of these predictions.

The only way for the cortex to predict the ever-changing pattern of column activation in V1 is to find, and learn, the patterns and regularities in the features that V1 encodes — features that predictably occur together in space and time. The manifestation of this strategy is immediately apparent to anyone with a functioning visual system — when you open your eyes, you aren't greeted by

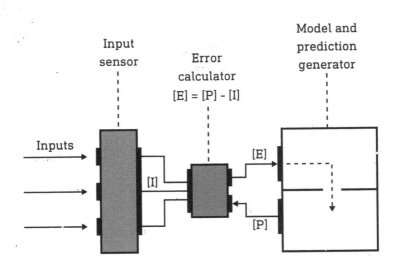

This prediction machine uses an internally-generated model to make predictions [P] about the patterns of inputs [I]. The difference between the actual inputs and the predictions is calculated to generate a prediction error [E], which is passed back to the model generator so it can be updated.

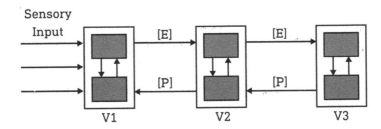

Each level of the cortical hierarchy is a prediction machine, using its internally-generated model to predict changes in activity in the level below. Only the prediction errors are passed up the cortical hierarchy and used to update each level of the model.

a world built as a pattern of moving lines and colours, but a world of objects you recognise. Your brain has learned to combine the low-order features encoded in V1 (see chapter 3) to build high-order object models — known as *object representations* — that fill your phenomenal world. It's the role of each level of the cortical hierarchy above V1 — V2, V3, and so on — to detect and classify the patterns of column activity in the level below and settle upon the most appropriate object representations (5).

The columns in V1 form convergent connections to columns in V2 — a single high-order column in V2 has a "bird's-eye view" of many columns in V1 and is perfectly positioned to detect patterns and regularities in their activity. By sculpting the connections between the V1 and V2 columns, the V2 columns become tuned to recognise — be activated by — high-order patterns in V1. For example, when this pattern of three lines below occurs in V1, columns in levels above rapidly detect and classify this pattern as a triangle. The pattern of column activation in the higher level that represents the triangle is the object representation — only the higher levels can "see" the shape, since outputs from many columns can converge on a single column in the higher level.

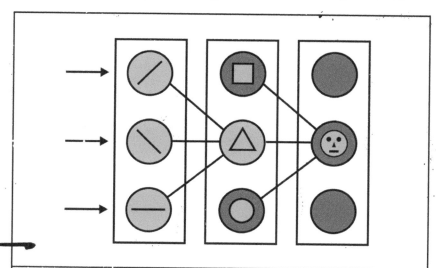

A column represents higher-order objects by receiving convergent inputs from lower-level columns representing lower-order features.

Geometric shapes, such as triangles, circles, and so on, can also be combined to form even higher-order object representations, such as faces, animals, etc, at even higher levels in the cortical hierarchy. Columns in V2, representing these basic geometric shapes, can converge their outputs onto even higher-order columns in V3 tuned to detect more complex objects built from these shapes. And, of course, other features — movement and colours — can also be brought into these high-order object representations.

If you look around now, you'll notice how the everyday objects around you are hierarchically constructed. Complex objects are built from smaller nested objects down to the lines in different orientations, colours, textures, and so on. Whilst the pattern of activity in V1 is the sensory information being predicted, the objects that you experience and recognise are the nested object representations spanning many levels of the cortical hierarchy.

It's simple to appreciate why this is an extremely effective predictive strategy. Imagine watching the top set of 10 dots (opposite) move around a computer screen. Your task is to predict the position of every dot in the next moment, just before it occurs. To make an accurate prediction, you must track the trajectory of every individual dot, and project this trajectory into the future (and hope for no sudden and surprising changes in direction or speed) — a task requiring 10 individual computations.

Now, imagine the same task with the lower 10 dots. It's obvious how much easier the task is. You immediately recognise that the dots form a basic geometric shape — a circle — and, assuming they didn't happen upon this configuration by random chance, you now only have a single trajectory to project from, and a single computation to perform: the trajectory of the circle. Of course, if the circle begins to break apart, then your predictions will be inaccurate. However, given the available information and what you know about circles, grouping the dots as a high-order object representation — a circle — is clearly the most effective strategy for predicting the movement of the dots. And, indeed, as you gaze at the image, you have no choice but to see the dots as a circle.

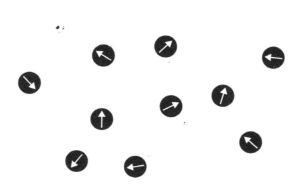

Tracking the movement of these dots requires 10 independent trajectory calculations.

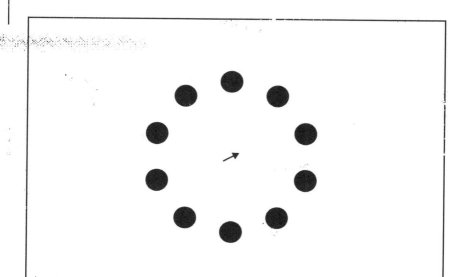

Tracking the movement of these dots requires a single trajectory calculation.

In a similar way, your brain is constantly trying to find object representations that are most likely to result in accurate predictions. When you observe a face, for example, rather than attempting to keep track of all the low-order features encoded in V1, by using stored "face" object representations your brain dramatically reduces the amount of information it must predict. Your brain has learned (and has encoded in its face object representations), for example, that the spatial relationship between the eyes, nose, and mouth is likely to remain constant. So, rather than trying to predict the sensory information from these five objects independently, it can treat them as a unified set of objects. And, most of the time, this prediction will be accurate (unless something very weird happens!). We can deconstruct the face even further: since the cortex has stored "eye" object representations, it can accurately predict the sensory information from each eye — the arrangement of the pupil, iris, and the white, for example. And so on down the hierarchy to the level of V1 itself. The cortex essentially "unpacks" the high-order object representation to predict the activity in the cortical level below, all the way down to V1, the level closest to the environment and where the evolution of sensory information must ultimately be predicted.

Using object representations, the inherent difficulty in attempting to predict the rapidly shifting and complex patterns of features encoded in V1 is greatly mitigated. Once a learned object representation that best explains the sensory data has been selected, the problem of predicting the evolution of sensory information is much easier. A single high-order object representation is essentially a highly compressed object model that can be unpacked to predict a large array of features, all of which would be almost impossible to predict if they were treated independently. The sculpting of cortical column connectivity we discussed in chapter 2 is partly the learning of these object representations used to organise and predict the contents of perception across all levels of the cortical hierarchy.

If you could visualise the pattern of column activation that encodes the model of, say, a face, you would see active columns at all levels of the cortical hierarchy, from V1 upwards. However, as you move up the hierarchy from V1, you would notice that the patterns of cortical activity begin to grow more and more stable since, although the pattern of V1 is ever changing, the high-order "face object representation" remains constant — there is always a face in the visual field, albeit a face that might be shifting in its location and expression.

So, at every moment, your brain is analysing the patterns of sensory information it's receiving, and attempting to find the patterns that it can group to form objects that it has learned — to activate stable object representations that it can unpack to make accurate predictions. If you've ever seen a face in the clouds, or burnt into a slice of toast, you'll have experienced this first-hand. Pareidolia — the experience of seeing familiar objects (often faces) in inappropriate places — is an expression of the brain's constant attempt to find patterns in sensory information that it can categorise into familiar objects. And faces are one of the most important types of objects that your brain has evolved to recognise and represent — so it's not overly surprising that people will often find them in even the most random patterns that occur in the environment.

No matter how accurate its predictions might be, the brain can never *know* whether the object representation it's selected to model a particular pattern of sensory information is somehow "correct" or "true". The best object representation is simply the one that best predicts the evolution of sensory information and minimises the prediction errors. In many cases, the appropriate choice of object representation will be unambiguous. But this is not always the case. A number of visual illusions exploit the fact that, in certain special cases, the same pattern of sensory information can be explained by two or more different object representations.

The particular object representation that the cortex settles upon is appropriately referred to as a *hypothesis* — the cortex's current best guess as to the most appropriate object representaiton to explain and predict the sensory information it's receiving. Whilst the entire visual world at any point in time is a unified pattern of cortical column activity spanning all levels of the cortical hierarchy, this overall pattern comprises a large number of these hypotheses, each itself a pattern of column activation nested within the larger pattern.

Different hypotheses generate different predictions that flow down the cortical hierarchy. From the top downwards, each level of the hierarchy is generating predictions about the activity in the level below. If these predictions fail to match the actual activity, prediction errors are generated. A rise in prediction errors prompts the cortex to refine, modify, or even switch to an entirely new hypothesis.

In the case of the Necker cube illusion, below, both hypotheses explain the sensory information equally well and there is no difference in the prediction errors generated by either hypothesis. The cortex can switch to and forth between the hypotheses and is never drawn to settle on one by an increase in prediction errors. However, these kinds of illusions are special examples designed to betray the cortex's world-building methodology. In the natural environment, such true ambiguity is relatively rare.

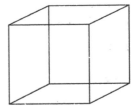

The Necker Cube can be seen as either pointing down-to-the-left or up-to-the-right. Both object representations explain the sensory data equally.

The image opposite shows what appears to be a face or mask — based upon the visual sensory information, and what your brain has learned about the structure of faces, it settles on "regular face" as the most likely hypothesis. So, this face object representation is almost instantaneously incorporated into your world model. Now, as the face begins to rotate, the "regular face" hypothesis leads to specific predictions about the evolution of sensory information that are unpacked down the cortical hierarchy: the characteristic convex shape of the face should become clear, the nose should

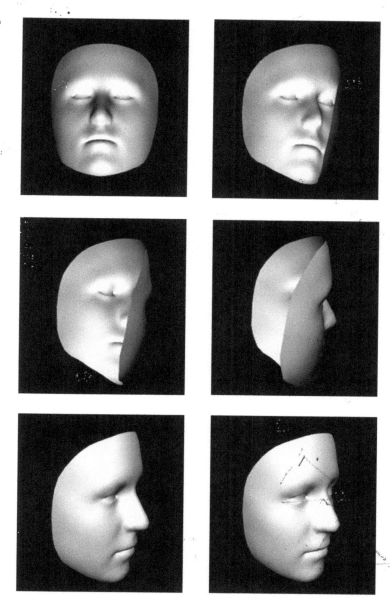

The Hollow Face Illusion (6)

From the front, the image appears to be of a regular face. However, upon rotation, it's revealed to be the concave reverse side of a mask.

move into profile, and so on. In other words, if the "regular face" hypothesis is correct, your brain should be able to predict the flow of sensory information — the changing pattern of column activity in V1 — as the face rotates. However, it quickly becomes clear as the face rotates that it is, in fact, the reverse (concave) side of a mask. The sensory information predictions are not fulfilled, predictions errors begin to accumulate and flow up the cortical hierarchy. In response, the brain quickly attempts to update its hypothesis to stem the flow of prediction errors; to find an alternative hypothesis that better fits the sensory information. The moment you realise that you're looking at the reverse side of a mask is precisely the moment at which your brain switches to the new hypothesis, triggering an updated set of predictions that cascade down the cortical hierarchy and quench the prediction errors. If you could observe the activity at the top of the cortical hierarchy, you would see the stable pattern of column activation representing the "regular face" hypothesis shift to a new pattern representing the updated "concave mask" hypothesis.

At any moment in time, your entire phenomenal world is a constellation of these hypotheses spanning all levels of the cortical hierarchy. Not just the high-order object representations, but also the lower-order hypotheses nested within them (the eyes, nose, and mouth hypotheses nested within the high-order face hypothesis, for example). It's hypotheses all the way down to V1. Each hypothesis is, of course, a pattern of column activation in a particular level of the cortical hierarchy and, together, these hypotheses form the overall hierarchical pattern of column activation which we defined in chapter 2 as a cortical state and is experienced as your phenomenal world.

Each hypothesis generates predictions that flow down the hierarchy in a never-ending fight against the upwards flow of prediction errors. In other words, the world model, built from hypotheses, is constantly being tested against sensory information. Prediction errors — the only information that flows up the cortical hierarchy — are both essential and dangerous. Without them, the cortex would be unable to detect when its world model was failing to

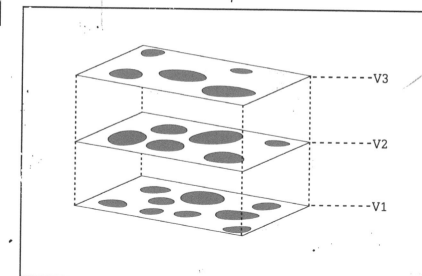

The world model is built from a constellation of hypotheses spanning the entire cortical hierarchy.

model the ongoing events in the environment whilst, conversely, an untrammelled flood of information would threaten to overwhelm the cortex, making it difficult to navigate and make sense of the world.

The cortex must maintain, at all times, a balance between the upwards flow of prediction errors and the downwards flow of predictions derived from the world model. This critical balancing act is one we will return to in later chapters, since it is highly susceptible to disruption by psychedelic molecules. However, before we can discuss these mechanisms, we need to look more deeply at the connections within the cortex that direct and control the flow of predictions and error signals.

デジタルリアリティ

リアリティ
スイッチ

<XXXXXX_3489_004_AO>

Chapter 5: Consensus Reality Space III

合意的現実空間：3

「ゴウイテキゲンジツクウカン」

"Each one of us is potentially Mind at Large. But in so far as we are animals, our business is at all costs to survive. To make biological survival possible, Mind at Large has to be funneled through the reducing valve of the brain and nervous system. What comes out at the other end is a measly trickle of the kind of consciousness which will help us to stay alive on the surface of this particular planet."

Aldous Huxley

現実△
制御学
研究所

The world model constructed by the brain is built from information, represented as a hierarchically-organised pattern of cortical column activation — a cortical state. Each of these states represents all the information contained within your phenomenal world at any particular moment. This overall model comprises a large number of hypotheses that are both distinct and yet unified as part of the same overall world model. These hypotheses, and the entire world model, must be continuously tested against sensory information to remain functional and stable.

Predictions are derived from the model hypotheses and flow down the cortical hierarchy, with each level of the cortical hierarchy attempting to predict the activity in the level below, all the way down to the lowest level, V1, which receives the dynamic patterns of information from the environment via the senses. The predictions are your brain's best guess as to what's happening in the environment and, as such, what should be happening in the next moment. Prediction errors must be calculated by comparing the predictions with the actual sensory information — the patterns of activity in V1 — received from the environment. If the prediction perfectly matches the sensory information, the prediction error is zero, meaning no such error information needs to be sent upwards through the cortical hierarchy. In effect, the sensory information has successfully been filtered or extinguished. Non-zero prediction errors, in contrast, must be transmitted through the hierarchy so that the model can be updated.

The neurons that comprise a cortical column organise themselves into several distinct layers that can be distinguished by the different types of neurons in each layer and by the way these neurons communicate with each other. We've already met the simple and complex orientation and movement selective neurons in chapter 3, for example. Since the columns sit side-by-side, the entire cortex displays this layered structure. Six distinct layers have been identified, with layer 1 being the outermost layer and layer 6 the deepest. For simplicity, we'll separate these layers into three groups: layers 1 to 3 we'll refer to as the *superficial layers*, and layers 5 and 6 the *deep layers*, with the input layer 4 sandwiched in between.

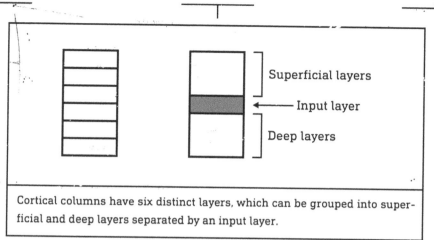

Cortical columns have six distinct layers, which can be grouped into superficial and deep layers separated by an input layer.

Although there are a range of different neuron types in each column, we'll focus only on those required for understanding world-building. The actual model is constructed by the deep layers. In particular, layer 5 contains a number of distinctively-shaped neurons called *pyramidal cells*. In the last chapter, we discussed how the world model is constructed as a hierarchical pattern of activation of cortical columns. Dissecting the layers and neurons of the columns, we can see that it's really a pattern of activation of pyramidal cells (sometimes referred to as *representation cells*) (1). Or, equivalently, when we refer to a cortical column as being active, it's the activation (firing) of the deep pyramidal cells that we're mainly referring to. The other layers are, of course, equally important, but have more of a computational data processing role. Another population of pyramidal cells are found in the superficial layers and form part of the group of neurons responsible for computing and propagating prediction errors (2).

Pyramidal cells are glutamate-releasing excitatory neurons that tend to activate other neurons (by delivering EPSPs) to which they're connected, whether in the same or different columns. Nestled amongst these pyramidal cells is a population of GABA-releasing inhibitory neurons. These are called *interneurons* since their main role is to sit between the major computational, information-generating neurons and regulate their activity. Across the brain, inhibition is as important as excitation and, without inhibitory interneurons, excitation would rapidly spread through the cortex in an entirely uncoordinated fashion and the world model would lose all structure. As we'll see when discussing the different classes of psychedelics, these interneurons have an important role in sculpting neural activity and the world model.

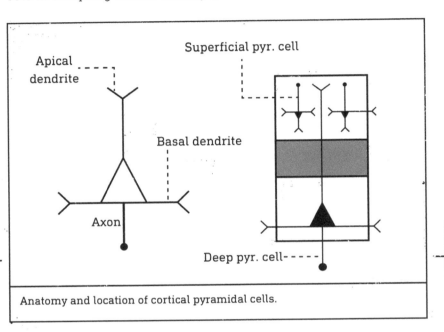

Anatomy and location of cortical pyramidal cells.

In the cortical hierarchy, connections fall into three categories:

Feedforward connections (carrying prediction errors)

Feedback connection (carrying predictions)

Lateral connections (within-level) (3).

Lateral connections are the connections between columns within a particular level of the cortical hierarchy, and are of crucial importance in sculpting the structure of that particular level of the model — the object representations we met in the last chapter. We'll focus mainly on the lateral connections between pyramidal cells, as well as those of the inhibitory interneurons.

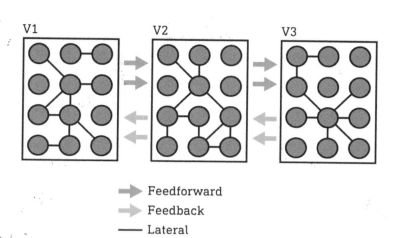

Column connection types within and between levels of cortical hierarchy.

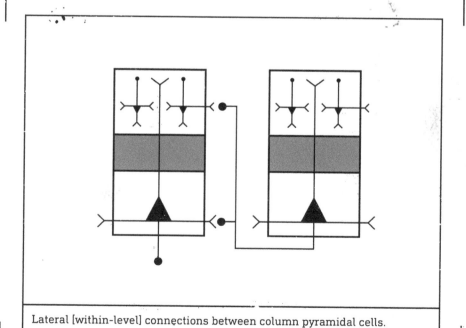

Lateral [within-level] connections between column pyramidal cells.

In addition to representing the hypotheses within its own level of the world model, each level must also "broadcast" its predictions — derived from the model — to the lower level in the cortical hierarchy. These are the feedback connections — since they pass *down* the cortical hierarchy — and are formed from deep layer pyramidal cells to neurons in the superficial layers of the level below, which have the role of computing the prediction error by comparing these predictions to the actual activity in the lower level. The prediction error must then be broadcast up to the level that made the predictions — using feedforward connections— and to its deep layers so that the model can be updated (4).

For example, in the last chapter, we saw how a single column in V2 can represent a "triangle object" by receiving convergent inputs from columns in V1 representing three lines in the appropriate orientations. Now we can see that these columns are connected by both feedforward and feedback connections:

The V2 "triangle object" column broadcasts a prediction from its deep pyramidal cells, using feedback connections, anticipating that the V1 columns representing three lines will either remain or become active in the following moment. If this prediction is fulfilled, the prediction error calculated by the superficial neurons will be zero, and no error signal will be propagated by the convergent feedforward connections from the V1 columns to the V2 column. If, on the other hand, the prediction is unfulfilled — meaning the sensory information isn't consistent with a "triangle object" — a prediction error will be generated and broadcast from the V1 columns to the V2 column. This will signal to the V2 column that it needs to update its predictions.

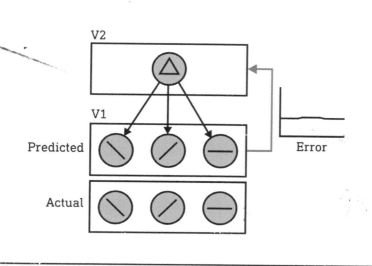

Column in V2 predicts activation of three columns in V1. Actual activation matches prediction. No error.

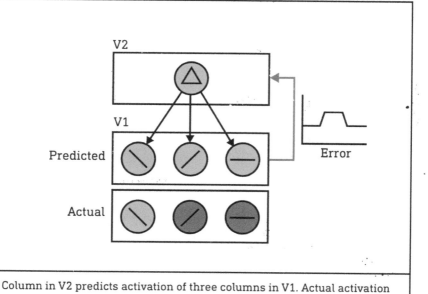

Column in V2 predicts activation of three columns in V1. Actual activation does not match prediction. Error.

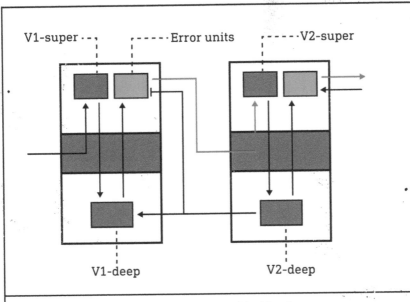

Schematic of connectivity between hierarchical levels.

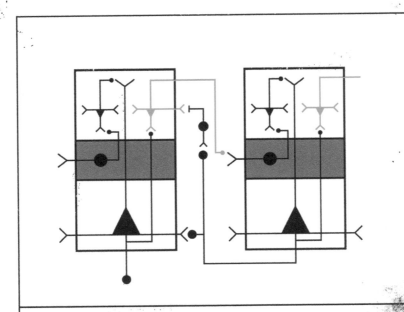

Neuronal connectivity between hierarchical levels.

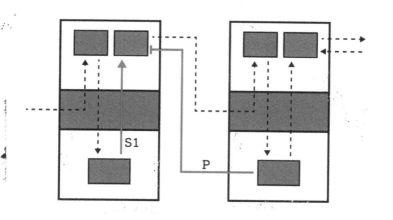

1. V2 deep pyr. cells broadcast predictions, P, to V1 superficial layers. V1 deep layers communicate current state, S1, to V1 superficial layers. Error units in V1 calculates pred. error, E.

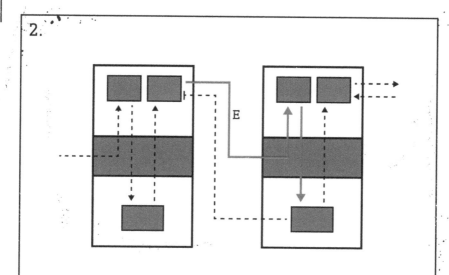

2. V1 error units broadcast error, E, to V2 input layer and then to V2 deep layers to inform model update.

The classical approach to explaining perception is that sensory information flows up the cortical hierarchy, with each level extracting features of the information and using it to piece together a world model. However, notice how this standard bottom-up approach is reversed. Each level of the cortical hierarchy actually generates its own "level" of the hierarchical model, which it uses to predict the activity in the level below, which also generates its own, lower-order, level of the model. Each level of the cortical hierarchy then adjusts its level of the model such that its predictions accurately predict the activity in (the model being generated by) the level below. This continues all the way down to V1.

So, overall, the cortex is attempting to generate — from the top of the hierarchy downwards — the pattern of column activation in V1 that will be stimulated by sensory information in the next moment. The model is being generated, not in a bottom-up fashion driven by sensory information, but in a top-down fashion driven by the cortex's high-order hypotheses. In the last chapter, we described this as an 'unpacking' of the high-order object representations to generate predictions in the levels below, down the hierarchy to V1. If the prediction perfectly matches this prediction (entirely unrealistic in a real brain), then no prediction errors will be generated by the superficial layers of the primary visual cortex and no information will flow upwards through the hierarchy. This means there is no surprising, unpredictable sensory information required by the brain to update its model. In other words, sensory information doesn't drive the generation of the model, but is only used as a kind of training signal to test whether or not the top-down generated model is working well.

The structure of the model at each level in the cortical hierarchy is determined by the connectivity between the columns and these connections are, of course, synaptic connections between neurons of one column and neurons of another. These lateral connections — since they connect columns in the same level — control the flow of information between columns within a level of the cortical hierarchy and sculpt the world model. We met these connections in chapter 3 when discussing how connectivity can sculpt the possible states — patterns of activation — that the cortical columns can adopt. Since the model is represented by deep pyramidal cells, we'll focus on the synaptic connections between these particular neurons, with the caveat that there are many other types of neurons and connections both within and between cortical columns.

Synaptic connectivity isn't a binary dictated by the mere presence or absence of a functioning synapse. Whilst new synapses form regularly, and disused ones can be "switched off" or deleted entirely, synapses can also vary in their strength (the size of response elicited in the postsynaptic neuron when a synapse fires) (see chapter 2). Having this kind of analogue control over a synapse's strength is essential for a cortex to learn the regularities in patterns of sensory information and construct object representations. Strong synaptic inter-column connections make it more likely that activity in one column will lead to activation of another. In this way, the flow of information between columns can be controlled, shaping their pattern of activity and the structure of the world model.

However, whilst this connectivity represents a storehouse of object representations — possible hypotheses — that can be drawn upon as needed, the brain must be able to select from the most likely of these object representations based upon sensory evidence, and incorporate them into the overall world model. In other words, the brain must select particular hypothesis from a set of competing hypotheses, and dismiss the alternatives. For example, if a cat suddenly appears before you, whilst it might startle you, once your brain has selected the "cat" hypothesis as the most likely explanation for this initially surprising sensory information, there isn't a jostling for alternative hypotheses in your cortex. At the highest levels of the cortical hierarchy, the pattern of cortical column activation that represents the "cat" hypothesis has situated itself within the world model. This high-level representation is then unpacked down the cortical hierarchy, broadcasting its predictions about the evolution of sensory information. From your subjective perspective, you watch the perfectly familiar and predictable experience of a cat padding across your path.

Whenever your cortex settles upon a particular hypothesis given the incoming sensory information, specific predictions about the evolution of that sensory information are generated. If this hypothesis fails to make accurate predictions and errors begin to accumulate, the hypothesis will either be updated or alternatives tested until the errors decline. Of course, when the brain is in a normal, sober, waking state, this all happens with such speed that it's entirely unnoticed, unless there is some obvious confusion over the interpretation of the information being received by the senses.

Although the brain is constantly refining its connectivity, the selecting and switching of hypotheses must occur much more rapidly than could be achieved by modifying synaptic connectivity (which takes minutes to hours). Rather, the cortex exploits its connectivity to rapidly generate the stable patterns of column activity that represent those hypotheses. Alternative hypotheses must compete for representation, with the winning hypotheses becoming enfolded into the world model and successfully broadcasting their predictions down the cortical hierarchy (5). The losing alternative hypotheses must be deactivated and discarded. However, should prediction errors begin to accumulate — indicating that a particular hypothesis is failing — the cortex must rapidly modify the hypothesis or switch to a new one entirely.

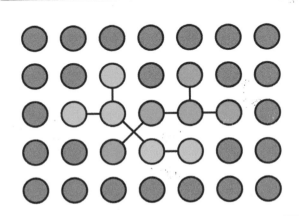

Two object representations within a hierarchical level.

Generally, the hypotheses most likely to win out for representation in the world model are those built from synchronously active columns generating a stable and robust pattern of activation (we'll discuss what is meant by "synchronised" activity shortly) that generates coherent downwards flowing predictions and keeps error signals at a low level. Such a hypothesis need only make minor updates, allowing its activity to further strengthen and stabilise. On the contrary, if a hypotheses fails to make good predictions, prediction errors will force major updates to the hypothesis, effectively distorting it and forcing a pattern of activation outside of the stored object representation. Eventually, the hypothesis becomes fragmented and incomplete and is unable to maintain itself, further weakening its predictions and making it even more susceptible to degradation by upwards flowing errors. These weaker hypotheses are rapidly extinguished by stronger competing hypotheses, until the cortex settles on the most likely explanation for the sensory information, which is the hypothesis that takes its place within the world model. The cat might initially have been mistaken for a small dog, a crow, or perhaps even a large rat. And, indeed, all reasonable hypotheses would have been rapidly explored and tested against the flow of sensory information. However, within a second or so, the "cat" hypothesis prevails, maintaining itself against sensory information testing and extinguishing the alternatives. It can then begin to broadcast strong predictions down to the next level of the cortical hierarchy.

This competition between alternative hypotheses relies on lateral connections to GABA-releasing inhibitory interneurons in the same level of the hierarchy (6). Whilst they only account for around 15% of neurons in the cortex, the role of interneurons in regulating the activity of other neurons cannot be overstated. These interneurons synapse with excitatory neurons and release GABA, which binds to the GABA receptors on the post-synaptic excitatory cell and pulls its membrane potential away from the firing threshold. A constant low-level — tonic — inhibition keeps the activity of excitatory neurons in check, and stronger inhibition can be used to effectively shut down excitatory activity as necessary to control the patterns of neural activity in the cortex. If this

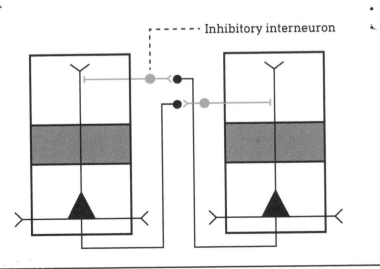

Columns use lateral connections to inhibitory interneurons to suppress the activation of competing columns.

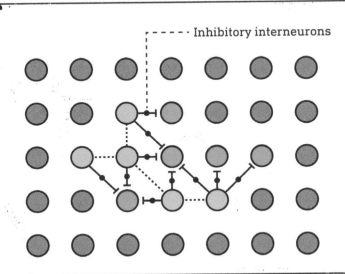

A hypothesis [object representation, blue columns] can use inh. interneurons to suppress competing hypotheses [red columns].

inhibitory activity is compromised, neurons will tend to fire more often and remain active for longer. In extreme cases, this can lead to seizures, in which neural activity becomes completely out of control. A set of columns that represents a particular hypothesis can activate — and effectively "recruit" — a set of inhibitory interneurons that will then inhibit, and ultimately extinguish, the activity of columns representing alternative hypotheses. A strong, coherent pattern of columns will be able to recruit more inhibitory interneurons and more effectively suppress other columns (and thus hypotheses). As one hypothesis begins to win out, other hypotheses are progressively prevented from maintaining themselves and generating predictions (7).

In addition to competing with alternate hypotheses by actively suppressing them using interneurons, a hypothesis will also attempt to maximise the impact of its predictions on the cortical level below. It can achieve this by ensuring that its columns synchronise their outputs from the deep layer pyramidal cells to the superficial layers of the level below. Predictions broadcast from deep pyramidal cells that are synchronised in their activity are more effective than those delivered by incoherent or random ones.

This makes sense for two reasons: Firstly, a single neuron in the superficial layers might receive input from a large number of deep pyramidal cells, all attempting to broadcast their predictions from the higher level. If those presynaptic deep pyramidal neurons are firing synchronously — if the columns of a particular hypothesis are synchronised in their activity — they naturally deliver their EPSPs within a very narrow time window. This makes it much more likely that these EPSPs can be integrated before decaying and successfully induce an action potential in the postsynaptic neuron (which is the measure of an effect). On the contrary, neurons that fire independently will have to rely on chance alone to deliver EPSPs within the time window required for integration. Most of these randomly-delivered EPSPs are likely to decay before being integrated with other EPSPs. Secondly, synchronised activity in the deep pyramidal cells is more likely to induce synchronised activity in the lower-level superficial neurons. In oth-

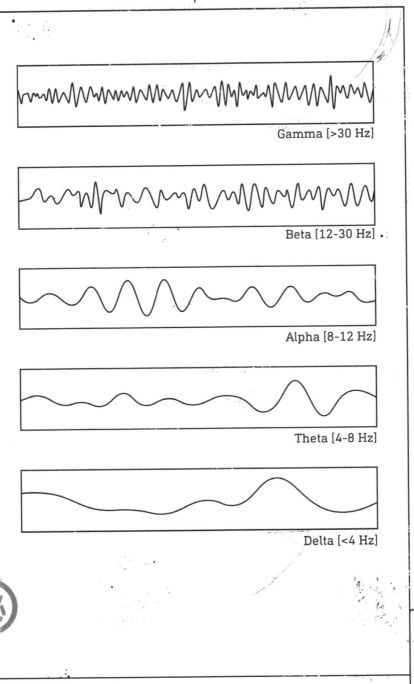

Gamma [>30 Hz]

Beta [12-30 Hz]

Alpha [8-12 Hz]

Theta [4-8 Hz]

Delta [<4 Hz]

Frequency bands measurable on a human EEG.

er words, a hypothesis built from synchronised columns is more likely to "implant" its predictions in the level below by inducing a pattern of self-sustaining coherent activity in the superficial neurons.

Despite the importance of synchronisation, the columns that comprise a particular hypothesis might well be distributed across columns not directly connected and, as such, synchronising their activity is far from trivial. Even though strongly connected columns in close proximity can influence each other's activity, the propagation of action potentials between columns isn't instantaneous, and synaptic delays make synchronisation more difficult. This time delay obviously becomes more of a problem the greater the distance between columns. The cortex solves this problem, not by relying on direct column-to-column connections, but by using neural oscillations.

Anyone who's seen an EEG (electroencephalography) trace is familiar with the complex patterns of oscillating electrical activity that can be measured through the skull. An EEG signal is a complex wave structure that can be decomposed to reveal a number of different electrical oscillations that emerge across the brain. These oscillations are separated into frequency bands ranging from low frequency (<4 Hz) delta waves to high frequency (>35 Hz) gamma waves. Depending on the state of the subject being measured — whether they're awake or asleep, sober or under the influence of a drug — the raw EEG signal will comprise varying proportions of these frequency bands (8).

These electrical oscillations aren't merely a consequence of the electrochemical processing — action potentials, PSPs, and synaptic activity — that underlies brain activity, but are actively generated and utilised by the brain in almost all aspects of its functioning, including construction of the world model. Oscillations can be measured in both individual neurons and in networks of neurons. So far, we've thought of the resting potential as being stable and static — the neuron sits at this negative potential "waiting" for inputs from other neurons. In reality, the membrane potential is almost never truly resting or constant. As we have seen, the membrane potential is constantly being manipulated by an array of inputs from other neurons — EPSPs and IPSPs that move the potential towards or away from the threshold potential. However, even in the absence of any input from other neurons, the resting potential doesn't remain perfectly stable, but tends to oscillate, periodically moving towards and away from the threshold. These so-called *subthreshold membrane oscillations* emerge from a range of different ion channels in the neuronal membrane that open and close periodically and according to the membrane potential. The frequency of these oscillations can vary depending on the type of neuron and the ion channels present in the membrane, allowing neurons to be 'tuned' to receive specific frequencies of inputs and, in turn, generate specific frequencies of output (action potentials).

Imagine two neurons connected in sequence, with the postsynaptic neuron's membrane potential oscillating at a specific frequency (i.e. oscillations per second, Hz). The presynaptic neuron fires an action potential, glutamate is released into the synaptic cleft, and an EPSP is generated in the postsynaptic neuron. If this EPSP occurs when the subthreshold oscillation is at its peak (and so closest to the firing threshold), rather than at its trough, it's more likely to push the postsynaptic membrane potential over the threshold and trigger an action potential in the postsynaptic neuron. Although a single EPSP is unlikely to trigger an action potential in the postsynaptic neuron, a series of EPSPs at a frequency such that each is generated at the peak of the oscillation are likely to rapidly drive it over the threshold. We can thus say that the postsynaptic neuron is 'tuned' to receiving input at this frequency. Further, the postsynaptic neuron will begin to fire action potentials at this frequency and affect downstream neurons to which it's connected. If we connect several of these neurons together in a loop then, very quickly, they will begin to synchronise their firing at this frequency. In the brain, neurons tend to form many different loops, circuits, and networks of varying sizes and complexity that become entrained in oscillations of different frequencies. However, when we say that a network is oscillating at a particular frequency, this doesn't mean that all the neurons in the network are firing at the same time (or even at exactly the same frequency), but that the overall network alternates between periods of high and low firing activity at that frequency.

A remarkable property of the thalamocortical column circuitry is its ability to generate and sustain oscillations at different frequencies. Networks of fast-spiking interneurons in the superficial layers of the cortex tend to exhibit sustained oscillations in the gamma range (>35 Hz) (8). Superficial pyramidal cells receive inputs from these interneurons and are themselves entrained to fire at this frequency — the interneurons provide a synchronised oscillatory inhibit-release cycle that gives the excitatory pyramidal cells a repeating window of opportunity to fire (in the release phase, when they're not being inhibited), but prevents them from firing whilst being inhibited (8). This can rapidly entrain large groups of neurons that aren't directly connected to begin firing in synchrony. And so, by extension, gamma oscillations within a single column can soon become synchronised with the oscillations of other columns, creating an assembly of active columns synchronised at the gamma frequency.

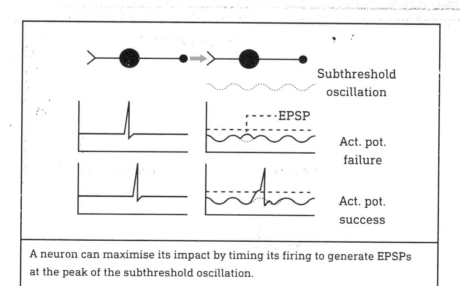

Subthreshold oscillation

EPSP

Act. pot. failure

Act. pot. success

A neuron can maximise its impact by timing its firing to generate EPSPs at the peak of the subthreshold oscillation.

The deep pyramidal cells, representing the world model and generating its predictions, naturally fire in the lower frequency (alpha and beta) bands and use networks of interneurons within the cortex and thalamus to maintain the oscillations that synchronise their activity (9). So, if a particular pattern of columns representing a hypothesis are able to synchronise their alpha-beta oscillations, then their outputs — predictions — will also be more synchronised and broadcast at this frequency (10). This entrains the neurons in the superficial layers receiving the predictions to also begin oscillating at this frequency. In effect, the hypothesis has induced its particular pattern of oscillations in the lower level superficial layer.

Notice that the lower-frequency alpha-beta oscillations arriving from the higher level "collide" with the higher-frequency gamma oscillations being generated in the superficial layers. Phase synchronisation between these high and low frequency oscillations helps in "matching" the downward-flowing predictions with the actual activity in the lower level (11). So, overall, both the downwards-flowing predictions using the alpha-beta channel and upward-flowing error signals using the gamma channel can maximise their impact by maximising the synchrony of their oscillations. The propagation of predictions down the cortical hierarchy can be monitored using EEG as backwards travelling alpha-beta waves (12), and are most pronounced when an EEG subject is in a resting, closed-eye state without sensory stimulation. When the eyes are opened and the world model again becomes accountable to sensory information, higher frequency gamma oscillations travelling in the opposite direction, up the cortical hierarchy, become more prominent (13).

Together with the dense network of interneurons that infiltrate the cortex, these oscillations help orchestrate the dance of cortical column activation that forms the world. Transient congregations of columns that jostle for representation in the world model, each attempting to prove itself against the noisy patterns of information that continuously arrive from the environment via the sensory apparatus.

Chapter Summary.

1. Hypotheses (different object representations) compete for representation in the cortex, and thus incorporation into the world model, by forming stable and synchronised patterns of column activation.

2. Competition between hypotheses is effected by the recruitment of inhibitory interneurons, allowing columns to suppress the activity of other columns.

3. Synchronisation of cortical columns (in the alpha and gamma bands, respectively) is important in maximising the impact of predictions on lower levels and error signals on the level above.

4. Deep layers synchronise in the alpha band, with backwards travelling alpha waves indexing the flow of predictions down the cortical hierarchy. The superficial layers synchronise in the gamma band, with forward travelling gamma waves indexing the flow of prediction errors up the cortical hierarchy.

When you open your eyes and view the world, you're confronted with your cortex's model of the environment built from a stable yet dynamic hierarchically-organised pattern of cortical column activation. By sculpting its connectivity, the cortex has constrained its state repertoire to a small region of the cortical state space — the Consensus Reality Space — containing those states that represent a useful and functional model of the environment. By learning object representations, rapidly selecting and incorporating these representations into the overall world model, and just as rapidly updating and switching to alternative representations in response to sensory information, your cortex has learned to tune into the environment. It's easy to assume that your brain has, in fact, learned to construct the truest model of reality and, perhaps, the only model that counts. But, psychedelic molecules reveal that the cortex is capable of reaching out of the Consensus Reality Space into the practically limitless and almost entirely unexplored terrains of its state space.

It's time to enter the World Space.

現実制御学研究所、東京

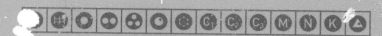

リアリティ
スイッチ.

<XXXXXX_3489_027_AO>

Chapter 6: The World Space

世界空間

「セカイクウカン」

"What happens is, the world is completely replaced, instantly, 100%. It's all gone. And not one iota of what's put in its place was taken from this world. So it's a 100% reality channel switch."

Terence McKenna

When Terence McKenna first smoked DMT in his tiny Berkeley apartment in 1965, he was catapulted from the old familiar world into a bizarre hyperdimensional reality that not only did he not expect, but which he could not have expected. He never got over that first trip and spent the remainder of his truncated life raving to rapt audiences about his wild sojourns in the impossible domains to which DMT grants access and the lively elfin beings that inhabit them.

> *"I had this hallucination of tumbling forward into these fractal geometric spaces made of light and then I found myself in the equivalent of the Pope's private chapel and there were insect elf machines proffering strange little tablets with strange writing on them, and I was aghast, completely appalled, because in a matter of seconds . . . my entire expectation of the nature of the world was just being shredded in front of me."* (1)

What's remarkable, and invariably shocking, about DMT is the ferocious efficiency with which it replaces the familiar waking world with one altogether unfamiliar and unexpected. The DMT space is not an alternate or distorted version of the consensus world, but another reality channel entirely. However, just like the normal waking world, it is a model constructed by the cortex, as all phenomenal worlds must be. Of course, the states of the Consensus Reality Space are mapped to an external environment, from which they receive information via the senses and against which they are continuously tested. But the model itself is always constructed by the cortex. The same is true for the DMT space, although it must remain an open question as to whether these strange realms are a model of some kind of freestanding external reality or, as many prefer to assume, a pure cortical fabrication. We will return to this issue in chapter 10, but it's important to stress again that all phenomenal worlds are built from information generated by the cortex, whether they're mapped to and tested against information from an external environment or not.

If we could freeze time and measure the activity in every cortical column responsible for constructing your phenomenal world, we would find a unique pattern of column activation that represented your world at that moment. Whether you're in a normal waking state, fast asleep and dreaming, or at the peak of a breakthrough DMT trip, each moment of your experienced world is built from the information generated by that particular state of the cortex being selected from countless others. Your experience of a world is the flow of your cortex from one unified hierarchical pattern of column activation to the next.

When you're awake and navigating the environment in a reasonably sober state, sensory information is used to guide the selection of states and the movement from state to state, which we described as a cycle of model testing and updating. But, even in the dream state, your cortex tends to adopt the same states as during waking, despite lacking the guidance of sensory input. Your cortex has sculpted its connectivity such that the states comprising the Consensus Reality Space are those it naturally moves through.

However, immediately after inhaling 30mg of DMT vapour, the cortex begins to adopt states that bear no resemblance to those of the familiar world — the cortex finds and reaches states entirely disjoint from those of the Consensus Reality Space and, quite literally, switches to a new reality channel. This naturally raises the question as to how and why this occurs and, tantalisingly, whether there are other reality channels available to the cortex, just waiting for the right pharmacological stimulation to reveal themselves.

The number of possible states (patterns of column activation) of the cortex is a number so massive as to be incalculable. But since it's impossible for the cortex to represent a world outside of this set of column activation patterns, this set of states forms a truly vast but finite *state space* representing all possible worlds. And, since each state represents your entire world at any moment, we'll refer to this state space as the *World Space*. It is within this World Space that alternate reality channels, including the DMT space, can be discovered and explored.

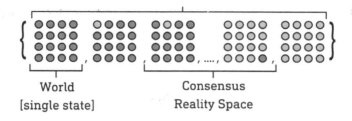

World
[single state]

Consensus
Reality Space

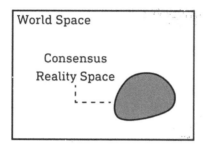

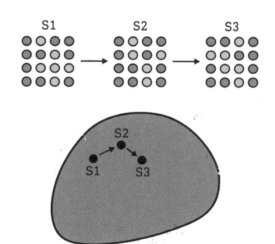

The experience of a world is the movement of the cortex through the World
Space, from state to state. The Consensus Reality Space is a subset of
states within the World Space.

Of course, most of the states within the World Space wouldn't represent anything like a coherent and meaningful reality, and we can't assume that all possible cortical states would be conscious states — deep sleep and anaesthesia, for example, are characterised by the lack of a world. The World Space includes only those states that represent phenomenal, experienced worlds. So, when we use the capitalised "World", we mean very specifically a single state of the cortex — a single pattern of activation — experienced as a phenomenal world at a point in time. We are not referring to "the world" in any other vague or general sense of the term (such as the "consensus world" or the "DMT world").

The movement of your cortex from state to state over time is precisely its movement through the World Space, from World to World. Your World changes with each passing moment, although the differences are usually subtle. The Consensus Reality Space occupies a (very large) set of states within the World Space, and your cortex has sculpted its connectivity such that it naturally moves through these states, which are those that comprise a functional model of the environment in normal waking life.

The states that the cortex naturally tends to adopt are determined by its underlying connectivity, the baseline activation of different types of both excitatory and inhibitory neurons, levels of endogenous neuromodulators and, of course, the presence or absence of exogenous molecules we know as psychedelics.

Complex systems, including the cortex, tend to move towards particular patterns of activity — these are known as attractor states, since the system is attracted towards these states in much the same way that a marble is attracted to the bottom of a glass bowl (2). Released into the bowl, the marble eventually finds its way to the lowest energy state and, similarly, the cortex tends to move towards certain states. Of course, whilst the bowl has a single attractor state, the cortex has a vast number of states and sculpts its connectivity to ensure that those states it tends to move towards are those that maximise its ability to predict the evolution of sensory information.

A Hopfield network is a simple type of artificial neural network — known as an *attractor network* — in which every node (corresponding to the cell body of a real neuron) is connected to every other node. Each node in the network can exist in either an active (1) or inactive (0) state, and all possible patterns of activation form the network's state space. No matter the starting state (activation pattern), a Hopfield network will always converge to one or more attractor states. However, the connection weights — equivalent to the strength of synaptic connections in the cortex — can be tuned such that any desired state becomes an attractor state (3). In other words, the network can be used to store any particular pattern to which the network will move. Since the network moves away from certain states and towards the attractor states, echoing the trajectory of a marble in a bowl, these are described as high and low energy states, respectively (although there is no simple relationship between "energy" as used here and energy in the more usual sense: electrical energy, gravitational potential energy, etc). Low energy states are favoured states, whereas unfavoured states are high energy. Despite being far more complex than any Hopfield network, by virtue of its connectivity, the cortex also tends to move towards certain low energy attractor states and away from other high energy states. It's the role of connectivity to ensure that the attractor states are those that represent functional models of the environment capable of predicting sensory information.

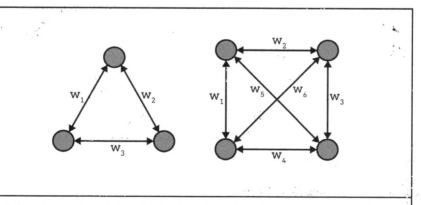

A 3-node and 4-node Hopfield network. Each node can occupy an active or inactive state with weighted symmetric connections between nodes.

If we were to plot every possible state of the cortex representing a conscious world — the entire World Space — on a plane, with the height above the plane representing the energy of the state, an "energetic landscape" or "attractor landscape" is generated, which we'll refer to as the *World Space Landscape* (4).

In an entirely unconnected cortex, in which every column is activated independently, every state would be equally likely and the landscape would be perfectly flat — the cortex wouldn't tend to move towards or away from any particular state, since there would be no relatively high and low-energy states. Of course, such a cortex would completely fail to represent any kind of meaningful model of the environment, and would wander randomly from state to state. But, by sculpting its connectivity, a landscape with distinct high-energy hills and low-energy valleys and basins develops.

Every low-energy state is essentially one that the cortex has "stored" by modifying its connectivity such that the state can easily be accessed. These are the states that represent a world model that successfully predicts the evolution of sensory information using a hieratically-organised system of object representations, and your experience of a dynamic yet stable and predictable world is the experience of your cortex gliding through these low-energy state valleys (5).

One can frame the entire process of tuning the connectivity between cortical columns as a sculpting of this World Space Landscape such that the low energy states form the most functional model of the environment. The shape of the World Space Landscape isn't fixed, of course, but can be further moulded as the cortex adjusts its connectivity during development and learning. And, by amplifying or suppressing certain types of connections, and by modulating the excitability of specific neuron types, neuromodulators can also temporarily distort the shape of the landscape, as can psychedelic drugs. In fact, many of the effects of the psychedelics on the structure and dyamics of your world can be explained by their effect on the World Space Landscape.

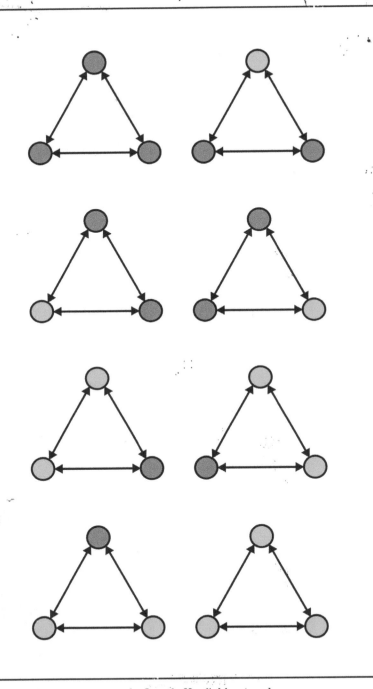

The complete state space of a 3-node Hopfield network.

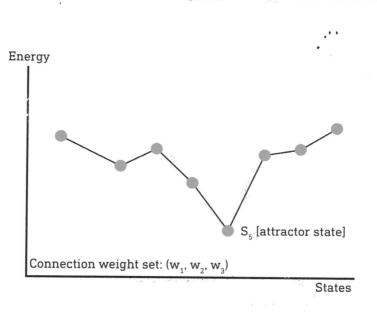

Energy

S₅ [attractor state]

Connection weight set: (w_1, w_2, w_3)

States

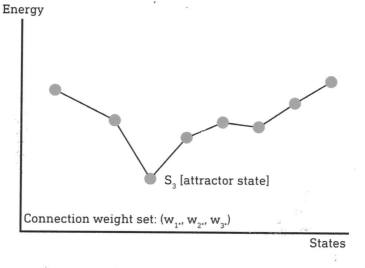

Energy

S₃ [attractor state]

Connection weight set: ($w_{1'}$, $w_{2'}$, $w_{3'}$)

States

A Hopfield network will always move towards the lowest energy attractor state, which depends on the connection weights, (w_1, w_2, w_3)

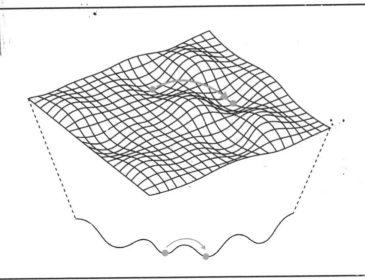

The cortical World Space forms a landscape of high-energy hills and low-energy basins and valleys.

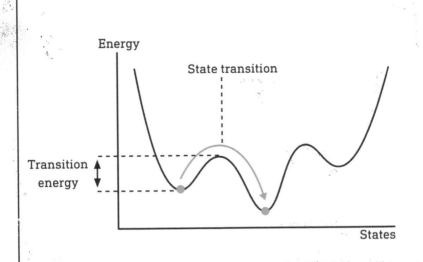

The cortex moves along the World Space Landscape by transitioning from state to state, guided by its geometry.

When a pattern of sensory information enters the brain, it stimulates cortical columns. This activity spreads through the cortical networks and threatens to push the cortex up a hill towards a disfavoured high energy state. If you've ever watched the rather terrifying "skeleton" event during the Winter Olympics, in which the competitors hurtle headfirst on a sled down a winding frozen track, you'll appreciate this effect: Although the shape of the track guides the sled even at (literal) breakneck speeds, any loss of concentration or interference from a careless spectator can lead to the athlete flying off the track with disastrous consequences.

Likewise, although the cortex will naturally glide from one low-energy state to the next, guided by the valleys of the attractor landscape, a flood of column-activating sensory information can quickly push it into a high-energy state. However, by predicting the sensory information, and reducing it to a minimal and tightly-regulated trickle of error signals, the sensory information can be used by the cortex to gently push it from state to state along the low-energy valleys. And whilst surprising, unpredictable, sensory information will tend to nudge the cortex up a hill, it quickly finds a new state — the best hypothesis — that drops it back into an attractor valley.

If the current hypothesis fails to predict the evolution of sensory information, we can say that the cortex is in the "wrong attractor" and a flood of error signals (unpredicted sensory information) will drive the cortex up a hill from which point into can drop back down into the "correct attractor" — the cortex updates its model with a new hypothesis.

When you view the hollow face illusion, your brain initially locates the best hypothesis — a regular convex face — and shifts into a valley of the cortex's attractor landscape. However, as the face rotates and error signals begin to accumulate, the cortex is pushed into a high energy state. The updating of the hypothesis — the reverse concave side of a mask — is the cortex dropping into a different low-energy attractor of the landscape from this high energy position.

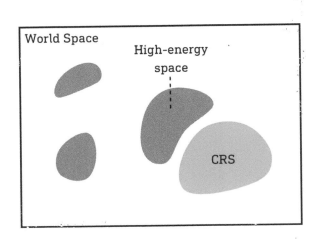

World Space

High-energy space

CRS

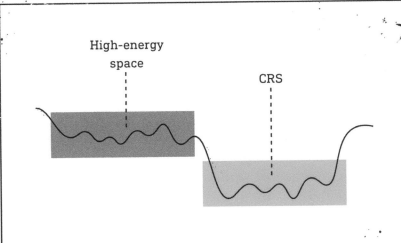

High-energy space

CRS

The Consensus Reality Space (CRS) forms a low-energy basin within which the cortex normally remains. Other high-energy regions are usually inaccessible.

In the dream state, without this gentle guidance from sensory information, the cortex wanders this World Space Landscape more freely. But, naturally, it wanders along the low energy basins and valleys. As such, the world model in the dream state tends to be as with the normal waking world, since the overall shape of the World Space Landscape remains similar to its shape during waking.

To reach and explore entirely separate regions of the World Space, the shape of the World Space Landscape must be distorted, lowering the energy of disfavoured states such that they become attractors, whilst raising the energy of the Consensus Reality Space states. The cortex will then move effortlessly away from these states and towards the new attractor states and into a new region of the World Space. Psychedelic molecules provide the molecular perturbation that causes this temporary World Space Landscape restructuring, making available normally inaccessible states within the World Space. This effect can be subtle or astonishingly dramatic, depending on the psychedelic molecule and dosage. Since the DMT world is represented by states completely disjoint from those of the normal waking world, we know that the DMT Space exists in a separate region of the World Space from the Consensus Reality Space. This means DMT must distort the structure of the World Space Landscape such that the states representing those bizarre realms become attractor states. But before we can explain how and why this distortion occurs, we need to begin at the lowest level, with the interactions between psychedelics and membrane-bound receptors.

Chapter Summary.

1. All possible states of the cortex that represent a phenomenal world form a World Space.

2. Channel Consensus Reality is one region of the World Space.

3. The World Space forms an attractor landscape (World Space Landscape) with a shape sculpted by the interactions between

columns (patterns of connectivity and strengths of connections).

4. A phenomenal world is experienced as a trajectory through the World Space dependent on the landscape structure. At any point in time, the cortex occupies a position within the World Space and will move to another point in the following moment.

5. Psychedelics can distort the shape of the World Space Landscape, changing the states that act as attractors, and/or the cortex's trajectory through the World Space.

6. Alternate reality channels exist within separate regions of the World Space and can only be accessed by major distortion of the World Space Landscape.

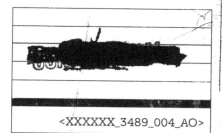

<XXXXXX_3489_004_AO>

リアリティ
スイッチ

Chapter 7: The World Space Switches

世界空間 スイッチ

「セカイクウカンスイッチ」

"And in the bloodlit dark behind his eyes, silver
phosphenes boiling in from the edge of space,
hypnagogic images jerking past like film compiled
from random frames. Symbols, figures, faces, a
blurred, fragmented mandala of visual information."

William Gibson,

When a psychedelic molecule reaches your brain, your world model, refined and perfected over evolutionary epochs and throughout your life, begins to change. Your brain's tuning becomes disrupted, nudged towards a new channel:

With low doses, these effects might well be subtle: colours become brighter, objects begin to breathe or shimmer, and the contents of your old familiar world begin somehow to take on an ineffably elevated presence and significance.

As the dosage is increased, alterations in the structure of your world become more dramatic and noticeable: what began as a subtle shimmer grows into an outright morphing and reconfiguration of the world. Objects dissolve and reform with entirely new identities, as the world becomes fluid and unstable, ever shifting before the eyes. Soon, the distinction between self and other begins to dissolve as you're enfolded into the unified field of conscious awareness.

At the highest doses, all semblance of the old world is lost and replaced in its entirety with one thoroughly strange and utterly new.

The switch complete, your brain has found a new reality channel.

You're greeted by strange creatures that inhabit this new realm. Intelligent and curious, they dance and sing as you stare back in disbelief and awe.

What has happened?

(S)

How is this possible?

How did I get here?

Have I died?

How will I get home?

The range of psychedelic molecules available to the modern psychonaut is extensive and growing, each transforming the world in its own distinct way. However, what all these molecules have in common is their altering of the structure and dynamics of the world model constructed by your brain. The key to understanding these changes begins at the lowest level in the brain's hierarchically-organised complex world-building machinery.

Like the brain, the neuron is a complex emergent structure whose function depends on a vast set of interactions between a multitude of components. However, whereas the brain emerges as a complex system of neurons, each neuron itself emerges as a complex system of interacting molecules: proteins, lipids, carbohydrates, minerals, and ions. And also, just as the brain uses sensory information from the environment to test and update its model, the neuron relies on information from outside of itself — from the surrounding milieu — to regulate its own function and behaviour. Whereas the cortex relies on the sensory apparatus to absorb information from the environment, neurons use receptors. We've already met two important receptors: the AMPA receptor, which binds glutamate and transmits sodium across the membrane, and the GABA receptor, responsible for passing negatively-charged chloride ions. In addition to these, every neuron boasts a gamut of different receptors embedded in its membrane designed to detect molecules in its environment.

Glutamate and GABA are the major wiring neurotransmitters providing the chemical connection between the pre- and post-synaptic neuron and eliciting the fleeting EPSPs and IPSPs integrated by the cell body. However, in addition to these fast neurotransmitters are a range of molecules — neuromodulators — that affect a neuron over more extended periods of time. Like neurotransmitters, neuromodulators are released from the axonal synaptic bouton in response to action potentials. However, the neurons releasing neuromodulators tend to form wider, more open, synaptic connections. This so-called volume transmission allows the neuromodulator to diffuse out of the synaptic cleft and affect large numbers of neurons at the same time (1). For example, serotonin (5-hydroxytryptamine, 5HT) is manufactured mainly by a small cluster of neurons in the brainstem, called the Raphe nucleus. Axons from this cluster of cell bodies reach out like long tendrils that infiltrate all areas of the cortex, pumping out serotonin which bathes large areas of the cortex.

The effect of a neuromodulator on a neuron depends entirely on the receptors with which it interacts. Serotonin binds to at least seven different receptor types (named 5HT1 to 5HT7), some of which also possess multiple subtypes (given additional subscripts, a, b, c, etc) (2). Each receptor type has its own characteristic effect on a neuron. So, overall, the effect of serotonin — or indeed any neuromodulator — on a neuron depends entirely upon the serotonin receptor types embedded in its membrane. Most neurons in the cortex will contain receptors for a range of different neuromodulators, perhaps several different subtypes, each modulating the activity of the neuron in its own subtle, or profound, way.

One of the most common effects of a neuromodulator receptor is to alter the membrane potential, similar to, albeit often in a much more sustained manner than, the AMPA and GABA receptors. The 5HT2A receptor, for example, exerts a long-lasting depolarising effect on a neuron, making it more likely that it will fire, since the sum of EPSPs from presynaptic activity will be more likely to nudge the membrane potential over the firing threshold (3). This is also called *excitation*, often described as increasing the excitability of the neuron. In contrast, the 5HT1A receptor has the opposite effect, hyperpolarising the neuron, pulling its membrane potential further from threshold and making it less likely that the neuron will fire, reducing its excitability. So, overall, the effect of serotonin on a neuron's membrane potential will depend largely on the balance of 5HT1A and 5HT2A receptors.

Of course, in addition to these particular receptor subtypes, a neuron is likely to contain other 5HT receptor subtypes and, as such, it can be difficult to predict how serotonin will affect a particular type of neuron's membrane potential without actually measuring it. More generally, the effect of any particular neuromodulator on a neuron will depend on the selection and arrangement of receptor types in its membrane. And, overall, the activity and behaviour of a neuron is regulated by the combined effects of large numbers of different neuromodulator receptors.

As well as the endogenous neuromodulators, exogenous molecules also interact with neurons via their receptors. This includes, of course, the so-called classic psychedelics, such as psilocybin, LSD, and DMT. And it is through the classic psychedelics' interactions with neuromodulator receptors that they elicit their remarkable effects on the brain and the structure of your world.

Neuromodulator receptors (including the serotonin receptors) are proteins that span the neuronal membrane, with an extracellular domain (containing the binding site for the neuromodulator) on the outside, a transmembrane domain passing through the membrane itself, and an intracellular domain exposed to the interior of the cell and its networks of molecules. The AMPA and GABA receptors are *ionotropic* (literally: ion-moving) receptors. Glutamate, for example, binds to a site on the extracellular domain of the AMPA receptor, whose transmembrane domain forms a channel through which sodium ions can flow. The 5HT receptors, however, belong to an entirely different neuromodulator receptor family known as the *metabotropic* receptors. Like the ionotropic receptors, metabotropic receptors also contain three distinct domains. However, unlike the ionotropic receptors, the metabotropic receptors don't transmit ions — or any type of molecule — across the neuronal membrane. The metabotropic receptors essentially allow the outside of the cell the speak to the inside, to signal the presence or absence of a particular molecule — a neuromodulator or an exogenous molecule — in the neuron's environment. In other words, metabotropic receptors transmit *information* across the membrane and into the complex network of signalling molecules inside the neuron. Whereas sensory information relies on the sensory apparatus to stimulate the cortex, molecules use receptors to stimulate the inside of the neuron.

Like all proteins, a receptor is constructed from a chain of ami-

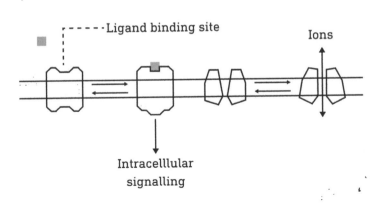

Ionotropic receptors [right] transmit ions across the neuronal membrane.
Metabotropic receptors [left] transmit information by perturbing
intracellular signalling.

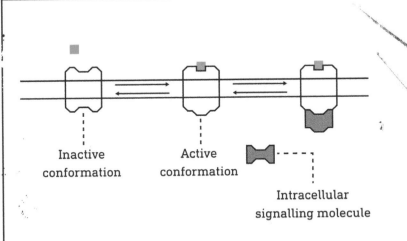

Binding of the ligand to the ligand binding site shifts the intracellular
domain into an active conformation, allowing it to interact with intracellular
signalling molecules.

no acids in a sequence defined by genes encoded in DNA. It is the folding of this chain into a precise 3-dimensional shape — its tertiary structure — that gives each protein type its characteristic structure and function. This folding is controlled by both weak and strong chemical interactions between the amino acids, including charge interactions (attractive and repulsive), hydrogen bonds, and strong covalent bonds. The overall 3-dimensional shape of the protein emerges from all of these interactions to form a precisely but delicately folded shape. A complete metabotropic receptor is actually composed of seven proteins (termed subunits) — the individual subunits join together to form the complete functional receptor. The same applies to ionotropic receptors, although they're usually built from three to five subunits.

The protein subunits of a receptor, whilst precisely folded, are often quite flexible and can flip between two or more distinct shapes or *conformational states* which control the function of the receptor. For example, we saw in chapter 2 how the AMPA receptor can exist in an open or closed state, with the glutamate molecule controlling which state is adopted by the receptor. In the absence of glutamate, the receptor sits in a conformational state in which the ion channel is blocked. However, when glutamate binds to the *ligand-binding site* (a ligand is simply any molecule or protein that binds to a receptor) on the AMPA extracellular domain, it causes the receptor protein to flip to a different conformational state in which the channel is cleared, allowing sodium ions to flow into the neuron. This same principle applies to all types of neurotransmitter and neuromodulator receptor: binding of the ligand — whether serotonin, LSD, or DMT — causes the receptor to flip to a distinct conformational state that alters the function of the receptor.

All molecules are defined as chemically-bonded sets of atoms that form a particular molecular structure — a certain shape. Furthermore, certain atom types — such as oxygen and nitrogen — tend to hold onto electrons more strongly than other atoms and, as such, molecules that contain such atoms tend to have an uneven charge distribution. This means that certain parts of the molecule contain a slight negative charge, balanced by parts with a slight positive

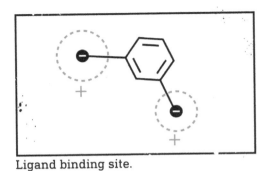

Ligand binding site.

Uneven electron distribution in a molecule create regions with full/partial negative/positive charge. When appropriately positioned, these charges form bonds with opposing charges within the receptor's ligand binding site.

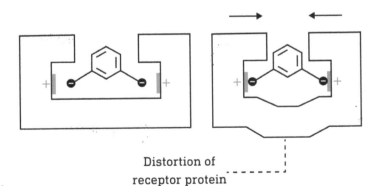

Distortion of
receptor protein

Binding of the ligand distorts the ligand binding site and induces a conformational change in the receptor intracellular domain, shifting the receptor into an active conformational state.

charge. The overall shape and charge distribution of a molecule will determine whether and how it can interact with a receptor. The ligand binding site of a receptor also has a precisely-defined shape determined by the folding of the protein chain and, since this protein chain is constructed from amino acid molecules, has areas of positive and negative charge. A molecule with a shape and charge distribution complementary to that of the receptor's ligand binding site will tend to interact with the site. This is often likened to the way a key fits into a lock. In addition to having the correct shape, it's important that repulsive like-charges (negative to negative or positive to positive) don't clash, as this is likely to push the molecule out of the binding site. In contrast, if positive charges on the molecule can interact with negative charges in the binding site (or vice versa) then these will tend to pull the molecule into the site.

Once a molecule has found its way into a receptor's ligand binding site, the molecular shape and the charge interactions will often pull on the receptor and distort its delicate 3-dimensional structure. Since the binding site is part of continuous amino acid chain, these distortions may not be restricted to the binding site, but can cause the entire receptor subunit to distort or twist out of shape. In other words, by occupying the ligand binding site, the molecule pulls the receptor into a different conformational state. This is the fundamental basis of the receptor mechanism. The molecule is effectively *selecting* a particular conformational state of the receptor and, by doing so, is generating information (refer to our definition of information from chapter 2: information is generated when a system — in this case the receptor — selects between a finite number of distinct states). This is the information that is passed through the neuronal membrane from outside to inside — the distortion of the receptor ligand binding site (on the extra-cellular side) creates a distortion of the 3-dimensional shape of the intracellular domain. This effectively informs the inside of the neuron that a particular molecule has bound to the ligand binding site and is thus present outside the cell. The molecule itself doesn't need to enter the cell, only the information in the form of the conformational shift that indicates its presence.

When a receptor's ligand-binding site is unoccupied, its conformational state is (usually) referred to as the *inactive state*. When the ligand binds, it shifts the receptor into an *active state* (4). In this state, the receptor can interact with a complex set of intracellular signalling pathways that generate the effect of the receptor on the function or behaviour of the neuron.

For example, when bound by serotonin, 5HT2A receptors depolarise a neuron, making it more excitable. This depolarisation requires more than just the receptor, but also the network of intracellular signalling molecules that actually cause the shift in the membrane potential. Molecules, such as serotonin, that activate a receptor in this way are known as *agonists*. However, other molecules — known as *antagonists* — also bind to the receptor but, by virtue of their structure and charge distribution, either shift the receptor into a conformation state that does not interact with any signalling pathways, or have no effect at all on the receptor conformation. Either way, the receptor isn't shifted into an active state and the antagonist has no effect other than to block the binding of any agonists floating in the vicinity of the receptors.

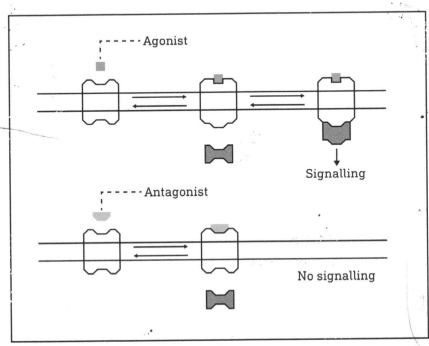

The idea that receptors can exist in either an inactive or active state — a simple binary switch — has now revealed itself to be rather simplistic, and we'll be looking at a more complete picture of receptor activation later. But, first, we need to think about the signalling pathways with which the active form of the receptor interacts, since these pathways form the central control panel of neuronal function. The receptor is the (rather complex) switch and the signalling pathways the intracellular "circuitry" that the switch activates.

Just like the brain itself, every neuron is a complex system, the function and behaviour of which emerges from the multitude of interactions of countless proteins, carbohydrates, lipids, small molecules, and ions (5). Everything a neuron does, whether regulating its membrane potential, generating action potentials, regulating the type and number of receptors in its membrane, or more mundane activities, such as dismantling and replacing old worn-out proteins, maintaining the lipid content of its membrane, or repairing its DNA, depends upon the interactions of large numbers of different molecules. An important function of a neuron is to regulate how all of these different processes work, rather like the way an electronic circuitboard controls the behaviour of an electronic device, such as a mobile phone. A neuron must be able to control when and in what direction its membrane potential should be shifted, for example.

Signalling molecules are a subset of these molecules that perform this role as "cellular circuitboard". Rather like electrical components — such as transistors, capacitors, and resistors — on an electronic circuitboard, these molecules interact with each other to control the flow of information through the cell (known as *signal transduction*). When a 5HT2A receptor is activated, for example, the intracellular domain interacts with one or more intracellular signalling molecules which then interact with other signalling molecules and so on, the information from the receptor flowing into this tightly regulated, and extremely complex, signalling network. The ultimate result is the shifting of the membrane potential towards the firing threshold.

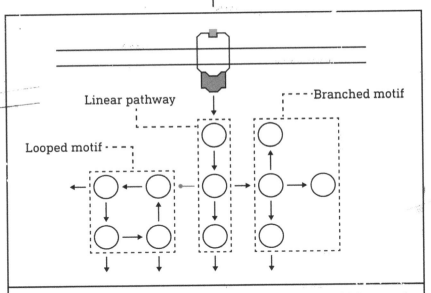

Signalling molecules form pathways that interact and from which a complex signalling network emerges, controlling neuronal function.

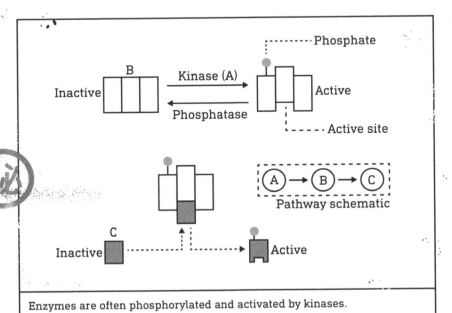

Enzymes are often phosphorylated and activated by kinases.
Phosphorylation distorts the enzyme protein and exposes the active site.

If you could open up any living cell and peer inside, you'd find it packed with a range of different proteins and other molecules swimming in the gel-like interior. Signalling molecules are often special types of enzymes (proteins that act as biological reaction catalysts), although there is also a large range of non-protein signalling molecules, including lipids and other small molecules.

Signalling molecules interact to form signalling pathways, which themselves interact to form highly complex signalling networks. A signalling pathway is a set of intracellular signalling molecules that interact with each other in an orderly sequence. "Interaction" usually means one molecule activates another molecule, which then activates another molecule downstream, forming a sequence of activation. Just as receptors embedded in the neuronal membrane can exist in both active and inactive states, the same can apply to signalling proteins diffusing freely in the cytosol. An inactive signalling protein is usually one in which the conformational state is such that the active site — the substrate binding and chemical reaction site of the enzyme — is either blocked or distorted such that the substrate is unable to bind. Flipping to the active conformational state opens up the active site such that the substrate can bind and the protein can perform its enzymatic function (which is often to activate another signalling protein).

Depending on the signalling protein, there are a number of ways that a protein can be activated. However, by far the most important mechanism is the chemical addition of a phosphate group (PO_4) to specific sites on the protein chain. This is called *phosphorylation* and is performed by a class of enzymes known as *kinases*. The attachment of a phosphate group to a protein will often cause it distort and flip to a different conformational state. In most cases, this is a flip from the inactive to the active state. However, many proteins are also inactivated — flip from the active to the inactive state — by phosphorylation. Another class of enzyme — *phosphatases* — has the role of clipping off these phosphate groups, inactivating the signalling protein by causing it to flip back to its inactive conformational state. Different kinases and phosphatases tend to be selective for specific signalling proteins.

It's also possible for certain signalling proteins to be activated by the binding of another signalling protein, but the principle is the same: the binding of the "activator protein" causes the other protein to distort and flip to its active conformation. It flips back and inactivates as soon as the activator protein unbinds. Since protein-protein interactions like this tend to be quite transient — unlike phosphorylation, which can persist from minutes to hours — this kind activation is useful for briefly activating a signalling protein.

One of the most important types of signalling pathway is the *kinase cascade*: The first kinase in the cascade phosphorylates and activates the second kinase, which can then phosphorylate and activate the third kinase, and so on. An important example of this type of pathway is the Ras-RAF-MEK-ERK pathway (the naming of signalling proteins can be confusing — don't be concerned about where these names came from). *Ras* is a small signalling protein (although it's not an enzyme) that's activated when it interacts with the active conformation of certain types of membrane receptor. Once activated, *Ras* can bind to and activate *RAF* — a kinase — which then phosphorylates and activates *MEK* — also a kinase — which phosphorylates and activates *ERK*, the third kinase in the cascade. ERK can phosphorylate a range of target proteins in a cell with diverse functions.

Notice that, when a signalling protein is activated, the protein selects a different conformational state and so generates information. Since the proteins in a cascade are activated in sequence, information is passed from one protein to the next. In the case of the Ras-RAF-MEK-ERK cascade, information is passed from the activated receptor along the cascade to ERK. In other words, ERK receives the signal that the membrane receptor has been activated. The activated ERK then initiates the intracellular processes that it controls. The Ras-RAF-MEK-ERK signalling cascade is switched off by specific phosphates — PP1 and PP2 — that cleave the phosphate groups from the kinases, switching them back to their inactive state. Each kinase in the cascade can also be regulated by other signalling proteins, providing several points of control.

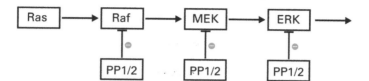

The Ras-Raf-MEK-ERK cascade is a signalling pathway of sequential kinase phosphorylations leading to activation of ERK. The phosphatases PP1 and PP2 inactivate the pathway by dephosphorylating the individual kinases.

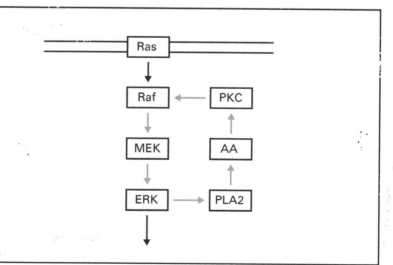

The Ras-Raf-MEK-ERK cascade can form a positive feedback loop by interacting with the PLA2-AA-PKC pathway, resulting in sustained activation of ERK lasting >20 minutes.

The Ras-RAF-MEK-ERK pathway is but one of a plethora of signalling pathways that have been identified. Whilst some, like the Ras-RAF-MEK-ERK pathway, are simple linear cascades, more sophisticated network motifs, including branching and looped systems, are also part of a cell's signalling toolbox. What all of these pathways have in common, however, is that they direct the flow of information through a cell. Looped motifs, for example, can exhibit sustained activity using positive feedback (6), whilst branched pathways allow information to spread and interact with other pathways to form the highly complex network of interacting signalling molecules necessary to control the diverse functions of a neuron (7).

It is from the activity of these interconnecting pathways that the complex multifaceted behaviour of a cell emerges. Much of the basic research in biochemistry during the last century was devoted to teasing apart these networks in an attempt to understand how they function. However, it is only relatively recently that their nature as complex systems — rather than merely complicated machines — became appreciated. As in the neocortex, the behaviour of the network emerges from the multitude interactions between the signalling molecules, and the role of each signalling molecule cannot be extricated from the system in which it's embedded. Its function is an irreducible part of the emergent complex system.

At any point in time, the intracellular signalling network of a neuron exists in a particular state, which can be defined as the particular pattern of active and inactive signalling proteins within the network. The obvious parallels between this intracellular pattern of activation and the pattern of activation of cortical columns in the neocortex is no coincidence. As above so below. When a molecule binds and activates a receptor, it perturbs the signalling network and induces a new and distinct pattern of activity, in much the same way that sensory information perturbs the cortex and induces a distinct pattern of cortical column activation. The gamut of different receptors embedded in a neuron's membrane provide it with constant stimulation, to which the intracellular signalling network constantly responds.

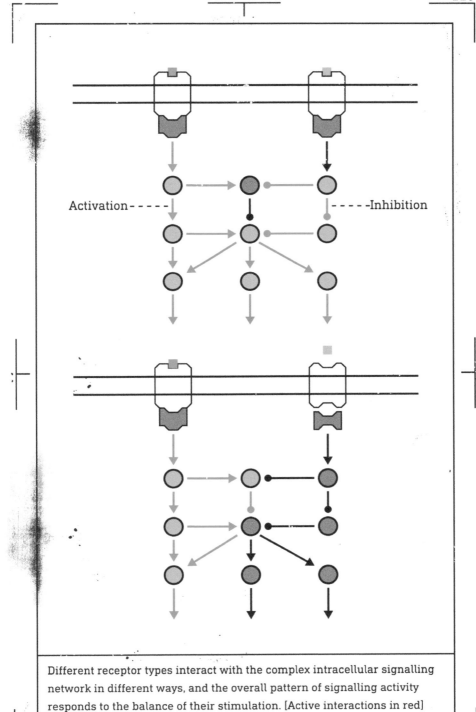

Different receptor types interact with the complex intracellular signalling network in different ways, and the overall pattern of signalling activity responds to the balance of their stimulation. [Active interactions in red]

Bearing this complexity in mind, we have to be a little careful when trying to describe the effects of a particular neuromodulator — or indeed a psychedelic drug molecule — on a neuron's intracellular signalling network. Whilst some of the primary effects will be clear and measurable — such as a shift in the membrane potential — more subtle effects can easily be missed and remain somewhat obscure. It's important to consider this when thinking about why certain psychedelic drugs have quite distinct effects on brain activity despite having the same basic mechanism of action. This remains one of the difficulties in studying and trying to understand complex systems. Having said that, there's still much to be learned by studying some of the more clearcut effects of neuromodulators and psychedelics on certain signalling pathways, but a truly comprehensive and definitive account remains out of reach.

The interaction between the intracellular domain of a receptor and an intracellular signalling molecule is regulated by its conformational state. When the receptor is in its inactive state, the conformation of the intracellular domain is such that it does not interact with any intracellular signalling molecules — the 3-dimensional shape and charge distribution of the domain doesn't complement that of the signalling molecule. When the intracellular domain flips to the active state — when a ligand binds to the extracellular domain — the change in conformation allows it to bind and activate a specific signalling molecule with the complementary shape. This is how a receptor is able to "switch on" a particular signalling pathway, which is ultimately responsible for the effect of the receptor on the neuron's function.

When a psychedelic molecule binds and activates a receptor, it perturbs the intracellular signalling network and induces a new pattern of signalling activity, which changes the behaviour of the neuron. This change in behaviour at the level of single neurons alters the manner in which these neurons communicate. This perturbation of the flow of information between neurons affects the flow of information between cortical columns which, ultimately, alters the structure of the world model, experienced as the psychedelic effect. Different classes of psychedelic molecules acti-vate particular receptor types on particular types of neurons, per-turb the intracellular signalling network in their own particular manner, and have their own particular effect at the level of the world model. A number of these World Space Switch mechanisms in the brain have been identified, and we'll begin with the most well-known: the C(lassic)-Switch.

現実制御学研究所、東京

This is a series of 7 advertisements for the now (presumably) defunct Laboratory for Reality Engineering, Tokyo [現実制御学研究室]

The purpose or target of these advertisements remains unknown, with no information presented beyond the Laboratory's logo and address. The first 5 advertisements possibly show the inside of the Laboratory, but this has never been confirmed.

The original site of the Laboratory, sitting below-ground, beneath the Parasitological Museum in Meguro Ward, Central Tokyo, no longer exists. It isn't known whether the Laboratory ceased all operations or relocated to an undisclosed site.

Former employees of the Laboratory were contacted but were unable to comment.

現実
制御学
研究所 ④

下目黒 4-1-1
目黒区
東京 153-0064

現実
制御学
研究所

下目黒 4-1-1
目黒区
東京 153-0064

現実制御学研究所

下目黒 4-1-1
目黒区
東京 153-0064

現実　▲
制御学
研究所

下目黒 4-1-1
目黒区
東京 153-0064

現実
制御学
研究所

下目黒 4-1-1
目黒区
東京 153-0064

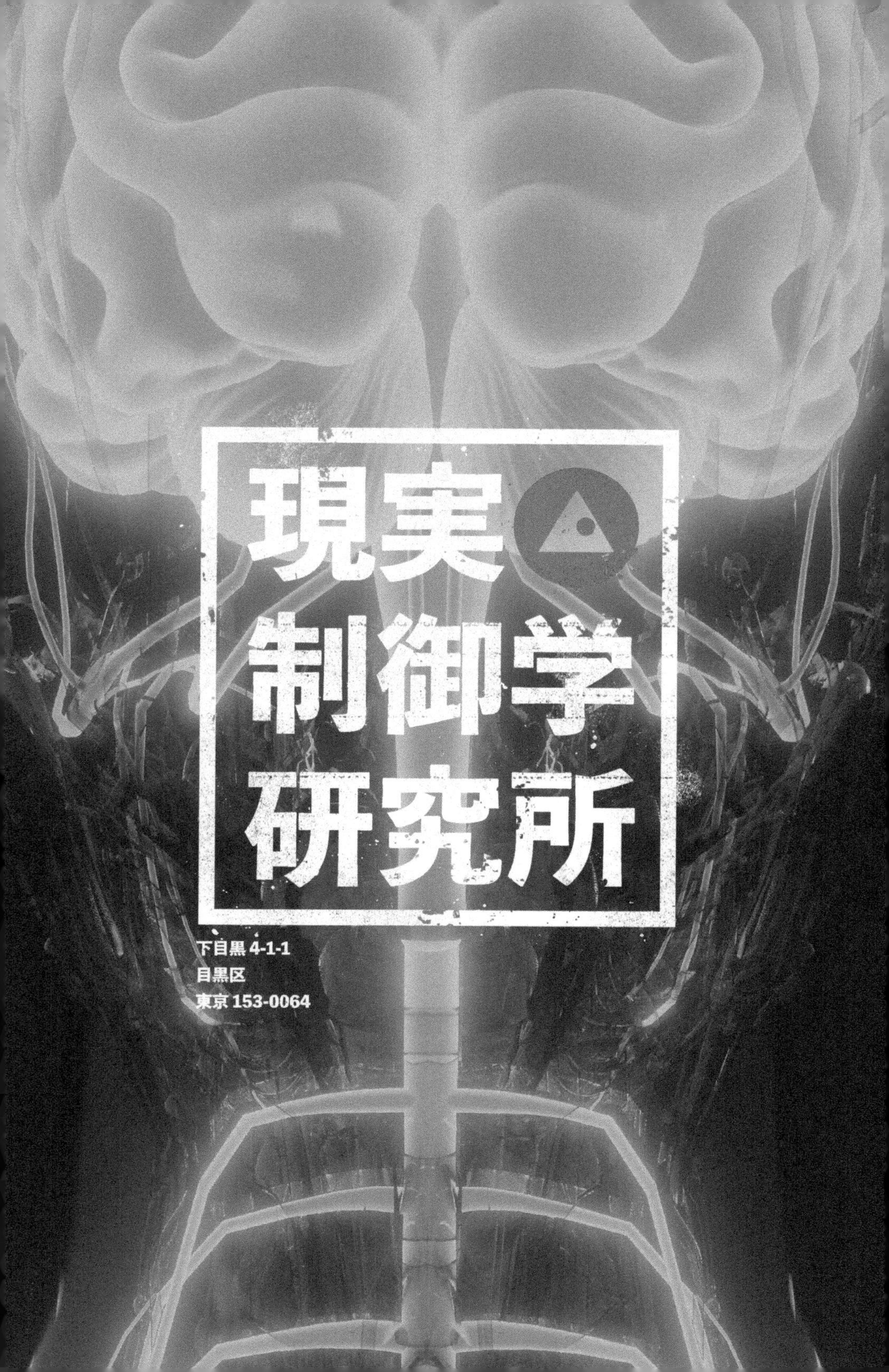

現実△
制御学
研究所

下目黒 4-1-1
目黒区
東京 153-0064

現実制御学研究所

下自黒 4-1-1
目黒区
東京 153-0064

現実管理課

<XXXXXX_3489_004_AO>

リアリティ
スイッチ

Chapter 8: The C-Switch I
[Level: Neuron]

世界空間 C－スイッチ

「セカイクウカンC－スイッチ」

" I felt faced by Death, my skull in my beard on
pallet on porch rolling back and forth and settling
finally as if in reproduction of the last physical
move I make before settling into real death — got
nauseous, rushed out and began vomiting, all
covered with snakes, like a Snake Seraph, colored
serpents in aureole all around my body, I felt like a
snake vomiting out the universe…"

William S. Burroughs

現実△
制御学
研究所

A World Space Switch comprises not just the receptor that binds to the psychedelic molecule, but the entire multi-levelled mechanism responsible for the change in the structure and dynamics of the world model. Binding of a psychedelic molecule to the receptor activates the Switch, but this is only the beginning: the perturbation of the intracellular signalling network (which might be different for different molecules acting at the same receptor), the effect on the behaviour of the neurons within which the receptor is embedded, and the consequent effects on the flow of information between neurons and the columns they form, are all important in eliciting the changes in the world model.

Of all the known World Space Switches in the brain, the C-Switch is by far the most well-known and understood, being the Switch activated by the so-called classic psychedelics, which include LSD, psilocin (from psilocybin), mescaline, and DMT. It also appears to be the most versatile, in that it's possible to activate this switch in a variety of ways, using a range of structurally diverse molecules. Each activation mode leads to a distinct effect on cortical activity and, as such, a distinct psychedelic effect.

All of the known classic psychedelics fall into three related molecular families:

> The tryptamines.

The lysergamides (a class of rigid tryptamines).

The phenethylamines.

The naturally-occurring tryptamines are all derived from the amino acid tryptophan. Conversion of tryptophan to tryptamine is a simple chemical transformation requiring of a single step: the removal of a carbon dioxide molecule (decarboxylation). The tryptamine molecule contains two important substructures:

The indole system.
A 2-carbon side chain terminating in an amine.

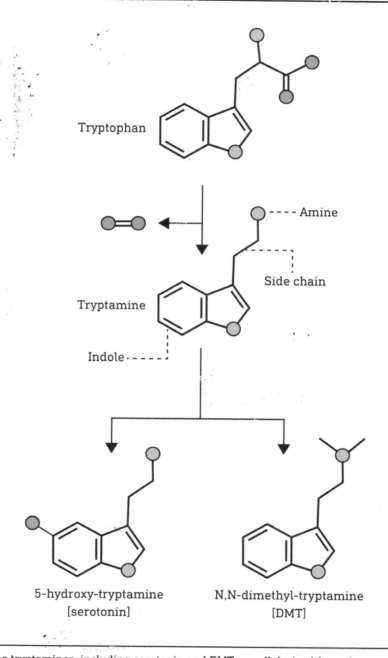

Tryptophan

Amine

Side chain

Tryptamine

Indole

5-hydroxy-tryptamine
[serotonin]

N,N-dimethyl-tryptamine
[DMT]

The tryptamines, including serotonin and DMT, are all derived from the amino acid tryptophan.

The indole system comprises two connected rings — a 6-membered ring of carbon atoms and a 5-membered ring that includes nitrogen. Indole is numbered from one to seven anticlockwise from the nitrogen (only those atoms to which other groups can be attached are given numbers). The side chain, comprising two carbons and an amine (NH_2) group, is attached at the 3-position.

Whilst tryptamine itself isn't psychoactive, it forms the basic skeleton for a range of natural and synthetic psychedelic molecules. The neuromodulator serotonin (5-hydroxytryptamine, 5HT) is derived from tryptamine by addition of a single hydroxyl (OH) group at the 5-position on the indole ring. N,N-dimethyltrypamine is the simplest of all the naturally-occurring tryptamine psychedelics and is generated by adding two methyl (CH_3) groups to the amine nitrogen. Further addition of a hydroxyl to the indole 4-position yields psilocin, the active component of *Psilocybe* "magic mushrooms" (1). If the hydroxyl is added instead to the 5-position of DMT, bufotenine (5-hydroxy-DMT) is produced, and is so named as being derived from the skin secretions of certain frogs of the *Bufo* genus, but is not particularly psychedelic (2). However, adding a methyl group to bufotenine's hydroxyl group yields 5-methoxy-DMT (5-MeO-DMT), which is an extremely potent and powerful psychedelic present in a range of plant species and the secretions of the Colorado River Toad, *Bufo alvarius* (3).

Beyond these naturally-occurring molecules, a variety of synthetic tryptamine derivatives have also been invented, most notably by the late psychedelic chemistry extraordinaire Alexander "Sasha" Shulgin. Some of his most interesting inventions include the auditory hallucinogen N,N-diisopropyltryptamine (DiPT) and the distinctly aphrodisiacal 5-methoxy-N,N-diisopropyltryptamine (5-MeO-DiPT, also known as "foxy methoxy") (4).

The lysergamides form a class of molecules based on tryptamine, but with a more complex four-ring structure. The tryptamine nucleus remains, but is held in place by two further rings stacked upon the indole system. From the uppermost ring extends an amide group to which a range of other groups can be attached (5).

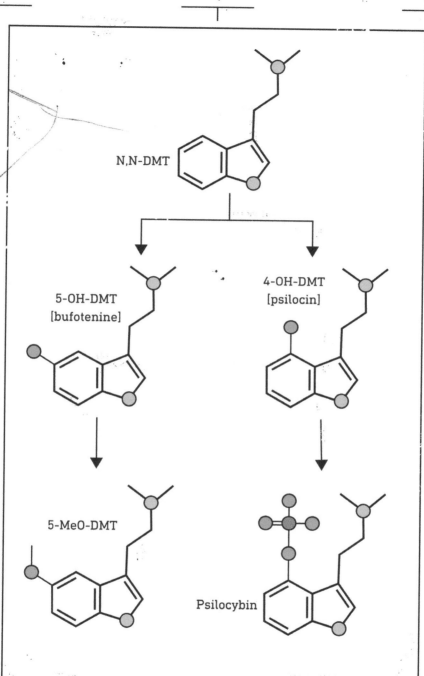

N,N-DMT

5-OH-DMT
[bufotenine]

4-OH-DMT
[psilocin]

5-MeO-DMT

Psilocybin

The other important natural psychedelic tryptamines, 5-MeO-DMT and psilocybin, are derived from N,N,-DMT.

The simplest psychoactive lysergamide is the parent molecule, lysergic acid amide (LSA), found in the seeds of various morning glory plants, including the South American vine *ololiuhqui* (*Ipomoea corymbosa*) and the Hawaiian Baby Woodrose (*Argyreia nervosa*) (6). Ergotamine is formed by the addition of a complex 4-ring structure to the amide, and is most notably produced by the ergot fungus (*Claviceps purpurea*) from which its name is derived (7). Although ergotamine itself isn't psychoactive, it's the most common precursor to lysergic acid diethylamide (LSD), first synthesised by Albert Hofmann in 1938 and by far the most famous of all the psychedelic molecules we'll meet in this book (8). LSD is synthesised by cleaving off the large 4-ring group from ergotamine to yield LSA. Addition of two ethyl groups (CH_2CH_3) yields a molecule around ten times more potent than LSA, with an active dose as low as 50 millionths of a gram (50μg).

The phenethylamines form the third class of classic psychedelic molecules, with mescaline — from the peyote cactus (*Lophophora williamsii*) — being the prototypic representative (9). The basic phenethylamine skeleton is a single phenyl ring (see the appendix) with a 2-carbon side chain (the ethyl part) terminating in an amine group. Mescaline is derived by attaching three methoxy groups (OCH_3) to the phenyl ring in the 3,4,5-positions (hence a more formal name for mescaline is 3,4,5-trimethoxy-phenethylamine). The simple phenethylamine skeleton provides extensive opportunities for chemical modification; an opportunity not lost on Sasha Shulgin, who created and personally assayed (read: tested on himself) over 150 entirely new phenethylamines. A handful of these have become popular amongst amateur psychonauts and other drug enthusiasts, most notably the empathogens MDMA and MDA, and the delightfully psychedelic 2C-B and 2C-T-7 (10).

Whilst belonging to distinct chemical classes, the classic psychedelics are unified in their activity at the 5HT2A serotonin receptor subtype, which is indispensable for their psychedelic effects (11). However, the structural differences and associated variations in charge distribution across the psychedelics mean each molecule binds and activates the receptor in its own way — depending upon

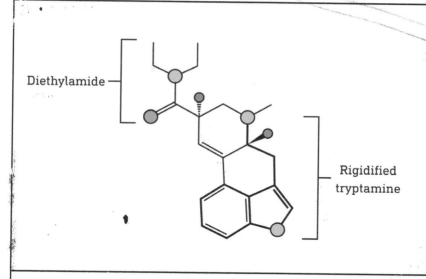

LSD [lysergic acid diethylamide] contains a tryptamine moiety rigidified by
the disinctive 4-ring structure, in addition to a crucial diethylamide group.

how the molecule sits in the receptor ligand binding site and interacts with the amino acids, each molecule will distort the receptor into a particular conformation, which can significantly affect
how the intracellular domain interacts with the intracellular signalling pathways.

The natural ligand for the 5HT2A receptor is, of course, serotonin.
Upon entering the ligand binding site, the side chain amine group
forms two hydrogen bonds with the hydroxyl groups of two amino
acids (a serine and an aspartate) within the protein chain of the
receptor (12). The hydroxyl group at the 5-position on the indole
ring also forms a hydrogen bond with a suitably positioned serine
(13), as does the nitrogen on the indole ring itself (14).

In addition to these strong ionic and hydrogen bonding interactions, a number of weaker, but equally important, interactions
work to stabilise the serotonin molecule in its own unique orientation in the ligand binding site. The indole ring is a flat structure
with clouds of electrons extending over both surfaces. These can

form weak interactions with amino acid residues that also contain flat ring structures, such a tryptophan (which also contains an indole ring) and phenylalanine (containing a phenyl ring).

A number of both tryptophan and phenylalanine residues work together to hold the serotonin molecule in place (15), although one tryptophan in particular acts like a kind of "toggle switch" that helps the serotonin molecule induce the conformational change in the receptor that shifts it into an active state (14). Together these interactions lock the serotonin molecule into a precise position within the ligand binding site and "pull" the receptor into an active conformation: the extracellular domain contracts as the serotonin molecule settles into place, and the intracellular domain opens out, allowing it to interact with signalling proteins inside the cell.

The psychedelic tryptamines, such as DMT and 5-MeO-DMT, also drop into the 5HT2A receptor and, since they are structurally very similar to serotonin, form some of the same bonds within the ligand binding site. The methoxy group of 5-MeO-DMT, for example, interacts with the same serine residue as serotonin, and both 5-MeO-DMT and DMT form a hydrogen bond with another serine using their indole nitrogen, as well as the important hydrophobic interactions with phenylalanine and tryptophan residues. However, unlike serotonin, neither of these psychedelic tryptamines are able to bind with the serine that interacts with the amine of serotonin (16) — the methyl groups ($-CH_3$) on the amine are bulky and prevent the amine from moving close enough to form a hydrogen bond. Overall, both DMT and 5-MeO-DMT sit in the 5HT2A receptor in their own particular orientation, depending on their shape and the interactions they're able to form. And, whilst both molecules are able to shift the receptor into an active state, each changes the conformation of the receptor protein in its own subtly different manner.

The phenethylamine skeleton is clearly distinct from the tryptamines, but possesses two of the same important structural features: a flat ring (a phenyl ring rather than an indole ring) and a two-carbon side chain with a terminal amine. As with the

Phenethylamine

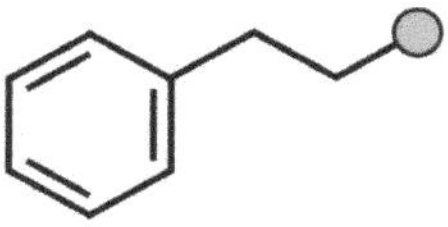

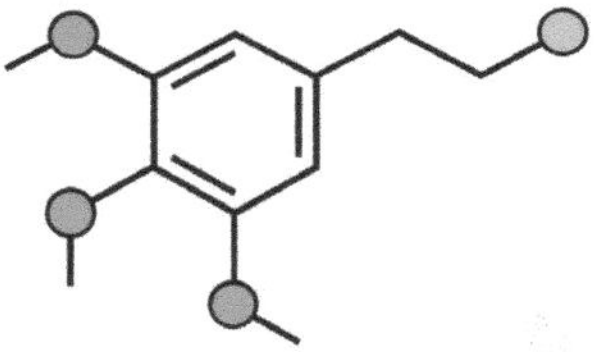

Mescaline

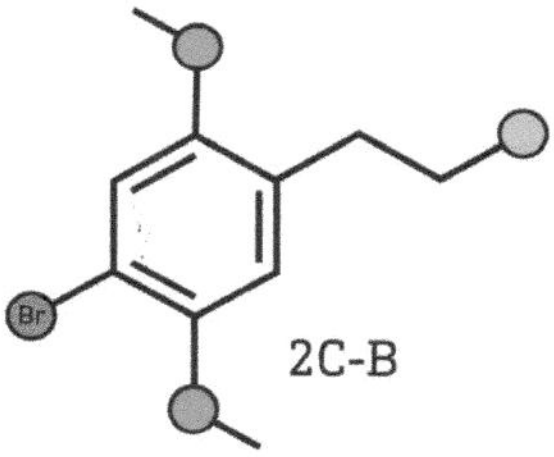

2C-B

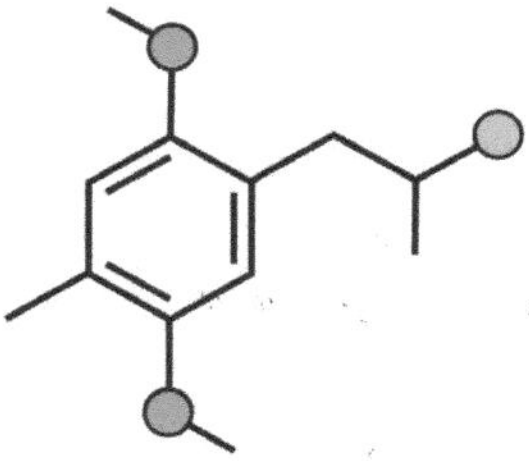

DOM [STP]

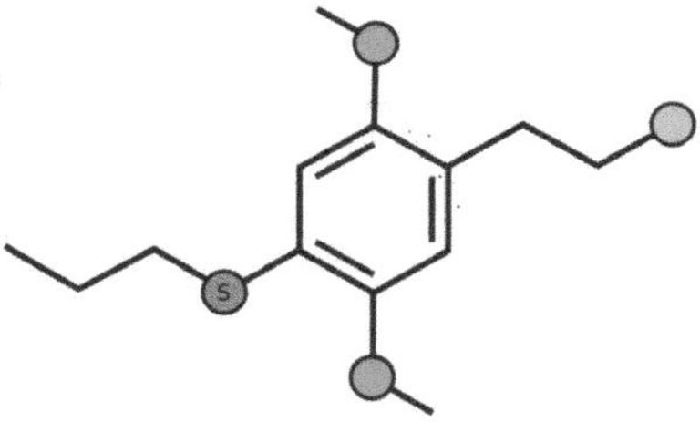

2C-T-7

The naturally-occurring psychedelic mescaline is derived from non-psychoactive phenethylamine. A large array of synthetic derivatives were invented by Alexander Shulgin.

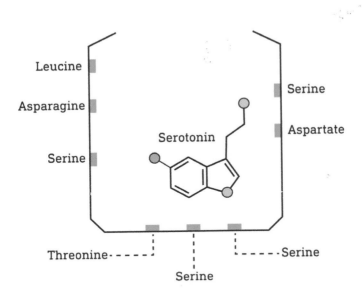

Leucine

Asparagine

Serine

Serotonin

Serine

Aspartate

Threonine

Serine

Serine

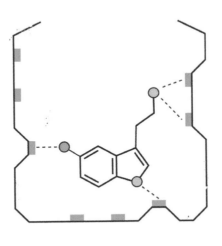

The 5HT2A receptor ligand binding site showing the key amino acids that interact with serotonin and the classic psychedelics. As serotonin enters the site, it interacts with 4 of these amino acids, distorting its shape.

tryptamines, the ring can interact with phenylalanine and tryptophan residues in the binding site, with the side chain amine forming an ionic bond with the critical serine residue. However, phenethylamine itself is unable to activate the receptor, and additional interactions are required. Mescaline, for example, contains three distinctive methoxy groups ($-OCH_3$) in adjacent positions on the phenyl ring, all of which are thought to be important for mescaline's ability to bind and activate the 5HT2A receptor. When mescaline drops into the ligand binding site, it orients itself such that each methoxy group can form a hydrogen bond with the hydroxy group of a specific amino acid within the protein chain of the receptor, one of which is the same serine bound by serotonin (17).

DOM (2,5-dimethoxy-4-methylamphetamine) is a potent psychedelic phenethylamine — again, first synthesised by Sasha Shulgin — that found its way onto the streets of the Haight-Ashbury in the late 1960s, originally distributed in 20mg pills and marketed as STP (often claimed to stand for "Serenity, Tranquility, Peace", but actually named after a chemically unrelated motor oil additive). Whilst a typical dose of mescaline is around 200-400mg, DOM is much more potent, being active at doses as low as 1mg, with 5-10mg being fully psychedelic (18). As such, the 20mg pills being shared around the Haight represented a massive overdose, with many users experiencing severe psychotic reactions requiring emergency medical treatment (19).

The potency of DOM can be explained by the distinct manner in which it interacts with the 5HT2A receptor. When compared to mescaline, the structure of DOM is noticeably distinct, both at the phenyl ring and the side chain. Specifically, the 4-methoxy of mescaline has been replaced by a methyl group (CH_3) and the 5-methoxy group shifted to the 6-position. Unlike mescaline, the side chain of DOM sports a methyl group attached to the same carbon as the amine (technically this makes DOM a type of amphetamine). This methyl group is bulky and affects the way DOM orients itself in the receptor, shifting the molecule into an optimal position for the 6-methoxy group to interact with the serine residue (20).

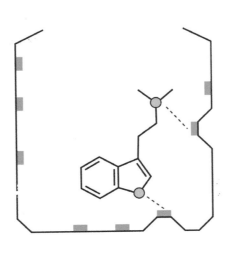

Interaction of N,N-DMT with the 5HT2A receptor ligand binding site.

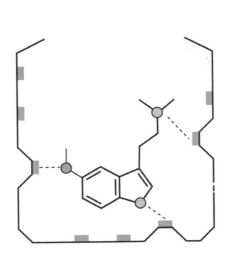

Interaction of 5-MeO-DMT with the 5HT2A receptor ligand binding site.

現実制御学研究所、東京

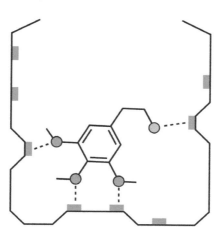

Interaction of mescaline with the 5HT2A receptor ligand binding site.

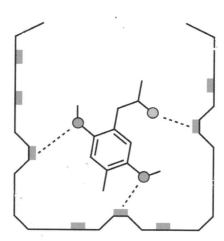

Interaction of DOM with the 5HT2A receptor ligand binding site.

The methyl group on the phenyl ring might also help to position the molecule favourably within the binding site and to optimise the interaction between the ring electrons and the phenylalanine and tryptophan residues, creating an overall much stronger and longer-lasting interaction with the 5HT2A receptor compared to mescaline (21).

DOM demonstrates how the particular structural features of a molecule can determine the strength with which it binds to the receptor, as well as the particular manner in which it distorts the receptor and shifts it into an active state. Not all active states are equal — the precise 3-dimensional shape of the intracellular domain induced by a molecule can be more or less conducive to sustained activation of the intracellular signalling pathways that engender the psychedelic effects.

The discovery of the psychedelic properties of LSD by Albert Hofmann was a monumental event from both a cultural and pharmacological perspective. As well as seeding the psychedelic revolution that would bloom in the decades that followed, LSD itself is something of a chemical marvel. The lysergamides, which include the naturally-occurring LSA, as well as Hofmann's synthetic derivative LSD, are essentially rigidified tryptamines — whereas the tryptamine side chain swings loose in other psychedelic tryptamines, in the lysergamides it's locked in position by the additional rings. Flexible molecules are better able to rotate their bonds to optimise their interactions in a ligand binding site and "relax" into position. However, the extra degrees of rotational freedom mean searching through a large number of potential orientations to find the one optimal for binding. Furthermore, once a ligand finds its position in the binding site, rotation of a single bond can cause it to slip out again. Flexibility is a double-edged sword. A rigid molecule, in contrast, must possess the correct shape to fit into the binding site from the outset. Otherwise the site will simply reject it. However, if the molecule is rigidified in the optimal orientation, the molecule will slip effortlessly into the correct position, rapidly establish the required interactions, and sit firmly in the binding site.

Remarkably, the lysergamides seem to have discovered the optimal way to rigidify the tryptamine side chain to achieve an almost perfect match with the crucial amino acid residues in the ligand binding site — as the indole ring slides into position, guided by the flat electron-rich rings of phenylalanine and tryptophan within the site, the indole nitrogen forms a hydrogen bound with a well-placed serine, and the side chain amine becomes perfectly positioned to interact with the critical aspartate residue (14, 22). Another distinctive feature of the lysergamides is the amide group sitting on the uppermost ring system. The oxygen of this amide can form a hydrogen bond with a suitably positioned asparagine (12, 22, 23), which helps to further stabilise the molecule in the binding site.

However, what's particularly interesting about the LSD is the pair of ethyl groups ($-CH_2CH_3$) on the amide that give LSD its name (lysergic acid *diethyl*amide). Compared to LSA, which has a free amide (no groups attached to the amide nitrogen), LSD is around ten times more potent: LSD is active above around 50μg, compared to around 500μg for LSA. Being the only structural difference between the two molecules, clearly these two ethyl groups have a central role in the striking difference in potency. Synthetic and modelling studies show that this diethyl group fits perfectly into a particular region of the ligand binding site, interacting with a critical leucine residue, and any changes to this group — such as increasing the length of the carbon chains or altering their structure in other ways — causes a dramatic loss in potency (24).

LSD is just right.

Other, ostensibly subtle, changes to the LSD molecule not only reduce its potency, but actually convert the molecule into a 5HT2A antagonist. Adding a bromine atom to the 2-position of the indole ring, for example, yields 2-bromo-LSD (also known as BOL-148) which, whilst binding to the 5HT2A receptor, has no activity whatsoever (20). A similar effect can be achieved by converting the carbon-carbon double bond in the uppermost ring to a carbon-carbon single bond.

Modification of diethyl group

Flipping this H

Conversion of double to single bond

The activity of LSD is highly sensitive to changes in its molecular structure. Any of the changes above either abolish or dramatically reduce potency.

Interaction of LSD with the 5HT2A receptor ligand binding site.

Despite their varying structures and potencies, all of the classic psychedelic molecules are unified not only in fitting into the 5HT2A active site, but also in being able to form the requisite interactions with binding site amino acid resides and pull the receptor into an active conformation. But we're still a long way from explaining how this subtle shift in the 3-dimensional shape of a receptor protein can elicit such dramatic effects on the structure of your phenomenal world, up to and including a complete reality channel switch to an alternate world constructed from higher-dimensional geometries and teeming with apparently intelligent entities. To bridge this gap, we first need to connect this conformational shift to the network of intracellular signalling proteins that regulate the function and behaviour of the neurons within which these 5HT2A receptors are embedded.

All metabotropic receptors transmit information from the outside of the cell to the inside — the conformational change in the extra-cellular domain induced by binding of an agonist also induces a conformational change in the intracellular domain, signalling the presence of the agonist, and shifting the domain into an active state (25). This connects the receptor to the intracellular signalling networks inside the neuron, and ultimately induces specific changes in the way the neuron functions. In the case of the 5HT2A receptor — the primary locus of action for the classic psychedelics — its activation has two key effects, which we'll discuss in turn before considering their consequences:

1. Slow depolarisation.

5HT2A receptor activation leads to a sustained depolarisation of the neuronal membrane, increasing the excitability of the neuron.

2. Inhibition of slow afterhyperpolarisation (SAHP)

The sustained hyperpolarisation that sometimes occurs following an action potential is inhibited by activation of the 5HT2A receptor.

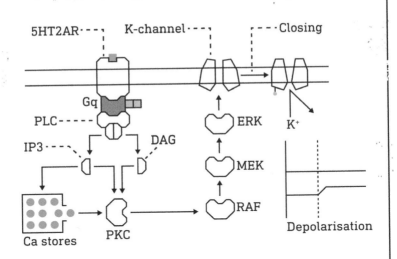

Activation of the 5HT2A receptor activates Gq, leading to ERK activation, phosphorylation of K-channels, and neuron depolarisation.

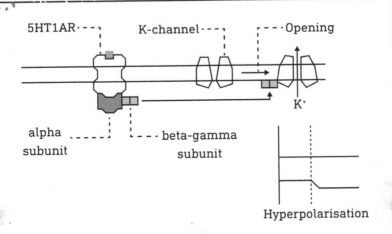

Activation of the 5HT1A receptor activates Gi, causing dissociation of the alpha-subunit and the beta-gamma-subunit, which binds and activates K-channels and hyperpolarises the neuron.

1. Slow depolarisation.

When the 5HT2A receptor is activated, its intracellular domain opens out and can interact with a type of membrane-associated signalling protein known as a G-protein. More specifically, the 5HT2A receptor interacts with the G-protein Gq. Upon binding to the 5HT2A receptor, Gq is activated and binds to a cytosolic enzyme, phospholipase C (PLC). In its active state, PLC breaks down a fatty molecule called PIP2 into two smaller molecules: DAG and IP3. These are two of the most important signalling molecules in biochemistry, and work together to activate another ubiquitous signalling molecule: a kinase called protein kinase C (PKC). PKC has a complex mechanism of activation: DAG binds and partially activates PKC directly, whereas IP3 binds to receptors on internal membranes and causes a massive release of calcium ions into the cyotosol from intracellular stores. Calcium also binds to PKC and, together with DAG, synergistically increases its activation (26).

The active form of PKC then activates the Ras-Raf-MEK-ERK pathway (see chapter 5): PKC activates the small signalling protein Ras, which activates the kinase Raf, which activates MEK, which finally activates the kinase ERK (27). So, overall, activation of the 5HT2A receptor activates a signalling pathway that results in the activation of ERK. Whilst ERK is responsible for phosphorylating a range of protein targets within cells, its most important role in the 5HT2A signalling pathway is in the phosphorylation of certain potassium channels.

So far, we've met the voltage-gated potassium channels responsible for the downward, repolarisation, leg of the action potential. However, the neuronal membrane contains a range of different potassium channel types, each with its own function and mechanisms of regulation. ERK phosphorylates one of the several types of potassium channels important in regulating the membrane potential of neurons in the cortex (28).

A neuron's membrane potential is constantly being pushed towards and away from the firing threshold potential by an array of ion channels that carry charge both into and out of the neuron. The resting membrane potential emerges from the balance of these impulses. Since potassium channels allow positively charged potassium ions to flow out of the neuron, they provide a negative pressure, pulling the membrane potential away from the firing threshold (to see this, it's simple to note that positive ions flowing *out* of the neuron are equivalent to negative ions flowing *in*). Sodium channels provide an opposing positive pressure towards the firing threshold, since they pass positively-charged sodium ions into the cell.

Many of these ion channels — potassium, sodium, chloride, etc — are regulated by phosphorylation (29). Addition of one or more phosphate groups by a particular kinase distorts the shape of the channel protein and either makes it more likely that the channel will shift to its open state or, conversely, that it will remain in (or shift to) its closed state. ERK phosphorylation of one particular type of potassium channel increases the proportion of time it spends in the closed state, stemming the flow of potassium ions out of the neuron (30). This reduces the negative pressure on the membrane potential and shifts the balance towards the firing threshold — the neuron is depolarised (31).

2. Inhibition of slow afterhyperpolarisation.

The action potential has two main phases: the depolarisation leg, driven by voltage-gated sodium channels, and the repolarisation leg, driven by the opening of voltage-gated potassium channels. At the end of this second phase, the membrane potential actually shoots past the resting potential before returning to its resting potential. This *undershoot* phase, known as *fast afterhyperpolarisation*, is largely caused by a delay in the closing of the potassium channels, meaning more potassium leaks out of the cell before the neuron is able to reset the potential. Whilst the neuron is in this hyperpolarised state, it's much more difficult for another action potential to be initiated, since the membrane potential is much further from the threshold potential than at rest. This gives the neuron a minimum *refractory period* between action potentials, which can be useful in controlling the rate at which it fires.

As well as the delay in potassium channels closing, other potassium channels can be activated towards the end of the repolarisation phase to increase the length of this refractory period of hyperpolarisation from a few milliseconds to up to a few seconds. This *slow afterhyperpolarisation* is often activated by increased intracellular calcium levels during a period of sustained firing or following a rapid burst of action potentials, and helps reign in overactivity by keeping the neuron in a hyperpolarised state for longer (32). The elevated calcium binds to protein calcium sensors which then bind and open special potassium channels (33). This allows additional potassium to leave the neuron, causing sustained hyperpolarisation. However, these potassium channels can be phosphorylated and inactivated by PKC, which is activated by 5HT2A. This blocks the slow afterhyperpolarisation from being initiated and the neuron remains able to maintain a high rate of firing.

In summary, activation of 5HT2A receptors has two distinct but related effects that increase the excitability of neurons. Firstly, sustained depolarisation brings the membrane potential closer to the firing threshold, making it more likely that a pattern of stimuli (EPSPs) will cause the neuron to fire (34). Secondly, 5HT2A activation inhibits the slow afterhyperpolarisation mechanism that regulates and limits firing activity, allowing a neuron to fire at a higher rate for extended periods of time (35).

If all neurons in the cortex relied on 5HT2A receptors alone to regulate their excitability, we'd expect serotonin (the natural 5HT2A agonist), when released into the cortex, to elicit a strong and straightforward excitatory effect. However, of course, the effect of serotonin on any particular neuron depends not only on the population of 5HT2A receptors embedded in its membrane, but also on the numbers of other types of serotonin receptors. The 5HT1A receptor is another important such receptor in the 5HT receptor family. This receptor works almost in direct opposition to the 5HT2A receptor, in that it actively hyperpolarises the neuron, pulling it further from the firing threshold. Whilst the 5HT2A re-

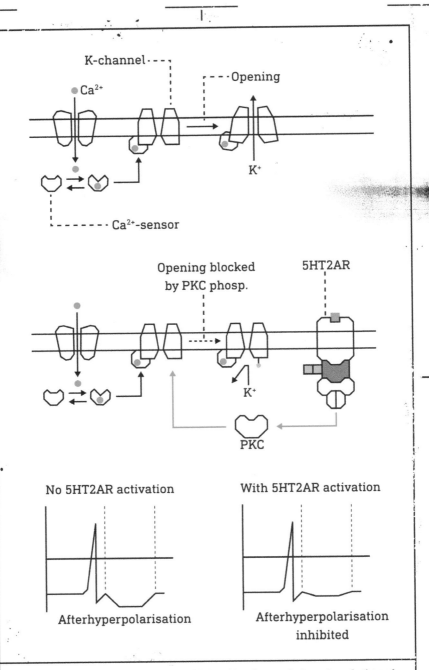

5HT2A receptor activation leads to PKC activation and phosphorylation of K-channels. This prevents the K-channels opening in response to Ca-sensor binding and blocks afterhyperpolarisation.

ceptor is coupled to the Gq type of G-protein (leading to potassium channel inactivation), the 5HT1A receptor binds and activates a different G-protein: Gi.

G-proteins are actually composed of three separate protein subunits — labelled alpha, beta, and gamma — and activation of the G-protein causes the alpha subunit to separate from the beta-gamma subunits, which remain together as the beta-gamma complex. Both the alpha subunit and the beta-gamma complex can bind and regulate other proteins and, in the case of the 5HT1A receptor, the beta-gamma complex directly binds and activates certain potassium channels (distinct from those inhibited by ERK phosphorylation) (36). So, activation of the 5HT1A receptor leads to the opening of these potassium channels, allowing potassium ions to leave the neuron and pulling the membrane potential in a negative direction away from the firing threshold.

So, overall, the effect of serotonin on a neuron's membrane potential will depend largely on the balance of 5HT1A and 5HT2A activation. Since serotonin binds and activates both 5HT receptor subtypes, it doesn't have a simple excitatory effect on neurons as would be expected were the membrane potential regulated by 5HT2A alone. 5HT2A receptor activation increases the excitability of the neuron and its response to strong stimuli, but this is counterbalanced by 5HT1A activation, which is important in suppressing responses to weak, noisy inputs, helping to increase the signal-to-noise ratio (37). Since the classic psychedelics tend to activate the 5HT2A selectively — but don't strongly activate 5HT1A, if at all — it might be assumed that disruption of this 5HT2A-5HT1A balance is responsible for their psychedelic effects. However, as is so often the case in biological systems, this picture turns out to be overly simplistic. Lisuride is a drug which, at first glance, appears structurally almost identical to LSD, and is used in the treatment of Parkinson's disease and in the prevention of migraine headaches. The receptor binding properties of lisuride and LSD are also remarkably similar, both being agonists at the 5HT2A receptor (38). Lisuride, however, is not psychedelic. To understand why, we need to consider yet another metabotropic receptor.

LSD   Lisuride

Structural comparison of LSD and lisuride.

mGluR2 is one of a family of metabotropic glutamate receptors coupled, like the 5HT1A receptor, to a Gi protein. Upon activation, the beta-gamma subunit activates a kinase — Src kinase — that phosphorylates the amino acid tyrosine in certain signalling proteins (39). Src kinase activation by the mGluR2 receptor is essential for the psychedelic effects of the classic psychedelics (40), since this kinase helps to support activation of the Ras-Raf-MEK-ERK pathway central to the 5HT2A receptor's action. However, also like the 5HT1A receptor, the beta-gamma subunit activates potassium channels, leading to hyperpolarisation (41). This directly counteracts the depolarising effect of the 5HT2A receptor to the extent that, for a molecule to be psychedelic, it must not only activate the 5HT2A receptor, but must also partially suppress the activation of mGluR2 by glutamate (which is present whenever a neuron is being stimulated). However, unsurprisingly, none of the classic psychedelics are able to directly bind and affect the activation of the mGluR2 receptor. They achieve this mGluR2 suppression by inducing a unique interaction between the 5HT2A receptor and the mGluR2 receptor.

Both 5HT2A and mGluR2 receptors are embedded in the neuronal membrane and can diffuse somewhat freely. When they meet, they bind to form a 5HT2A-mGluR2 complex, allowing the two normally independent receptors to influence each other's activity (42). The difference between psychedelic and non-psychedelic 5HT2A agonists lies in the way they modulate this interaction. When a classic psychedelic, such as LSD, binds the 5HT2A receptor, it induces a conformational change in the receptor protein that also distorts the mGluR2 receptor to which the receptor is complexed. This inhibits the mGluR2 receptor's ability to activate the Gi protein and reduces the overall hyperpolarising effect of the receptor (43). Lisuride, however, fails to induce this particular conformational change and the activity of the mGluR2 receptor is unaffected. So, overall, rather than simply tipping the balance of 5HT1A-5HT2A receptor activation, psychedelics tip the balance of Gq-Gi signalling in favour of Gq via both activation of 5HT2A and suppression of mGluR2 (43, 44).

In summary, activation of the 5HT2A receptor by the classic psychedelics — but not by non-psychedelic 5HT2A agonists — has two primary effects on these neurons:

> 1. Gq pathway activation leading to sustained depolarisation, with concomitant Gi pathway inhibition (by 5HT2A-mGluR2 dimerisation).

> 2. Inhibition of slow afterhyperpolarisation.

We're now ready to discuss why this excitatory effect at the neuronal level elicits such dramatic effects on the world model.

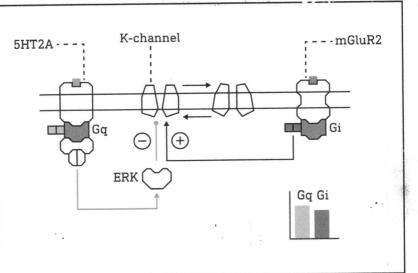

5HT2A receptor activation (via Gq) blocks the opening of K-channels, whereas mGluR2 receptors (via Gi) promote their opening.

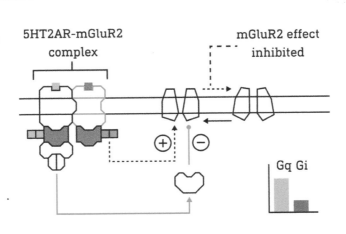

The 5HT2A receptor forms a complex with mGluR2 and inhibits its activation, reducing its ability to activate K-channels and oppose the 5HT2A receptor's depolarising effect on the membrane potential.

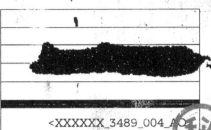

<XXXXXX_3489_004_A0

リアリティ
スイッチ

コピーは全て
破棄された

㊙

Chapter 9: The C-Switch II
[Level: Network]

世界空間 C－スイッチ

「セカイクウカンC－スイッチ」

"A hyperreal henceforth sheltered from the imaginary, and from any distinction between the real and the imaginary, leaving room only for the orbital recurrence of models and for the simulated generation of differences."

Jean Baudrillard

現実△
制御学
研究所

Your experience of a world is of the movement of your cortex from state to state, from one unified, hierarchically-structured, pattern of cortical column activation to the next.

> State follows state follows state through the vast state space of the cortex: the World Space.

The classic psychedelics alter both the structure and dynamics of the phenomenal world by increasing the repertoire of reachable states and lowering the energetic barriers between them.

Pyramidal cells in the deep layers of the cortex (see chapter 5) have a central role in the representation of the world model, as well as in generating predictions based on this model that are broadcast down the cortical hierarchy, and help to maintain the relationship between the model and the environment. Together with the interspersed inhibitory interneurons, this crucial neuron population also sports one of the highest concentrations of 5HT2A receptors in the cortex and, as such, when the classic psychedelics enter the brain and bind 5HT2A receptors, it is these deep pyramidal cells that are disproportionately affected (1). As discussed in the last chapter, 5HT2A activation by the classic psychedelics, coupled with mGluR2 receptor signalling suppression, increases the excitability of the pyramidal cells by sustained depolarisation and inhibition of slow afterhyperpolarisation.

Having explicated these effects at the level of individual pyramidal cells, we're now ready to consider how this increase in excitability leads to the effects of psychedelics on the networks of cortical columns that construct and maintain the world model, bringing us closer to a complete picture of the C-Switch mechanism.

Sustained depolarisation by activation of the 5HT2A receptor, when accompanied by mGluR2 suppression, makes it more likely that a pyramidal cell will fire in response to excitatory activity from other neurons — the depolarised neuron sits closer to the threshold potential, effectively lowering the barrier to firing. This effect is augmented by inhibition of slow afterhyperpolarisation, since

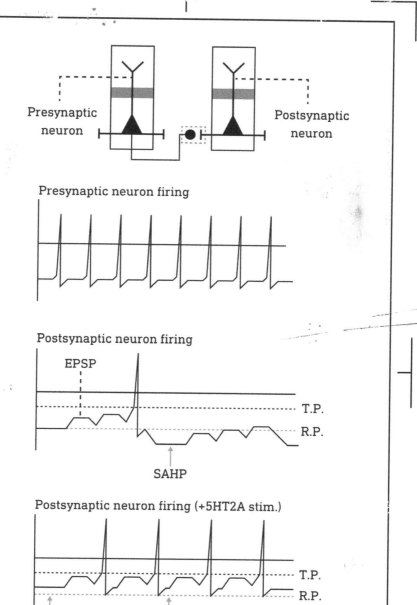

Activation of 5HT2A receptors depolarises deep pyramidal cells, whilst simultaneously inhibiting slow after hyperpolarisation [SAHP]. This both increases excitability and allows sustained rapid firing.

the neuron will spend less time in the hyperpolarised state — further from the threshold potential — after firing an action potential, expanding the window of opportunity for another set of EPSPs to push it over the threshold again. Overall, this depolarisation and inhibition of afterhyperpolarisation increases the response of a pyramidal cell to its excitatory inputs from other neurons, as well as increasing the effect a pyramidal cell has on other pyramidal cells (since it fires more often and generates a larger number of EPSPs).

The tuning of the synaptic connection strengths between pyramidal cells is essential for controlling the flow of information between columns and maintaining the structure of the world model. Recall that the cortex's ability to activate stable object representations — the hypotheses from which the world is constructed — depends upon the patterns of connectivity and connection strengths between cortical columns, controlling the flow of information between columns and allowing the columns that form an object representation to become stably active. By selectively activating 5HT2A receptors and causing sustained depolarisation of the deep pyramidal cells across all the columns of the visual cortices responsible for constructing your visual world, the classic psychedelics effectively override these finely-tuned connections, since even weak connections become able to transmit information between columns. Whilst this might be a small effect between any particular pair of columns, the effect over the entire cortex is more dramatic: Columns become hyper-excitable, responding strongly to weak inputs and delivering flurries of signals to other hyper-excitable columns. Information begins to flow out of the normally well-demarcated networks and the structure of the world-model begins to break down. The cortex loses control of the information flowing from column to column, losing its ability to construct the stable and well-defined set of hypotheses that comprise the world model (2).

Since the connectivity between cortical columns normally restricts the states (column activation patterns) that the cortex can reach — defining the Consensus Reality Space — this loss of con-

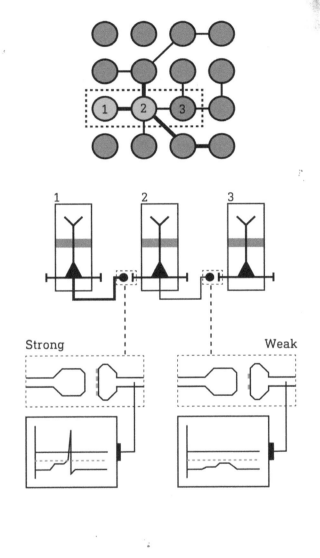

The cortex controls the flow of information by regulating the strength of synaptic connections between columns. Columns connected by weak synapses are less likely to activate each other than those connected by strong synapses.

trol over the flow of information through the cortex allows the brain to reach outside of the Consensus Reality Space into areas of the World Space unavailable in the absence of the psychedelic molecule. The states within the Consensus Reality Space are destabilised — their energy is raised — and the energies of states outside of it are lowered. This amounts to a flattening of the World Space Landscape, which the cortex can wander more freely. In functional neuroimaging studies, this is observed as an increase in the cortex's "state repertoire" — the cortex adopts patterns of activity not seen in the normal waking state and is observed to move from state to state in a more random fashion (3).

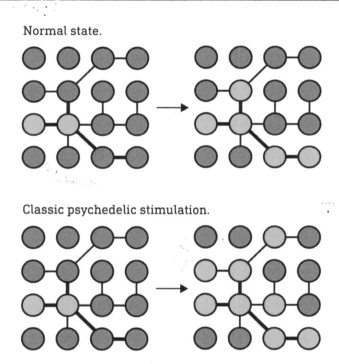

Normal state.

Classic psychedelic stimulation.

Normally, the cortex maintains column activation within the patterns defined by the tuned connections. In the presence of a classic psychedelic, depolarisation and inhibition of SAHP allows even weak connections to activate columns, causing the novel patterns of activation to emerge, as information flows out of the normally well-defined networks.

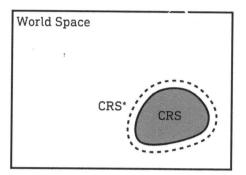

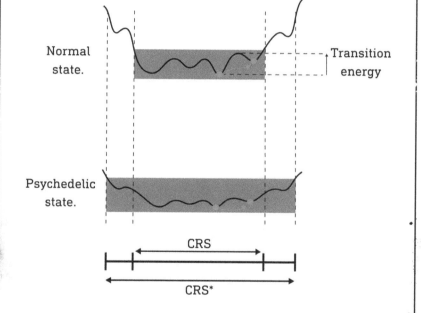

The classic psychedelics increase the size of the accessible state repertoire, effectively expanding the Consensus Reality Space [CRS -> CRS*]. The World Space Landscape is flattened, lowering the state transition energy and allowing the cortex to explore an expanded set of states more freely than in the normal waking state.

Alpha-beta oscillations in the deep layers of the cortex are important in synchronising the columns that represent the world model. As well as forming stable and well-structured object representations, the deep pyramidal cells can maximise the impact of their predictions on the lower level of the cortical hierarchy by synchronising their oscillations. As we discussed in chapter 5, both the pyramidal cells and inhibitory interneurons are important in establishing and maintaining these synchronised oscillations between separated cortical columns. Crucially, the generation and synchronisation of these oscillations across the cortex depends upon a finely-tuned balance between the excitatory activity of the pyramidal cells and the inhibitory activity of the interneurons (the "E-I balance"). Since the classic psychedelics increase the excitability of the deep pyramidal cells, they push the E-I balance towards excitation, which results in the suppression and desynchronisation of cortical oscillations (4). But, this is not the end of the story.

As well as activating the 5HT2A receptors on the pyramidal cells, the classic psychedelics also activate the same receptors embedded in the inhibitory interneurons. This depolarises and so increases the activity of these interneurons, increasing their inhibitory effect on the pyramidal cells to which they're connected. This, of course, is in direct opposition to the direct excitatory effect of the psychedelics on the 5HT2A receptors embedded in the pyramidal cells. However, only a relatively small proportion — around 25% — of these interneurons express the 5HT2A receptor (5), and so the increased inhibitory activity is insufficient to offset the elevated excitation. Furthermore, this selective increase in inhibition disrupts the pattern of organised interneuron activity that helps maintain synchronisation of the oscillations. Together with the shifting of the E-I balance, this causes the oscillations to weaken and desynchronise (6). This is observed on an EEG trace as a decrease in the power of the alpha-beta band (the sum of these oscillations), and is one of the most consistently observed effects of the psychedelics in human neuroimaging studies (7). Poor synchronisation in the alpha-beta band decreases the impact of downward-flowing model predictions. Secondly, the well-coordinated recruitment of interneurons by pyramidal cells is critical for strong hypotheses to outcompete and extinguish weaker ones. Coordinated recruitment becomes more difficult when the interneurons are non-uniformly activated by the classic psychedelics.

So, rather than a set of strong and stable hypotheses extinguishing weaker rivals and delivering robust and synchronised predictions down the cortical hierarchy, the strong hypotheses are weakened and destabilised and the weaker ones are able to maintain themselves in the absence of well-coordinated inhibition. Model predictions become weaker and more disorganised and, naturally, error signals begin to accumulate (8). The cortex loses its ability to predict and thus filter sensory information, which begins to flow untrammelled (in the form of error signals) up the cortical hierarchy. So, overall, the brain loses control not only of the flow of information within itself but, also, into itself. Sensory information that would normally be perfectly predictable and successfully filtered out suddenly begins flowing into the cortex. In short, the cortex becomes much more sensitive to sensory inputs.

In his psychedelic classic, The Doors of Perception, Aldous Huxley eloquently describes this state whilst gazing at a bunch of flowers:

> *"He could never, poor fellow, have seen a bunch of flowers shining with their own inner light and all but quivering under the pressure of the significance with which they were charged; could never have perceived that what rose and iris and carnation so intensely signified was nothing more, and nothing less, than what they were - a transience that was yet eternal life, a perpetual perishing that was at the same time pure Being, a bundle of minute, unique particulars in which, by some unspeakable and yet self-evident paradox, was to be seen the divine source of all existence." (9)*

In the normal waking state, the observation of a flower — or even a bunch of them — is a fairly trivial and entirely familiar affair.

Your brain settles upon the best hypothesis for the sensory information it's receiving from the flowers, and you duly experience this model of those flowers. The brain is able to filter out a large proportion of the sensory information arriving from the flowers. But, when a psychedelic is ingested and the filtering mechanism disrupted, the flower appears entirely new, novel, surprising, and imbued with significance. It's tempting to dismiss this effect as some kind of illusory perception or distortion of reality. However, the removal of the brain's filtering mechanism actually increases the amount of information absorbed and processed by the cortical hierarchy. When you ingest a psychedelic drug, you really are absorbing more information from the environment.

The process of neural development from birth to adulthood is one of honing the cortex's filtering mechanism to discard all but the most important — that's to say, predictable — information from the environment. As you grow and develop, your world becomes, quite literally, more and more predictable as your cortex perfects its predictive skills. By shaking up these abilities, psychedelics remove that filtering mechanism and return your world to a more childlike state, when all is new.

The increase in upwards information flow is met by a swift response from the cortex. The role of prediction errors is to inform the update of the model and, even in the presence of psychedelic 5HT2A stimulation, model updates are still applied. As the prediction errors begin to accumulate, the cortex responds by attempting to update its world model. Under normal, unperturbed, circumstances, the brain continuously modifies and updates its world model in an attempt to keep prediction errors low. Often this requires only subtle alterations in the model, although shifting to entirely new hypotheses about the contents of the world is also common, as we saw with the hollow face illusion. However, model updates are usually much more subtle and entirely unnoticed, occurring all the time.

In the presence of a psychedelic molecule, the disrupted model, and the predictions derived from it, lead to increased prediction errors that the cortical hierarchy attempts to quash. However, unlike the normal waking state, when stable and coherent alternative hypotheses can be selected and established, this is not possible in the psychedelic state. Despite its best efforts, the disrupted model will continue to fail in generating accurate predictions and the prediction errors remain. This results in a fluid and unstable world model, as the cortex constantly modifies its model hypotheses in a repeatedly futile attempt at neutralising the elevated errors flowing unabated up the cortical hierarchy. The brain shifts from hypothesis to hypothesis in an often highly apparent and striking manner, as objects visibly morph and change their identity before the eyes. Competing hypotheses jostle for representation and, although one might manage to establish itself, its reign is soon toppled by yet another alternative.

Alexander Shulgin describes this effect during a mescaline trip:

> "I sat there on the seat of the car looking down at the ground, and the earth became a mosaic of beautiful stones which had been placed in an intricate design which soon all began to move in a serpentine manner. Then I became aware that I was looking at the skin of a beautiful snake — all the ground around me was this same huge creature and we were all standing on the back of this gigantic and beautiful reptile" (10)

In a normal sober state, "the earth" would be experienced as a perfectly stable and predictable model. However, under the influence of mescaline, the pattern of column activation representing the hypothesis is degraded, and is less able to generate strong and coherent predictions. As the error signals grow, the model is forced to update and an alternative hypothesis — a mosaic of beautiful stones — manages to establish itself. But, again, the column pattern is unstable, predictions remain poor, and error signals remain. Yet another hypothesis takes the stage — a gigantic snake writing beneath the car — which was likely maintained only briefly before being replaced again.

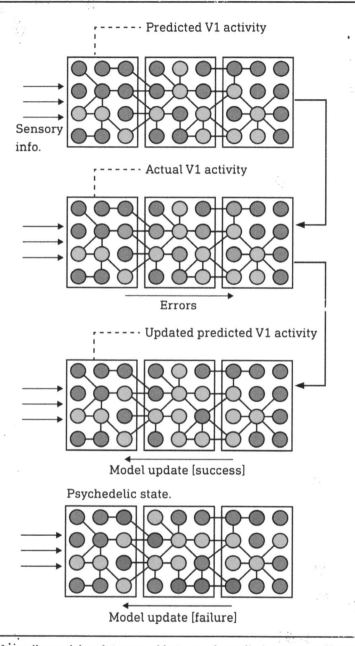

Predicted V1 activity

Sensory info.

Actual V1 activity

Errors

Updated predicted V1 activity

Model update [success]

Psychedelic state.

Model update [failure]

Normally, model updates are able to quash predictions errors. However, in the psychedelic state, the disrupted model fails and errors remain, forcing frequent updates to the model (which also ultimately fail to stem errors).

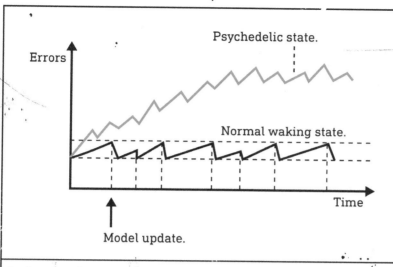

In the normal state, prediction errors are quashed by model updates and remain low and range-bound. In the psychedelic state, however, even frequent model updates fail to quash the accumulating errors.

So far, we've only focused on the world model as the brain's attempt to construct a functional model of the environment, and how this can be disrupted by psychedelics. However, your phenomenal world also contains a very high-order model of yourself as distinct from the environment. You possess an ego, a sense of self, an agent acting in the world whilst remaining distinct from it. This "self model" emerges from high-order cortical networks across a number of areas of the cortex.

Each level of the cortical hierarchy is a network of cortical columns and, since these levels are heavily interconnected, can be thought of as a network of networks. In fact, all brain areas that perform a specific function, whether involved in sensory perception, movement, or speech, for example, are networks of columns connected to other networks, forming networks of networks. A number of these high-order networks have been identified and shown to be important in brain function. For example, producing speech requires not only the appropriate movement of the lips and tongue, but also the recall of word meanings, auditory processing and refinement of the speech as it's being produced, as well as other language-related processes. Coordination of these processes requires communication between several distinct brain areas, and this specialised "speech network" comprises those brain areas important for all the different aspects of speech production (11).

Two of the most important brain area networks include the *task-positive network (TPN)* and the *default mode network (DMN)* (also called the *task-negative network*). The TPN is a network of brain areas activated during attention-demanding goal-directed tasks, such as solving a mathematical problem or writing a letter. In contrast, the DMN is activated during daydreaming, when thinking about the future or reminiscing about the past, or just letting the mind wander, and is often considered the resting state of the brain (hence *default* mode network). The TPN is directed out towards the world, away from the self, whereas the DMN is inwardly-focused (12). The TPN and DMN are anti-correlated, meaning they actively inhibit each other — when the TPN is active, the DMN is inhibited, and vice versa (13). These networks of brain areas give the brain another level of control over its activity and the way information flows through itself. The ability of brain area networks to regulate other networks is important in this control, allowing activity to be controlled and focused on a particular task. Obviously, it's difficult to focus on a cognitively-demanding task if you're also daydreaming about your future career or who you might marry. The DMN is thought to be a critical component of a set of large scale networks that represent the "self/ego model" distinct from the environment (14). If you've ever "lost yourself" whilst deeply focused on a task demanding all of your attention, you'll know what it feels like to deactivate your DMN, giving full reign to the TPN.

The classic psychedelics' ability to disrupt and allow information to flow out of the brain's well-demarcated column networks also applies to these higher-level networks of brain areas. Whilst, in normal waking life, the DMN and TPN are diametrically opposed — helping to maintain the experience of separation between the self and the environment — under the influence of the classic

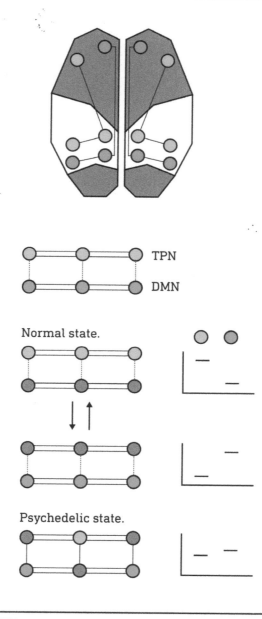

TPN

DMN

Normal state.

Psychedelic state.

The DMN and TPN are normally anti-correlated by actively inhibiting each other. However, in the psychedelic state, the networks are disrupted, with information flowing between them. Novel patterns of activity emerge and the differentiation between the networks is degraded.

psychedelics, information begins to flow between these networks and their distinction begins to blur. This is experienced as a dosage-dependent dissolution of the sense of self — culminating at high doses in so-called "ego death" — and a loss of the distinction between oneself and the outside world (15). This is also described as a feeling of *oceanic boundlessness* — an overwhelming sense of merging, or becoming "one", with the world or, indeed, the entirety of existence itself (16).

So, in summary, depolarisation of pyramidal cells and non-uniform depolarisation of inhibitory interneurons disrupts the structure of the world model, and the experienced world becomes less defined, more fluid, and objects begins to lose their well-defined structure and identity. Loss of control over the flow of information between columns allows the cortex to explore an increase repertoire of states more freely, including those outside of the Consensus Reality Space. The effect on inhibitory interneurons causes desynchronisation of alpha oscillations, which further disrupts the structure of the world model and degrades the impact of predictions as they flow down the cortical hierarchy. This results in an increase in prediction errors and an increase in the flow of information up the cortical hierarchy — the world becomes richer, more salient, surprising, and novel as information that would normally be filtered out floods the cortex. The cortex responds to this dramatic increase in prediction errors by shifting from hypothesis to hypothesis in a vain attempt to quench them — the world becomes unstable and objects morph and change their identity, often in rapid succession. Disruption of high-order networks — specifically the DMN — causes a loss of differentiation between the self and the environment, ultimately resulting in ego death and oceanic boundlessness.

Of course, not everyone who ingests any of the major classic psychedelics will experience all of these effects, which are somewhat dose-dependent. At low doses, only subtle changes in the world model are likely to be experienced: colours appear brighter and more vivid, object and surfaces seem to "breathe" or appear larger or smaller than usual, and a general increase in the richness and novelty of the world emerges. As the dosage is increased, the cortex loses more and more control over its world model, culminating in the more dramatic, and often disorientating, world destabilisation, hypothesis shifting effects, and ego death. However, this is by no means the end of the story.

The effects described so far, whilst dramatic, are really only the beginning of something far far stranger. Whilst moderate doses of most classic psychedelics disrupt the structure and dynamics of the world model, there remains a clear relationship to Channel Consensus Reality, as if it was merely nudged out of tune. But certain molecules, including DMT, transcend this and reach for new reality channels entirely.

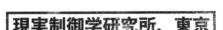

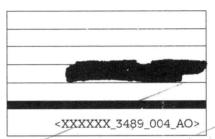

リアリティ
スイッチ

<XXXXXX_3489_004_AO>

Chapter 10: The C-Switch III
[Level: World Space]

世界空間 C－スイッチ

「セカイクウカンC－スイッチ」

"The world is in the act of creating itself. Mind is
a creature of four dimensional space but only by
habit, enforced by necessity. Sufficiently perturbed
mind recrystallises with a higher geometry that
represents a more elegant solution to the problem
of distributive energy mechanics within the mind/
organism."

Terence McKenna

C₃

現実△
制御学
研究所

DMT — N,N,-dimethyltryptamine — is arguably the simplest of all the naturally-occurring psychedelics. Enthnobotanist Dennis McKenna, brother of Terence, likes to say that "nature is drenched in DMT", such is its ubiquity in the natural world, manufactured by countless plant species across the globe. In one sense, this is hardly surprising, since DMT can be derived from the amino acid tryptophan in two trivial chemical steps requiring enzymes that are just as common. What *is* surprising is that this common plant alkaloid also happens to be the most efficient reality-switching molecule currently known to exist, almost instantaneously trans-porting the tripper from the Consensus Reality Space to a bizarre hyperdimensional ominverse teeming with superintelligent enti-ties of every (un)imaginable form and character.

The reality-switching properties of DMT were discovered in 1956 by Hungarian physician Stephen Szára (1), who both synthesised and self-administered the drug by intramuscular injection:

> "Within three minutes the symptoms started, both the autonomic (tingling, trembling, slight nausea, increased blood pressure and pulse rate) and the perceptual symptoms, such as brilliantly coloured oriental motifs and, later, wonderful scenes alter-ing very rapidly." (2)

Excited by his discovery, Szára recruited 30 subjects from the hos-pital where he worked and began the very first study of DMT in humans. Almost immediately, subjects began reporting strange worlds with even stranger occupants:

> "The room is full of spirits...the images come in such profusion that I hardly know where I want to begin with them! I see an orgy of color, but in several layers one after the other... Everything is so comical...one sees curious objects, but never-theless everything is quickly gone, as if on a roll-er-coaster." (3)

DMT's ability to rapidly and completely replace the normal waking world with a bizarre alien one was unlike any of the other psychedelics known at the time. And once it found its way out of the clinic and into the hands of the burgeoning population of 1960s psychedelic enthusiasts, its reputation as the ultimate psychedelic soon grew. Renegade psychologist and psychedelic spokesperson of the era Timothy Leary was as amazed by DMT as anyone else, describing it as "the nuclear bomb of the psychedelic family":

> "Eyes closed... suddenly, as if someone touched a button, the static darkness of retina is illuminated . . . enormous toy-jewel-clock factory, Santa Claus workshop . . . not impersonal or engineered, but jolly, comic, light-hearted. The evolutionary dance, humming with energy, billions of variegated forms spinning, clicking through their appointed rounds in the smooth ballet..." (4)

Of course, it was the baroque orations of the late great psychedelic bard Terence McKenna from the 1980s until his untimely death in 2000 that cemented DMT's status as the apotheosis of Mind-blowing Molecules, promising nothing less than "Death by Astonishment":

> "I sank to the floor. I had this hallucination of tumbling forward into these fractal geometric spaces made of light and then I found myself in the equivalent of the Pope's private chapel and there were insect elf machines proffering strange little tablets with strange writing on them, and I was aghast, completely appalled, because in a matter of seconds . . . my entire expectation of the nature of the world was just being shredded in front of me. I've never actually gotten over it." (5)

5-MeO-DMT, DMT's slightly less famous and slightly more complex chemical cousin, requires two additional enzymatic steps from DMT: hydroxylation (addition of an OH group) to yield bufotenine (5-OH-DMT), followed by methylation (addition of a CH_3 group). Such is the close chemical relationship between these molecules, it is common to find them together in the same plant species. For example, the Amazonian snuffs prepared from the resin of the *Virola* tree contain varying mixtures of both DMT and 5-MeO-DMT amongst a handful of other tryptamines (6).

Until relatively recently, both DMT and 5-MeO-DMT were mainly acquired from the laboratory, with both having straightforward synthetic routes. However, more recently, *Mimosa hostilis* has become by far the most commonly-used source, its root bark being a relatively high concentration source of smokeably clean DMT, with the Formosa acacia, *Acacia confusa*, running a close second (7). A metabolic quirk of the Colorado River toad — *Bufo alvarius* — endows it with the ability to methylate the more common toad alkaloid bufotenine to yield high concentrations of 5-MeO-DMT in its parotid glands, which can be milked and the venom smoked (8). Sadly, in recent years, an explosion of interest in 5-MeO-DMT and awareness of this poor amphibian's unique secretion has led to a decimation of wild populations by countless self-proclaimed "toad shamans" chasing it across the desert and almost driving it to extinction.

Both DMT and 5-MeO-DMT are short-acting tryptamines, their effects running their course in a matter of minutes rather than hours. 5-MeO-DMT, however, is severalfold more potent than DMT, with a fully active dose in the 5-10 milligram range, compared to around 30-50 milligrams for DMT. Pharmacologically, both are classic psychedelics in that they are (partial) agonists at the 5HT2A receptor (9). Both also display activity at the 5HT1A receptor subtype (10), as well as activating a number of other 5HT receptors to varying degrees. Despite these pharmacological similarities, their effects could hardly be more different.

Vaporisation of DMT in a small glass pipe remains the most popular mode of administration, although electronic vaporising devices, such as those used to vaporise cannabis resins and waxes, are becoming increasingly popular amongst amateur psychonauts.

DMT can also be dissolved in a high propylene glycol "e-liquid" and vaporised in an electronic vaping mod, which many find offers a much greater degree of control over the experience and, since it avoids open flames and scolding hot glass, is much safer when tripping alone. With vaporised DMT, the onset is rapid and overwhelming, the user being hurtled through a rapidly changing procession of extremely complex geometric imagery. If the dose is sufficient, this eventually gives way, and the user bursts through a kind of membrane into an entirely novel domain unlike anything within this universe. The most striking feature of this "DMT space" is its structure, often described as "hyperdimensional" (11). Users typically describe a place filled with beings of an unreckonable intelligence and power:

> "I did see intelligent insect alien god beings who explained that they had created us, and were us in the future, but that this was all taking place outside of linear time. Then they telepathically scanned me, fucked me, and ate me." (12)

Whilst the structure of the DMT space is characterised by its astonishing complexity and visual content, 5-MeO-DMT, in stark contrast, is notable for its striking lack of structure. Unlike the high-dimensional geometries, hypertechnological cityscapes, and intelligent entities of the DMT space, the 5-MeO-DMT experience is usually almost visual-free, and colours are rare. Rather, the experience is likened more to the "white light", an immeasurably vast and formless space into which the user dissolves until only pure conscious awareness remains. The 5-MeO-DMT space seems somehow to move *past* the highly structured worlds reached using DMT — all form and content dissolve leaving only awareness within an infinite void. The experience is understandably overwhelming and, for many, utterly terrifying, often requiring months to integrate and come to terms with:

> "At about 60 seconds after I smoked this freebase, I beheld every thought that was going on everywhere in the universe and all possible realities while I

was wracked out with this horrible ruthless love. It scared the hell out of me. When I could see again, it was almost as if there was an echo of a thought in my head saying that I was given an extremely rare look at the true consciousness of it all." (13)

Without an understanding of the brain's world-building mechanisms, it's difficult to comprehend how a pair of molecules so closely related could have such profound and yet strikingly different effects on the structure of the world model. DMT and its 5-methoxy counterpart seem to sit at opposite ends of a form spectrum — at one end is immense structure and complexity and, at the other, pure formless existence itself.

Overall, in a dose-dependent manner, the classic psychedelics increase the number of states available to the cortex, reducing the stability of states within the Consensus Reality Space and allowing the cortex to reach states outside of it. The cortex moves more freely from state to state, experienced as a more fluid and unstable world in which the structure and even the identity of objects can shift rapidly in surprising ways. In functional neuroimaging studies, this effect has been observed in real time in the brains of participants under the influence of psilocybin or LSD (14). In these studies, the cortex is parcellated into discrete areas and patterns of activity across these areas measured and recorded. Soon after a dose of the psychedelic, the participants' brains begin to explore an expanded "repertoire" of patterns in an apparently more random fashion over time (15). This is precisely what would be predicted to happen given what we know about the effect of psychedelics at the receptor level and how these effects perturb the construction and maintenance of the world model.

The World Space Landscape is an attractor landscape comprising all possible cortical states that represent a phenomenal world — "low energy" states are favoured and "high energy" states disfavoured. A low energy state is simply one that the cortex is more likely to move towards relative to a high energy state and, as we discussed in chapter 6, the cortex sculpts its connectivity (and thus the structure of the World Space Landscape) such that the low energy states are those that represent the most functional (that is, predictive) model of the environment.

By increasing the number of available cortical states, the classic psychedelics are effectively lowering the energy — increasing the favourability — of normally high-energy, less functional states, whilst raising the energy of the favoured low-energy states. This amounts to a flattening of the World Space Landscape — the low-energy basins and valleys become shallower and the high-energy hills drop lower. So, the energetic difference between favoured and disfavoured states becomes smaller, the cortex is no longer guided as strictly by the basins and valleys of the landscape and is more likely to access formally disfavoured states. Sensory information, in the form of error signals, effectively nudges the cortex from state to state, which we described as forcing updates of the world model. By disrupting its prediction/filtering mechanism, the classic psychedelics increase the flow of sensory information into the cortex and force more frequent updates — the psychedelics push the cortex around the flattened World Space Landscape, making it more likely that the cortex will jump from valley to valley. Again, this is the same 'hypothesis shifting' effect described in the last chapter but viewed from the World Space Landscape perspective.

So, overall, the classic psychedelics cause the cortex to move more freely across the World Space Landscape, and allow it to explore regions outside the Consensus Reality Space. However, at regular doses, these novel states remain within the same "district" of the World Space as the Consensus Reality Space and are usually experienced as a modified version of the normal waking world.

In stark contrast, at breakthrough doses, the DMT and 5-MeO-DMT worlds bear no resemblance whatsoever to the normal waking world. We'll refer to the sets of states that represent the DMT and 5-MeO-DMT worlds as the DMT Space and the 5-MeO-DMT Space, respectively. Reaching these areas of the World Space requires a more pronounced restructuring of the World Space Landscape than the flattening produced by moderate doses of the other classic psychedelics. Both DMT and 5-MeO-DMT provide a highly specific receptor-level perturbation that causes the World Space Landscape to move beyond the transitional flattening and 'collapse' into an entirely new structure in which the attractor states are located in an area of the World Space completely disjoint from those of the Consensus Reality Space. We can understand this behaviour by thinking about other highly complex systems.

An ant society beautifully illustrates how a complex system can emerge from the interactions between large numbers of components: the individual ants. A large ant colony might comprise several million ants, with each ant type assigned its own roles in the organisation of the society. The queen is the leader and founder of the colony, her eggs fertilised by the male drone ants. Female worker ants are responsible for maintaining the nest, as well as protecting it from intruders. Each individual ant is a rather simple creature and interacts with the other ants in rather simple ways. However, the entire colony can display highly sophisticated emergent behaviours: building elaborate networks of underground tunnels, delineating routes to food sources, defending against intruders, or even forming themselves into bridge-like structures over water (16). Which behaviour emerges — which pattern of activity of the colony — depends upon the interactions between the ants. The Defend Against an Intruder behaviour is entirely distinct from the Build a Bridge behaviour, and the switch between them occurs because of highly specific changes in the interactions between the ants, mediated by pheromones and other signals (17).

Notice that the ants aren't simply switching to a new state, but to an entirely new behaviour. Each dynamic behaviour comprises a set of states within a state space and, by altering their interactions, the ant society temporarily reshapes its attractor landscape such that the attractor states become the states that generate the required behaviour — whether building bridges or fighting intruders — at that time. Once the intruder has been defeated, the interactions are again modified, the attractor landscape collapses into another shape, and another behaviour emerges.

We can also see this effect with Hopfield networks (see chapter 6), as well as more complex neural networks. Tweaking the connection strengths or the basal activation of the nodes (how close they are to the firing threshold) can shift the states that act as attractors, which amounts to a restructuring of the attractor landscape (18). Whether it's an ant society, an artificial neural network, or the human neocortex, certain highly specific perturbations or alterations in the interactions between the system components have the potential to distort the attractor landscape, change the states that act as attractors, and so shift the system towards radically different behaviours. In the case of the classic psychedelics, this perturbation is of the complex intracellular signalling network inside pyramidal cells and the interspersed inhibitory interneurons. Whilst acting primarily at the 5HT2A receptor subtype, the classic psychedelics differ in their molecular structure and charge distribution and, as a result, each activates the receptor in its own way. The 5HT2A receptor is not an on-off switch, but a protein ensemble that can exist in a range of conformational states and interact, to greater or lesser extent, with a range of intracellular signalling proteins (19).

Whilst reducing the effects of the classic psychedelics to 5HT2A ERK-mediated K-channel inactivation is an instructive simplification, we must keep in mind that the subcellular network perturbed by the 5HT2A receptor is itself a complex system and different molecules will activate different pathways to different degrees (20). Overall, this leads to a pattern of signalling network activation unique to a particular drug. Furthermore, the balance of activity across different receptor subtypes will also vary depending on the molecule and, again, this results in a distinct pattern of emergent signalling specific to that molecule. For example, DMT and 5-MeO-DMT exhibit different degrees of activity at the depolarising 5HT2A receptors versus their hyperpolarising 5HT1A counterparts, causing distinct effects on the neuron's excitability. And, do all the classic psychedelics inhibit slow afterhyperpolarisation in the same way? Almost certainly not. And there are certainly other, more subtle, effects on a neuron's behaviour that will depend on the pattern of signalling induced by a particular molecule.

Whilst these differences might seem insignificant at the neuronal level, even subtle changes in the behaviour of a single type of neuron can have dramatic effects at the column and network level, since the patterns of activity displayed by these networks emerge from vast numbers of interactions. Subtle changes in low level neuron-neuron interactions can be amplified through the levels of the organisational hierarchy and lead to a far more pronounced effect at the cortical level at which the world model emerges. Whilst a number of generalisations can be drawn regarding the mechanism of action, and the broad effects on the world model, of the classic psychedelics, it shouldn't be surprising that subtly different molecules can have profoundly different subjective effects. In fact, these differential effects ought to be expected, but are extremely difficult to predict in a hierarchically-organised complex system such as the cortex.

DMT and 5-MeO-DMT both provide a robust and highly specific neuron-level perturbation that causes the World Space Landscape to collapse into a new, temporarily stable, structure in which the attractor states are completely separate from those of the Consensus Reality Space, forming the DMT and 5-Meo-DMT Spaces. In the case of DMT, this proceeds through distinct phases: firstly, the world begins to break down as the complex geometric forms at first veneer the world and then replace it entirely as the visions become increasingly wild and chaotic. Then a new world emerges from this chaos. Overall, there is a progression from order (the normal waking world) to disorder (the pre-breakthrough imagery) to a new order (the DMT worlds). This procession corresponds to the cortex's attractor landscape firstly being heavily disrupted and then collapsing into the new geometry, which only occurs if the dose is sufficient and "breakthrough" is achieved. The experience of the DMT worlds is the cortex gliding through the valleys of this dramatically restructured World Space Landscape within the DMT Space. 5-MeO-DMT delivers a distinct but equally powerful perturbation of the cortex and, again in a dose-dependent manner, results in its own particular restructuring of the landscape experienced as the formless 5-MeO-DMT worlds represented by states within the 5-MeO-DMT Space.

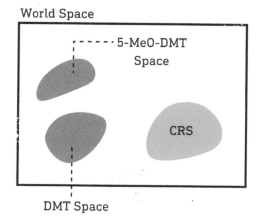

DMT.

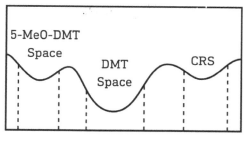

5-MeO-DMT.

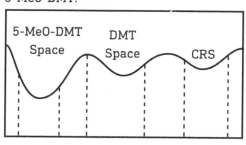

Perturbation of the cortex by a sufficient concentration of DMT causes the World Space Landscape to collapse into a new geometry in which the states of the DMT Space become attractors. The states of the 5-MeO-DMT Space become attractors under a 5-MeO-DMT perturbation.

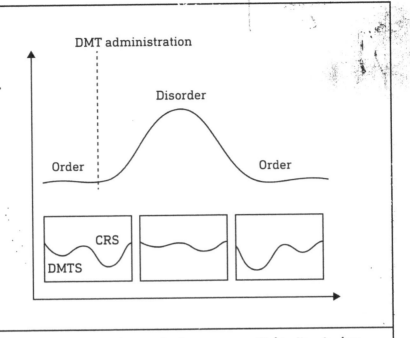

The DMT trip progresses from order [consensus reality] to disorder [pre-breakthrough imagery] to a new order [DMT reality] as the World Space Landscape flattens and then collapses into a new geometry in which the states of the DMT Space (DMTS) become attractors.

This progression from order to disorder to new order can be observed in subjects given a psychedelic before undergoing functional neuroimaging, including EEG, which can be used to monitor in real-time the neural oscillations in subjects under the influence of the drug. Changes in the power of certain frequency bands, as well as their synchronisation across the cortex, can reveal many of the changes in cortical activity produced by these molecules. Desynchronisation of alpha oscillations is a hallmark of psychedelics, indicating the disruption of the world model and an increase in disorderly cortical activity (21). However, modern EEG techniques can also monitor the way these oscillations propagate across the cortex.

Synchronised alpha oscillations are an indicator of a robust and coherent world model broadcasting its predictions down the cortical hierarchy and can be observed to propagate in that direction (towards the back of the brain where V1 is located). Gamma oscillations travel in the opposite direction, since they are generated by error-carrying superficial layer neurons. So, the balance of backward-travelling alpha waves and forward-travelling gamma waves provides a measure of the balance between downward-flowing predictions and upward-flowing prediction errors. This balance is highly dynamic and can vary depending on your state: if your eyes are open and you're viewing the world, this balance shifts towards forward-travelling waves, since your cortex's world model is being actively tested against sensory information. However, as soon as you close your eyes, visual sensory information drops off sharply and the balance tips in the opposite direction towards backward-travelling waves.

As expected, the classic psychedelics, by disrupting alpha oscillations, tip the balance further towards forward-travelling waves, indicating an increase in error signals and loss of sensory filtering. This is particularly striking with DMT — the closed-eye state at the peak of a breakthrough DMT trip is virtually indistinguishable (in terms of the forward-backward wave balance) from a normal (non-drug) open-eye state (22). In other words, it appears as if you're actually viewing a world from behind closed eyes during a deep DMT trip. Considering the highly visual nature of the DMT state, this isn't too surprising, but reveals an intriguing propensity of the lower ends of the cortical hierarchy to generate emergent patterns of activity, even in the absence of sensory stimulation.

Reducing visual sensory information doesn't cause the lower end of the cortical hierarchy to simply 'shut down', since cortical networks are always active to some degree. Downward-flowing predictions are suppressive, in that their function is to suppress activity in V1 and the upwards flow of error signals. When these predictions are disrupted by a psychedelic and visual sensory information is reduced or cut off entirely, patterns of activity in V1 emerge from spontaneous activity sculpted from the patterns of column connectivity in this area of the cortex.

With low doses of the other classic psychedelics — LSD, psilocybin, etc — these closed-eye visuals usually appear as geometric patterns known as *form constants*, of which four distinct types have been identified: spirals, funnels, cobwebs, and honeycombs (23). These recurring patterns are thought to emerge spontaneously from V1's underlying patterns of connectivity, and are naturally most pronounced when the eyes are closed. Whilst these form constants are often also experienced at the earliest phase of a DMT trip, with a sufficient dose these stereotypical visual motifs are rapidly transcended and an entirely new pattern of activity emerges, experienced as breakthrough into the DMT Space. This is the collapse into the restructured World Space Landscape caused by the DMT perturbation.

This switching to the DMT Space is also evident in the EEG data: although there is an initial drop in power and desynchronisation across all frequency bands, the breakthrough phase is accompanied by a striking increase in the delta (1-4 Hz) and theta (4-8 Hz) bands. These types of low frequency waves are also typically measured during dreaming (24), when the cortex is constructing a world model unmodulated by sensory information, and likely indicates the transition from the disordered early phase of the DMT trip to the emergence of the new order and the new world.

Now, the DMT worlds have properties, structure, and content that are entirely characteristic of DMT. It is natural to wonder how and why this particular ubiquitous naturally-occurring molecule ought to cause the human brain to switch to what amounts to an entirely new reality channel teeming with superintelligent entities and hypertechnological cityscapes. This is where questions as to the "reality" of the DMT worlds begin to arise: Are the DMT worlds mere hallucination or do they in fact exist as a freestanding objective reality populated by intelligent conscious beings? Firstly, it's important to frame this question correctly: Whether the DMT Space comprises states that form a model of an objective reality to which DMT gates access, or are a complete fabrication of the brain, or something else entirely, the cortical states within the DMT Space form a model constructed by the brain. The DMT Space sits within the World Space of the cortex, albeit in an entirely separate area from the Consensus Reality Space. The question then is thus: Does the DMT Space form a model of a world modulated by — being tested against — an extrinsic sensory information source? Does DMT somehow allow the brain to access sensory information from this free-standing reality?

In a sense, all experienced worlds are equally "real" in that all are built from the same stuff: information generated by the thalamo-cortical system. However, there is a reasonably well-understood mapping between the normal waking world and the environment, despite the brain never gaining direct access to the external world. If we are to surmise a mapping between an objective DMT reality and the experienced DMT worlds, then we must also deal with the nature of that mapping — where is this DMT reality and how does DMT gate the flow of information from its normally inaccessible domains? If, on the other hand, we assume the DMT worlds to be constructed entirely without modulation by some alternate source

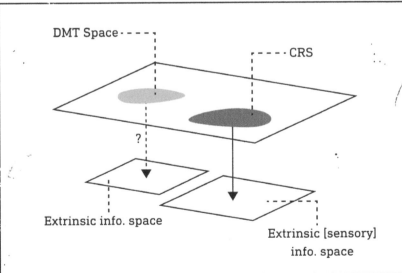

The DMT world is represented by states within the World Space and is as real as the normal waking world. However, whether, like the CRS, the DMT Space is mapped to an extrinsic information space is an open question.

of sensory information, the brain's ability to effortlessly construct such bizarre worlds remains puzzling.

Although, as we have discussed, perturbation of the interactions between the components of a complex system can cause it switch to entirely new patterns of emergent activity, it's not easy to explain why the most common naturally-occurring psychedelic molecule achieves a perturbation that reliably fires countless independent users into the same kind of hypertechnological space bursting with wildly giggling elves and other characteristic denizens of that realm.

The ant society doesn't shift from the Fight an Intruder to the Build a Bridge behaviour by random chance — the ants have evolved and honed their interactions (chemical, visual, etc) such that these behaviours become, in a sense, built into the system. The ants drive the restructuring of their society attractor landscape — to switch to the alternative behaviour — by temporarily modifying their interactions in a manner honed throughout the course of their evolution as a society. As such, the cortex's ability to suddenly restructure its attractor landscape such that the new attractor states just happen to model a hypertechnological alien world bearing no relationship whatsoever to the normal waking world is as confounding as a 5-year-old British child suddenly switching from English to fluent Central Siberian Yupik. Or, one might compare it to finding an entirely new channel on your TV set and then discovering that the aerial has been disconnected.

Where did this bizarre world come from?

How did the brain learn to construct a model of it?

Of course, it would be much easier to explain this if, as countless DMT users are convinced, the states of the DMT Space are mapped to — receiving and processing information from — an alternate reality existing independently of our brains and, most likely, outside of our Universe.

The DMT world is a world that's not only entirely unexpected, but a world that *cannot* be expected. It is inconceivable. Even after returning to the old familiar reality, DMT users often struggle to comprehend the experience that this simple compound afforded them. It is truly stranger than we can suppose. 5-MeO-DMT also has a tendency to leave users breathless and shaking with awe, but for different reasons. Both of these molecules are difficult to understand, and feel almost impossible to explain, but with an understanding of the dynamics of the brain's complex world-building machinery, we can at least try and get to grips with what's actually going on in the brain when they're ingested. However, definitive answers as to the objective nature or otherwise of these spaces, and what they might mean, remain out of reach for the time being. The best we can do is to withhold judgement and see ourselves as explorers of these strange domains. In the final chapter, we'll discuss how we might learn to navigate and explore the cortex's vast World Space, but first we'll turn our attention to the three other known reality channel switches embedded in the brain's world-building networks.

現実制御学研究所、東京

コピーは全て
破棄された

リアリティ
スイッチ

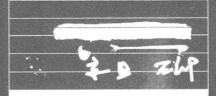

`<XXXXXX_3489_053_QX>`

Chapter 11: The M-Switch

世界空間 M—スイッチ

「セカイクウカン M—スイッチ」

"Indians lived here long ago, they had a drug
cult, smoked *toloache* which is jimsonweed, gave
themselves hallucinations, deluded themselves they
were visiting other realities — why, come to think of
it, not unlike the hippie freaks of our present day."

Thomas Pynchon, Inherent Vice

M

現実△
制御学
研究所

Despite their being amongst the oldest of the psychedelics, the use of tropane-containing plants by modern psychonauts is generally restricted to the more intrepid of such explorers.

And for good reason.

From an early age, children are warned about wild botanicals with bright and alluring but deadly berries, and the Solanaceae, or nightshades, feature prominently in such counsel. The most infamous members of this broad family are the Old World plants Deadly Nightshade (*Atropa belladonna*, from which the alkaloid name tropane is derived), mandrake (*Mandragora officinarum*), and henbane (*Hyoscyamus niger*), all of which contain varying concentrations of the psychedelic deliriant tropane alkaloids (1).

Tropane-containing plants have a history as intoxicants reaching back to pre-Bronze Age eras more than 5,000 years ago (2). Extracts of the mandrake root were used to enhance the psychoactive effects of beer in Egypt over 3000 years ago, with the Russians and Chinese opting for Datura extracts (3). In Europe, mandrake and henbane have historically played roles as the major active constituents of witches' ointments, allowing them to communicate with spirits, demons, and perhaps even Old Nick himself (4). Plants of the Datura and closely-related Brugmansia genus — specifically *Datura innoxia* (Toloache) and *Datura stramonium* (Thorn Apple) — have roles in the sacred rituals of the New World (5).

Three closely-related alkaloids are responsible for the psychoactive effects of these plants. All contain the unusual tropane ring system as their structural base: a 6-membered ring containing a single nitrogen atom, with a distinctive 2-carbon "bridge". Atropine and hyoscyamine are essentially the same molecule, except the latter is one mirror image isomer (optical isomer) of the molecule, whereas atropine is an equal (racemic) mixture of both (see appendix). Scopolamine (also known as hyoscine) differs from atropine/hyoscyamine only in sporting an epoxide ring on the main tropane ring, and is thought to be primarily responsible for the unique psychedelic state induced by these plants.

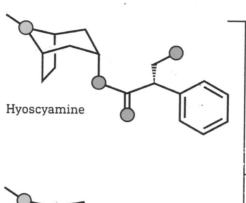

Hyoscyamine

Atropine

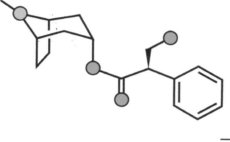

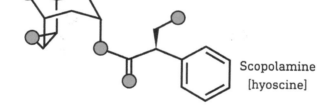

Scopolamine
[hyoscine]

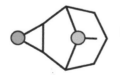

Scopolamine
ring system

The major tropane alkaloids responsible for the psychedelic effects of
Solanaceae (nightshades).

The tropane alkaloids are often referred to as deliriants and many are uncomfortable adorning them with the "psychedelic" moniker they'd prefer reserved for the less menacing reality-switching molecules (6). However, there can be no doubt that these molecules have the potential to swallow the user and ferry them into worlds as unusual as, albeit entirely distinct from, those visited under the influence of the classic 5HT2A agonists.

The tropane alkaloids are notable in that they often elicit what are called true hallucinations — these aren't visions that are recognisable as such, but hallucinations that blend perfectly with the environment (7). With the classic psychedelics, the user is, more often than not, aware that their eyes-open visuals are distinct from the normal waking world. Using psychiatric parlance, the classic psychedelic user maintains *insight* into his drugged state. However, this is not always the case with the tropanes. "Phantom smoking", for example, is a curiously common effect reported after consumption of tropane-containing plants (8). Trippers will not only smoke an imaginary cigarette for extended periods of time but then, finally noting its absence, scramble around on the floor searching the 'dropped cigarette' before it should set the house alight. When consumed orally, the effects are often delayed and can sneak up on the user, who might assume the plant to be inactive, only to realise some time later that they spent the preceding two hours entertaining guests at a party that never happened.

The tropane alkaloids are extremely strange, unpredictable and, undoubtedly, rather dangerous. Somewhat dependent on dose, their world-switching effects can vary between mild intoxication and immersion in an entirely fantastical reality filled with intelligent entities.

As with the classic psychedelics, the tropanes' world-switching effects depend upon their ability to manipulate the brain's world model and its interaction with the environment. Indeed, this is the defining effect of *all* psychedelic molecules. However, the manner in which this manipulation is achieved will affect the manner in which it manifests. Clearly, the tropanes elicit a distinctive, often rather sinister, change in the phenomenal world not elicited by the classic psychedelics. But, just as with the classic psychedelics, we can understand these changes by studying their effects on the construction and maintenance of the world model.

Unless you happen to be asleep and dreaming, your brain's world model is constantly tested against sensory information. A successful model is one that accurately predicts sensory information from moment to moment, meaning the amount of potentially disruptive information from the environment that must be processed by the cortical hierarchy is kept to a minimum. Your brain learns to construct a successful model by learning about the patterns and regularities in the environment, which it gleans from the patterns of sensory information that enter the brain via the sensory apparatus. Successful predictions provide accumulating evidence that the model hypotheses are appropriate and functioning well, whereas prediction failures indicate that they need to be updated. However, this somewhat oversimplifies the problem the brain must overcome in building a successful model, since it assumes that sensory information is always perfectly reliable. In other words, if a sensory prediction is unfulfilled, we have so far assumed that this must be because the model is somehow flawed. But is this necessarily the case? What if the sensory information is flawed and isn't providing reliable information about the environment? Can your brain always trust the sensory information it's receiving? Now, of course, your brain only ever has access to the environment via the patterns of sensory information it receives, so this information has a critical role in maintaining the integrity of the world model. On the other hand, it's important that your brain doesn't trust all sensory information without question, and it must learn to detect when it might be misleading.

Imagine you're talking to a friend over a rather crackly long-distance telephone line. He says:

"I'm meeting my (*unclear*) this afternoon."

The word sounds a bit like "dolphin", but being fully aware that your friend neither owns nor fraternises with dolphins, you assume you misheard and that he actually said "girlfriend". In other words, you trust your "model" (what you know about your friend and that "girlfriend" makes more sense in this sentence than "dolphin") more than you trust the information arriving along the noisy telephone line, and you complete the sentence accordingly. Visual sensory information entering the brain is also inherently noisy and cannot be assumed perfectly reliable (9). Even under strict experimental conditions when a visual stimulus is kept as stable and invariant as technically possible, the absorption of photons by the light-sensitive cells of the retina is a quantum-level process with inherent randomness that cannot be eliminated (10). Under low-light conditions or when light is obscured by fog, for example, noise levels are even higher, further decreasing the quality of visual sensory information.

Fortunately, as well as learning the patterns and regularities in sensory information received from the environment, your brain has learned that it must *expect* varying levels of random fluctuation in this information and, consequently, the low-level prediction errors this noise generates. Sensory noise is, by definition, unpredictable and, as such, even a perfect model of the environment is unable to predict these random fluctuations. In other words, low-level prediction errors are unavoidable, even when the world model and its predictions are working perfectly. The cortex ought only to update its working hypotheses if there's good evidence that they're failing. Prediction error resulting from low quality sensory information and random noise isn't good evidence. By learning how much of this noise-generated prediction error is to be expected under different conditions (low light, fog, etc), your brain can assess whether a particular pattern of prediction error is likely to be newsworthy and indicative of important unpredicted changes in sensory information or, conversely, if it can safely be ignored.

The more noisy and unreliable sensory information becomes, the less your brain is able to trust it, and the more it relies upon its internally-generated model. Just as you didn't trust the word "dolphin" when speaking to your friend over the crackly telephone line, your brain doesn't trust sensory information it considers to be unreliable. If all sensory information was trusted without question, flawed information would be allowed to modify the model and, potentially, degrade it. Information judged to be reliable ought to be allowed to enter the brain more freely than unreliable information, and your brain has evolved mechanisms to control the flow of predictions errors (and thus sensory information) depending on how reliable it considers them to be. Naturally, of course, since only prediction errors are broadcast upwards through the cortical hierarchy, curbing prediction errors means restricting the flow of sensory information into the brain. If this is pushed too far, the world model will soon become disconnected from, and unaccountable to, the environment. On the other hand, opening the gates completely will allow poor quality or noisy sensory information to flow into the cortical hierarchy and force inappropriate updates to the model. If your cortex updated its model in response to every random fluctuation in sensory information, your world would rapidly become unstable and completely useless as a model of the environment. The brain must strike a balance between trusting sensory information and continuing to sample from the environment, and relying more on its internal model (11).

Predictions errors are propagated up the cortical hierarchy through the superficial layers of the cortex. The brain tunes the balance between trusting sensory information and trusting the internal model by modulating the gain ("volume") of these error signals (12). If the prediction errors are the result of sensory information that the brain has determined to be unreliable, then these errors are dampened or "turned down" and not allowed to progress deep into the cortical hierarchy. If, on the other hand, the errors are seen to be the result of reliable sensory information, then the gain of these errors is "turned up" — they pass up the cortical hierarchy and are used, hopefully, to drive necessary updates to the world model.

This gain modulation can even be performed selectively in particular areas of the visual field, or for particular patterns of sensory information. If you're focused on watching a movie, your cortex

Sensory information reliable.

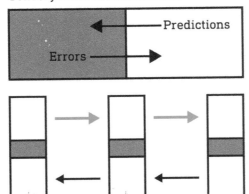

Sensory information unreliable.

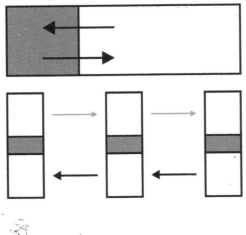

Depending on the perceived reliability of sensory information, the cortex can control the balance between trusting error signals and trusting its internal model.

increases the gain on columns in the centre of your visual field where your gaze is directed and, if you're particularly engaged in the action on the screen, you're unlikely to notice events unfolding in your peripheral vision where the prediction error gain is turned down. This doesn't mean your peripheral field of vision becomes empty or "blank", but that your cortex's model of this area of the visual field is less likely to be updated by sensory input and the dampened error signals. In effect, your brain has decided that the most important and newsworthy error signals are likely to be found in the centre of your vision, with peripheral error signals being ignored, unless something particularly startling happens. Or, if you've ever misplaced a possession with a particular colour — say a set of car keys with a bright blue keyring attached — as you scan the room in an attempt to locate the keys, you're likely to find that every blue object in your visual field pops out and grabs your attention. Your cortex has temporarily increased the gain on error signals from cortical columns representing the colour blue. So, prediction error gain isn't only useful in curbing the flow of unreliable sensory information into the brain, but can be used to amplify some elements of the sensory signal and disregard others, according to the particular demands of the task or focus of your attention (13).

Unlike the classic psychedelics, which disrupt the high-level world model by exciting deep pyramidal cells, the tropane alkaloids disrupt the gain modulation system that the cortex uses to sculpt the volume and patterns of prediction errors. To understand why this elicits the peculiar effects of the tropanes on the structure of the world model, we need firstly to look at the particular type of receptor with which the tropane alkaloids interact, and the effects these receptors have on the neurons within which they're embedded.

Whilst the classic psychedelics act as agonists at the 5HT2A receptor to elicit their effects on neural activity, the tropane alkaloids act as antagonists at another type of membrane-embedded metabotropic receptor: the M1 subtype of the muscarinic receptor (14). The muscarinic class of receptors is so-called since all of its subtypes bind to the alkaloid muscarine, which is found most notably in the famously red and white-spotted *Amanita muscaria* — Fly Agaric — mushroom (15). However, the natural endogenous agonist of the muscarinic receptor is the neuromodulator acetylcholine. Like serotonin, acetylcholine is part of the brain's molecular toolbox which it uses to modulate the function and behaviour of neurons and thus regulate cortical activity.

There are two classes of acetylcholine receptor, each of which comprises more than one subtype. The nicotinic receptors — so-called since they are activated by the tobacco alkaloid nicotine — are found in both the central and peripheral nervous system, where they control muscle contraction at a specialised synapse called the neuromuscular junction, as well as having important roles in the brain. However, it is the second class of receptors, the muscarinic receptors, that form the locus of action of the tropane alkaloids. Five subtypes of muscarinic receptors are known — labelled M1 to M5 — and each exerts its own specific type of effect on the neurons within which it's embedded. The tropane alkaloids act as antagonists at the M1 subtype in particular, meaning they bind to the receptor but elicit no activating conformational change in the receptor, merely blocking acetylcholine from binding (16).

Just like 5HT2A receptors, the M1 receptor sits within the neuronal membrane, with a ligand binding site in the extracellular domain, and an intracellular domain that interacts with the molecular signalling network within the neuron's interior. The binding of acetylcholine to its extracellular binding site elicits a conformational change in the receptor that's transmitted to the intracellular domain which, once activated, binds to the G-protein, Gq, (see chapter 5) and, as with the 5HT2A receptor, leads to depolarisation of the neuron. Activation of the 5HT2A receptor causes depolarisation mainly via activation of the kinase ERK, which phosphorylates and inactivates a specific type of potassium channel. M1 receptor activation also results in the inactivation of potassium channels, albeit by a different mechanism, and several different types of potassium channels are likely involved. However, arguably the most important in the signalling mechanism of the M1 receptor is a channel known as TREK (17).

The TREK channels, in their open state, allow potassium ions to flow out of the cell, pulling the membrane potential in the negative direction away from the threshold potential (hyperpolarisation). As such, together with the gamut of other ion channels in the neuronal membrane, they contribute to the overall balance of charge across the membrane and thus the resting membrane potential.

As with most gated ion channels, TREK has a complex regulation mechanism. However, two ubiquitous signalling molecules, PIP2 and DAG (both of which we met when discussing the 5HT2A receptor in chapter 8) both bind to the TREK channel, but have opposite effects on its gating:

> When PIP2, which is abundant inside the neuron and its membrane, binds to the TREK channel, it shifts it to the *open* state.

> DAG, on the other hand, binds and inactivates the TREK channel by nudging it into the *closed* state (18).

When acetylcholine binds to the agonist binding domain of the M1 receptor, the Gq-protein binds to the intracellular domain and is activated. Active Gq then binds to and activates PLC, an enzyme that specifically breaks down PIP2 to form IP3 and DAG.

So, activation of PLC — via activation of M1 by acetylcholine — leads to a *decrease* in PIP2 levels and a concomitant *increase* in DAG levels (19). This means the TREK channel receives a *weaker* activating signal from PIP2 and a *stronger* inactivating signal from DAG and, together, these cause TREK channels to close throughout the neuronal membrane.

Naturally, closure of these channels reduces the flow of potassium ions out of the cell and, in precisely the same manner as with the 5HT2A receptor, pushes the membrane potential towards the firing threshold. In short, activation of the M1 receptor increases the excitability of the neuron, and can be observed in cultured neurons as a slow and sustained depolarisation (20).

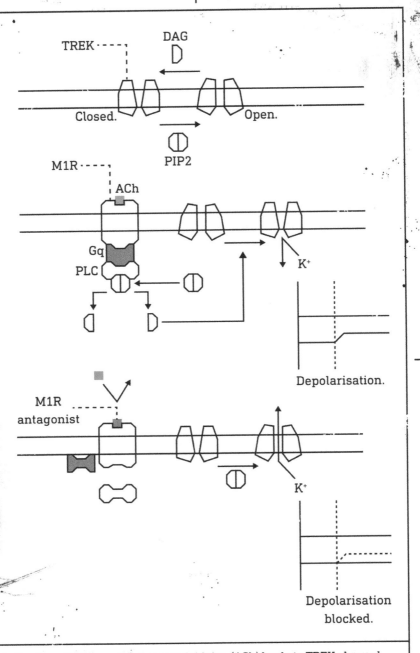

Activation of M1 receptors by acetylchloine (ACh) leads to TREK channel closure and depolarisation. M1 receptor antagonists block this effect by occupying the receptor ligand binding site and preventing Ach binding.

Error signals are transmitted up the cortical hierarchy using superficial pyramidal cells. Axons from the superficial pyramidal cells transmit the errors signals to neurons in the input payer of the level above in the hierarchy. So, if the brain wants to control the flow of sensory information — based on the perceived reliability or importance of that information — then it must control the volume of these error signals. Acetylcholine and M1 receptors play an important role in this process (21).

Much like those from serotonergic neurons, axons from specialised cholinergic neurons deep in the base of the brain project across large areas of the cortex and release acetylcholine into the world-building cortical hierarchy (21). In particular, these axons synapse with neurons in the input and superficial layers that receive the error signals from lower levels of the cortical hierarchy. So, if the brain trusts the sensory information arriving from the environment, acetylcholine is released and activates M1 receptors on these post-synaptic neurons, increasing their excitability and elevating their response to the incoming error signals (22).

If, on the other hand, the sensory information is believed to be unreliable (under low-light conditions, for example), acetylcholine release is reduced and the input layer neurons become less excitable — errors signals are effectively dampened (23). So, overall, by regulating acetylcholine release, the brain is tuning that all-important balance between trusting sensory information and trusting the world model.

The synchronisation of gamma oscillations in the superficial layers is also important in regulating the impact of error signals as they flow up the cortical hierarchy — synchronised error signals, generated by synchronised gamma oscillations, have a stronger impact on the cortical level above, in much the same way that synchronised alpha oscillation increase the impact of predictions flowing down the hierarchy. As well as exciting neurons in the input layer, acetylcholine also promotes gamma oscillations by stimulating superficial pyramidal cells (24) and so supports the generation of robust error signals.

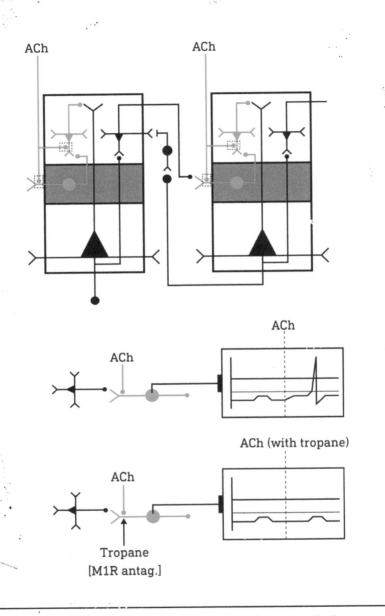

Acetylcholine (ACh) is released onto the postsynaptic neurons in the input and superficial layers of the cortical columns that receive the error signals from the lower hierarchical level. This increases the excitability of the neurons, increasing their response to incoming error signals.

In addition to these effects on superficial pyramidal cells, M1 receptors are also found in the membrane of GABA-releasing inhibitory interneurons. As discussed in chapter 7, inhibitory neurons are as important as excitatory ones in sculpting neural activity — it's just as important for the cortex to be able to suppress the activity of neurons as it is to excite them. By activating M1 receptors on inhibitory interneurons, acetylcholine increases their activity and helps to keep the background activity of pyramidal cells at a low level, which is important for maintaining a stable and coherent world model (25). By stimulating M1 receptors on both excitatory pyramidal cells *and* inhibitory interneurons, acetylcholine reduces any noisy background activity whilst, at the same time, increasing the response to actual input from the environment. This further helps to ensure robust and newsworthy error signals are transmitted but random noise is not.

When a tropane alkaloid finds its way into the brain, it competes with acetylcholine for the M1 receptor binding site. However, the tropanes bind to the M1 receptor around 10,000 times more strongly than acetylcholine, so it's not really much of a contest (26). In a dose-dependent manner, this dampens the response of the superficial pyramidal cells to sensory inputs, whether or not acetylcholine is present, and the brain loses the ability to increase the volume of error signals flowing up the cortical hierarchy. By suppressing gamma oscillations, the tropanes further reduce the impact of error signals generated at the lower levels of the cortical hierarchy. This tips the balance strongly towards trusting the world model (and its predictions) and away from trusting sensory information. Or, equivalently, this mimics a low acetylcholine state in which the brain strongly distrusts the sensory information it's receiving, even when the sensory information is perfectly reliable. The world model and its constituent hypotheses become divorced from the environment, since they're no longer subject to the strict testing against sensory information.

Furthermore, since the tropanes also block the stimulating effect of acetylcholine on inhibitory interneurons, the deep pyramidal cells that represent the world model and the superficial ones that

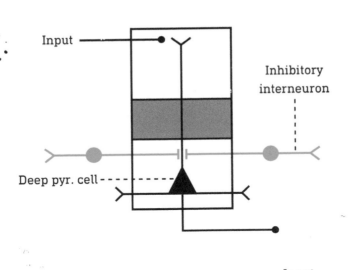

Input

Inhibitory
interneuron

Deep pyr. cell

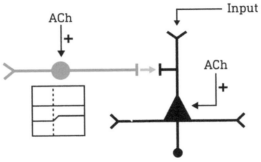

ACh

Input

ACh

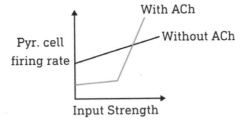

With ACh

Without ACh

Pyr. cell
firing rate

Input Strength

Acetylcholine (ACh) both directly stimulates deep pyr. cells (via M1R) and suppresses their firing via M1R on inhibitory interneurons. This keeps keeps pyr. cell responses to noisy background activity low, but enhances their response to strong inputs.

transmit error signals become overactive, but not in response to robust inputs from the environment. So, not only are the all-important "real" error signals dampened, but low-level noisy activity isn't quashed by inhibition from interneurons, since their stimulation by acetylcholine is also blocked by the tropane antagonist. The signal-to-noise ratio collapses.

The classic psychedelics strongly disrupt the world model by selective stimulation of deep pyramidal cells. The flow of information — the error signals — up the cortical hierarchy, however, isn't stymied. In fact, as we discussed in the chapters on the C-Switch, error signals actually *increase* in response to this model perturbation. In contrast, the tropanes' major effect is in *reducing* the upwards flow of information and preventing the world model from being held to account by those error signals. This alone allows hypotheses with little sensory evidence to become established in the world model (27). Entirely fleeting ideas — *Did I just light a cigarette?* — would normally be extinguished momentarily by generating predictions that would be met by a barrage of error signals: the characteristic appearance of a cigarette and the curl of smoke isn't present in the visual field, nor is the sensation of the cigarette between the fingers. But, in the tropane intoxicated state, these predictions, based on spurious hypotheses, are never corrected. This "cigarette" rapidly becomes part of the world model and isn't updated. Only after some time, with a moment of lucidity and focused attention, does your brain notice the error and you realise that the cigarette never existed. It's common for this to be repeated throughout the trip.

Again and again.

When you smoke a phantom cigarette during a tropane trip, your world model contains that cigarette in precisely the same way that your normal waking world contains a cigarette when you're actually doing so. Of course, this also applies to smoking in a dream. The difference, as always, lies in the relationship these models have with the environment. When error signals are muted by the tropane, the model loses its moorings and becomes detached

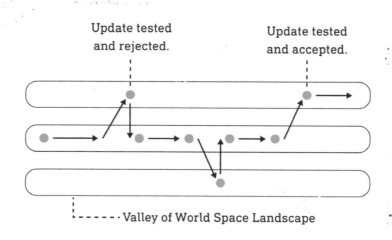

Update tested
and rejected.

Update tested
and accepted.

- - - - - - Valley of World Space Landscape

Potential model updates are tested against sensory information. If an
update fails to reduce error signals or causes them to increase, the
update will be rejected.

Tropane State.

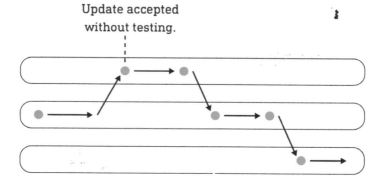

Update accepted
without testing.

Under the influence of tropane alkaloids, error signals are blocked.
Entirely spurious hypotheses can be rapidly and stably incorporated into
the world model without any protest from errors.

from the environment, which is unable to provide a challenge to the veracity of this entirely bogus and non-functional model. But the cigarette model is the same. Of course, this also applies to hallucinated people and even entire scenes which play out as if in normal waking life:

> "I remember walking around my dorm thinking I was naked, and there were at least 10 people in every room. I didn't know any of them, but I was able to talk to quite a few of them. They seemed to ignore my nudity, and I understood this to be a sign of friendship. In my room there were 4 people I've never seen before, my little brother, and a hallucinated version of my sober friend (who at the time was actually trying to help the other guy was tripping off the floor). We all talked for what seemed like years, discussing many things from the roman empire to how butterscotch was made." (28)

In contrast to the classic psychedelics, which employ a robust stimulation of deep pyramidal cells to disrupt the world model, at low doses the tropanes' disinhibition of these cells (by suppressing the activity of inhibitory interneurons) is more of a "tickling" of the model, unchastened by error signals. The visions induced by the classic psychedelics also tend to be unstable, since the elevated errors signals force frequent model updates (the hypothesis shifting effect). Since these error signals are muted by the tropanes, the visions tend to be more stable and often indistinguishable from the entirely adaptive remainder of the world. And this is perhaps why the experience is often described more as a delirium or waking dream than a psychedelic trip. The more dynamic classic psychedelic visions announce themselves as being distinct from the stable and familiar consensus world. Tropane visions do no such thing:

> "Everything seemed incredibly real, and I found it impossible to separate reality from fantasy. Because as far as I knew, everything was real." (29)

Having said that, these true hallucinations are not limited to the mundane — the tropanes' reputation as insanity-inducing agents is well-founded. At higher doses, the disinhibition of the deep pyramidal cells becomes more pronounced and, in a manner similar to the classic psychedelics, information begins to flow more readily between cortical columns and entirely novel patterns of activity — and the worlds they represent — can become established and remain stable without any robust challenge by error signals.

> "I began to have unpleasantly vivid, tactile hallucinations of translucent spiders with long, curly tails composed of what seemed like fishing line. They had made me very agitated and paranoid because they had been crawling up the walls, on the floor around me, up my legs, in my hair and up the curtains... The hallucinations were so overwhelmingly vivid and tactile because whenever I stepped on their 'tails' they illusively tripped up, or got snagged beneath my feet and struggled to go anywhere, whether along the floor, or up the walls." (30)

At regular "open eyes" dose levels of the classic psychedelics, when navigation and exploration of the external environment remains possible, such vivid and compelling visions are relatively rare. When they do occur, they tend to be transient and unstable, quickly giving way to new forms and structures as error signals force model updates. Closing the eyes, and thus cutting off visual sensory information, can help to stabilise the visuals and allow more complex and sophisticated visions to establish themselves. However, since the tropanes mute these error signals even when the eyes are open, the strangest of hypotheses can insinuate themselves into the world model and remain stable for long periods of time. This is remarkably similar to the REM dream state, except the mechanism of disconnection from sensory information is different. The tropane user is carried away by this waking dream, punctuated by moments of almost perfect lucidity. It's all over. But then it's not again:

"Next thing I know its already 6:46am and I am running late. My mom tells me I only got a half hour to get ready or I'll get a Saturday detention. I scramble out of bed and run into the bathroom to take a shower... Then I run into my room and get dressed and go downstairs to the kitchen. Right then I noticed something was wrong, the clock said 1:00am and the calendar was on July. Nobody was up. My mom was asleep and had been asleep. She didn't wake me up for school, I did not have school in summer." (31)

Whilst terrifying, often traumatic, and not particularly worthwhile for most people, the tropanes provide a penetrating insight into the way the world is built from a dynamic, labile, and delicate assembly of hypotheses requiring constant testing against sensory information. Without the error signals that this information generates, the model can quickly lose its moorings and, in some cases, become entirely divorced from the environment. It's not unusual for a flick of the head to transport the tripper from the kitchen to a busy airport terminal, complete with bustling crowds. In this way, it's very much like a waking dream. Unlike dreaming, however, in which the dreamer's motor function is mercifully inhibited to save them acting out their dreams, there is no such mercy for the tropane tripper, who will often begin interacting with the non-existent people and objects in their own private fantasy world.

To an outside observer — a trip sitter is obviously recommended for such voyages — the tripper's behaviour will often appear frighteningly bizarre, and it's often at this point that medical assistance is sought. Unfortunately, the motives and intent of anyone attempting to assist the tripper will likely be entirely unappreciated, and attempts at encouraging or coercing them tend to be met with resistance or, in some cases, outright violence.

As if it needs repeating:

The tropanes are not to be played with.

Despite their risks, the tropanes represent another tool for exploring the World Space which, in the right hands, is not completely without merit. As with the classic psychedelics, the effects of the tropanes can be viewed as a temporary restructuring of the World Space Landscape, albeit in a different manner and using an entirely different mechanism.

The classic psychedelics both flatten the World Space Landscape *and* cause an increase in error signals. The reduced energetic gap between high and low energy states makes it more likely that the cortex will reach disfavoured states, increasing the size of the state repertoire. The elevated error signals force more frequent model updates, actively pushing the cortex around the World Space Landscape, experienced as a novel and unstable world with frequent hypothesis shifts.

In contrast, at low doses, the tropanes flatten the World Space Landscape only slightly (since disinhibition of pyramidal cells is relatively modest) whilst dramatically *decreasing* error signals. So, although the cortex is more likely to reach novel high-energy states, it's just as likely to glide along the valleys of the Consensus Reality Space. However, unlike in the normal waking state, the impetus from error signals to correct the cortex's trajectory through the World Space is lost. So, if the cortex wanders into the wrong valley, it's likely to remain there for some time. Again, this is very much like the dream state, in which the cortex wanders the World Space Landscape without the guidance of sensory information. The phantom cigarette isn't extinguished and the "visitors" in the kitchen are entertained for hours.

At higher doses, when the disinhibition of pyramidal cells becomes more prominent, the World Space Landscape is flattened more dramatically (32), and the effects of the tropanes draw closer to those of the classic psychedelics. However, unlike the classic psychedelic state, the cortex can more freely wander into normally high-energy states completely separate from those of Channel Consensus Reality without any protest from error signals. Users can find themselves in alternate realities as stable and coherent

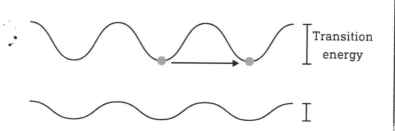

Transition energy

Normal state.

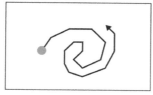

World Space trajectory guided by landscape geometry and sensory testing.

Tropane state.

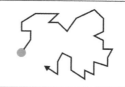

Wandering World Space trajectory without sensory testing.

The tropane alkaloids both flatten the World Space Landscape, reducing the state transition energy, as well as reducing the guidance from sensory testing, resulting in a dream-like wandering trajectory.

as the normal waking world but completely disconnected from the environment. It's at these doses, under similar closed-eye conditions as employed for the short-acting tryptamines, that the discovery and exploration of new regions within the World Space becomes feasible.

However, the dangers inherent in the tropanes render this tool suitable for only the most seasoned voyagers. Nature doesn't always provide the safest tools for switching reality channels and, sometimes, we can do better.

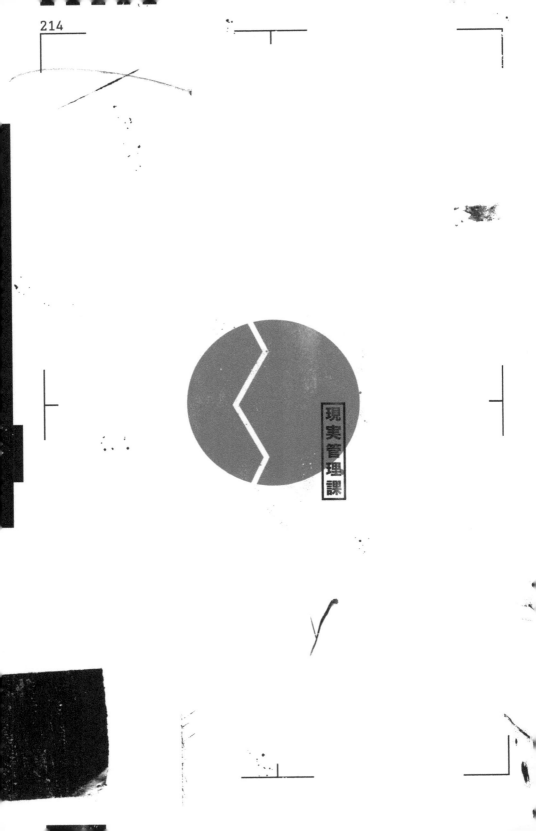

現実管理課

リアリティ
スイッチ

<XXXXXX_3489_055_AS>

Chapter 12: The N-Switch

世界空間 N-スイッチ

「セカイクウカンN-スイッチ」

"Would you like me to inject you again?"

"Yes, but it is too soon."

Samuel Beckett

Not all psychedelic molecules spring from, nor are they even inspired by, the natural world. Plants and fungi are masterful chemists, manufacturing a bewildering array of structurally diverse organic molecules from the simplest of chemical building blocks. Many of those that still await discovery will turn out to be psychoactive and, a handful at least, psychedelic. However, we shouldn't underestimate the potential of human invention in the creation of molecules with psychedelic, reality-switching, properties.

The arylcyclohexylamines, of which phencyclidine (PCP) and ketamine are the most (in)famous members, are unlike the psychedelics we've discussed so far in that they're entirely synthetic — they have no natural basis. Unlike LSD, which finds its inspiration in ergot's natural apothecary, or the phenethylamines based upon mescaline, the arylcyclohexylamines are a product entirely of the human mind. They are synthetic drugs in the purest sense. And yet, they possess reality-switching properties as dramatic and confounding as any of the natural psychedelics. But, as with any molecule that interfaces directly with the human brain's world-building apparatus, there is the potential for both terror and wonder.

PCP was first synthesised in 1956 by medicinal chemist Harold Maddox and given the moniker CI-395 (1). Animal trials began, in the usual way, from rodents upwards. Rats became agitated and "drunken" when injected with the drug, pigeons were immobilised, dogs grew delirious and, finally, monkeys were put to sleep (2). Perhaps the varied and frankly paradoxical effects across the species might have provided an omen of things to come. However, the highly apparent anaesthetic effects in monkeys were enough to convince clinicians to begin trials in humans undergoing surgery.

Whilst promisingly effective as an anaesthetic, many patients returned from their slumber in a state of pronounced delirium, sometimes requiring restraint from medical staff. Somewhat tellingly, some patients reported vivid hallucinations during the anaesthetised state:

"One thought he had become a grub and another was convinced he had been shot into space in a sputnik; the third was under the impression he had died and ascended into heaven; the fourth believed herself to be listening to the Halle Orchestra in the Free Trade Hall in Manchester." (3)

It soon became clear that the psychological side effects of PCP were intolerable and the drug was abandoned as an anaesthetic (4). However, the drug development team at Parke-Davis wasn't ready to abandon the arylcyclohexylamine class of molecules entirely, and a team of chemists set about synthesising a series of analogues with the hope of finding one with the desired anaesthetic properties but without the unpleasant side effects. CI-581, soon to be renamed ketamine, was one of those new analogues found to be a highly effective short-acting anaesthetic and analgesic, but without the accompanying delirium that disqualified PCP from clinical use.

The first human was given ketamine via intravenous injection on August 3, 1964. As the dosage was gradually increased, the patient experienced the now familiar tiers of the ketamine state:

At very low doses, no effect was apparent.

At higher doses, the patient experienced an entirely alert but "spaced out" state.

The highest doses resulted in an unresponsive anaesthetised state.

This pattern was repeated with a number of subjects, many of whom reported feeling detached from their bodies, floating in outer space, and completely disconnected from the outside world. This sensory detachment inspired the name of what would soon become an entirely new class of psychoactive molecule with ketamine as its founding member: the dissociative anaesthetics. Modern psychonauts, however, are more likely to consider ketamine and PCP as types of psychedelic since, at low doses, they share many of the types of effects experienced with the classic psychedelics, including a restructuring of the world model and alterations in its relationship to the environment (5). At higher, more challenging doses, ketamine can also gate access to entirely new reality channels populated by intelligent entities. Outside of the clinic, where high doses of ketamine are delivered intravenously over extended periods of time, "dissociative psychedelics" is perhaps a more fitting moniker and the one we'll adopt here.

Both PCP and ketamine have an underlying arylcyclohexylamine molecular skeleton — a 6-membered carbon ring (the cyclohexyl part), with an amine group and an aryl group (see appendix) attached to one of the ring carbons. This basic molecular foundation can be modified to generate a large (and growing) range of arylcyclohexylamine drugs related to PCP and ketamine (6). These structural analogues can be created by modifying the type of amine or aryl group, as well as attaching additional groups on the cyclohexyl ring. PCP bears a simple phenyl ring and an amine embedded in a 6-membered ring. Ketamine sports a simpler amine, but contains a chlorophenyl ring, as well as a ketone (C=O) on the cyclohexyl ring.

The arylcyclohexylamine psychedelics are unified in binding to a specific type of glutamate receptor: the NMDA receptor (NMDA = N-methyl-D-aspartate, a synthetic agonist of the receptor). We've already met the AMPA receptor, which forms a ligand-gated ion channel, and the metabotropic mGluR2 receptor. Like the AMPA receptor, the NMDA receptor is part of a positive ion (cation) channel gated by glutamate and, as such, its activation generates an excitatory postsynaptic potential (EPSP) in the dendrite of the postsynaptic neuron. However, activation of the NMDA receptor is rather more complex than the AMPA receptor. Whereas the AMPA receptor ion channel can be gated by glutamate alone, at the resting membrane potential the NMDA receptor channel is blocked by a magnesium ion (Mg^{2+}), even if glutamate is bound. However, if the membrane potential is pushed towards zero — depolarised — the magnesium ion becomes more and more likely to dissoci-

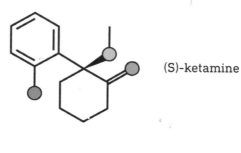

(S)-ketamine

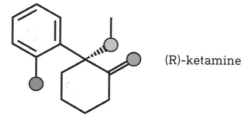

(R)-ketamine

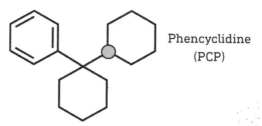

Phencyclidine
(PCP)

Structures of the major psychedelic arylcyclohexylamines.

ate from the channel and allow ions to pass through (7). So, for the NMDA ion channel to be opened, the neuron must be in a de-polarised state when glutamate binds to the ligand binding site. This can occur when a neuron is receiving excitatory inputs via its AMPA receptors — which depolarise the neuron — with simul-taneous glutamate inputs that activate its NMDA receptors. If the NMDA receptors alone are stimulated, the magnesium blockade will prevent any ions flowing into the neuron. So, rather than act-ing alone, NMDA receptors tend to amplify a neuron's response to excitatory AMPA inputs (8). Also, NMDA channels remain open for much longer than the AMPA receptor ion channel, generating a slower and weaker but longer lasting EPSP (9).

NMDA receptors are found on neurons throughout the brain, but they have a particularly important role in maintaining the struc-ture of the world model. We'll consider the function of NMDA re-ceptors in three locations:

1. Dendrites of neurons in the superficial layers of the cortical columns.

2. Deep pyramidal cells.

3. Inhibitory interneurons amongst the deep pyramidal cells.

Recall that the world model generates predictions which flow *down* the cortical hierarchy. These predictions are mediated by *feedback* connections, which can be defined as any connection that con-nects a column to one or more columns in the cortical level below. The predictions are generated by the deep pyramidal cells and sent to the superficial layers of the level below (see chapter 5 for a detailed reminder of how this works). Pyramidal cells release glu-tamate and so form their synaptic connections by releasing gluta-mate onto the dendrites of neurons in the superficial layers. The feedforward connections that carry error signals up the cortical hi-erarchy use AMPA receptors — the faster and more detailed AMPA receptor transmission allows any errors to be swiftly broadcast up

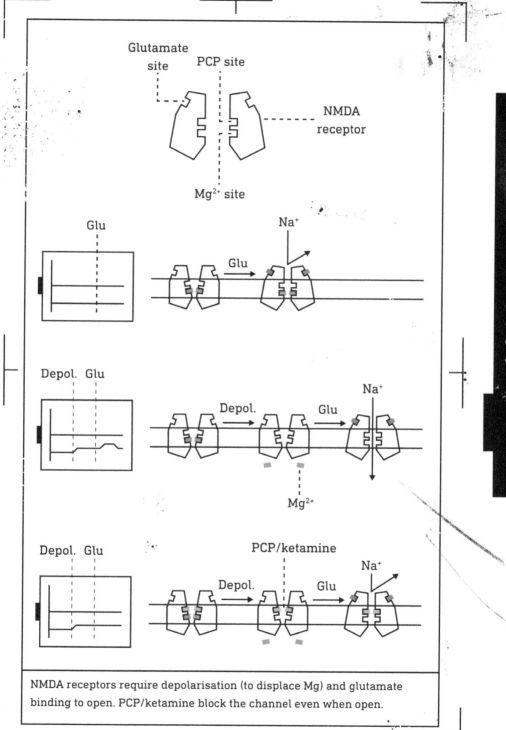

Glutamate site · PCP site · NMDA receptor · Mg^{2+} site

Glu · Na⁺

Depol. Glu · Na⁺ · Mg^{2+}

Depol. Glu · PCP/ketamine · Na⁺

NMDA receptors require depolarisation (to displace Mg) and glutamate binding to open. PCP/ketamine block the channel even when open.

the cortical hierarchy. However, the long-lasting NMDA signalling is more suitable for the downward-flowing feedback connections, since the high-level model and its predictions are likely to remain largely unchanged over longer periods of time. This is because the updating of the model and its predictions follows the accumulation of prediction errors over time, so predictions change more slowly than error signals (10).

NMDA receptors are also found on the deep pyramidal cells responsible for representation of the world model. Since both receptor types are excitatory, along with AMPA receptors, NMDA receptors play an important role in communication between neurons, including the deep pyramidal cells, and in maintaining the activity in the networks they form throughout the cortex (11). A single neuron might receive thousands of connections from other neurons that generate EPSPs via NMDA receptors, and a constant low level activation of NMDA receptors in pyramidal cells is essential for maintaining the alpha-beta oscillations that are crucial in synchronising the activity of large groups of columns across the cortex (12).

In chapter 9, we discussed how inhibitory interneurons, which regulate the activity of the excitatory pyramidal (and other) neurons, have a crucial role in sculpting the world model. In addition to the M1 acetylcholine receptors, NMDA receptors are also heavily expressed on the dendrites of these interneurons. Since their axons are heavily branched, each of these GABA-releasing interneurons can synapse with large numbers — often more than 200 — of pyramidal cells, providing broad control over their activity.

For the world model to be stable, it's important that the desired pattern of cortical column activation is properly structured and controlled — those groups of columns that form the world model representation should be activated, and potentially allowed to activate each other, with other columns being inhibited and prevented from becoming active. Groups of cortical columns must compete with other groups of columns to have their particular pattern of activity — which represents some hypothesis — represented in the overall world model. Strong hypotheses tend to be built from highly synchronised patterns of column activation that recruit inhibitory interneurons to extinguish weaker hypotheses built from poorly synchronised columns.

As well as being synchronised, strong hypotheses are often represented by tight clusters of column activity, whereas random or weak activity is often more sparse. When a cortical column is activated, excitatory neurons within the column synapse with inhibitory interneurons using their NMDA receptors and increase their activity. An individual interneuron might receive synaptic connections from a number of cortical columns within the same area and, as such, when a cluster of these columns is activated, the interneurons will receive a large number of excitatory NMDA inputs from these columns. In other words, clusters of columns are much better at recruiting inhibitory interneurons than scattered ones. These recruited interneurons then inhibit the competing cortical columns with which they are connected. Overall, this competition helps to ensure that strong and well-structured column activity wins out over weaker and more sparse activity (14), ensuring a stable, well-defined world model.

So, what happens when these receptors are compromised? Both ketamine and PCP bind to the same site on the NMDA receptor, and both act as antagonists in that they prevent activation of the receptor by glutamate. However, unlike the tropane alkaloids, which compete for the M1 receptor ligand binding site with acetylcholine, both ketamine and PCP are *non-competitive antagonists*, meaning they bind to the receptor at a location separate from the ligand (glutamate) binding site. Once bound, they cause a change in the receptor conformation that blocks the flow of ions through the channel whether or not glutamate is bound — the receptor ceases to function as a gated channel (15).

In experimental studies, ketamine produces cortical activation — the inhibitory interneurons no longer receive NMDA-mediated stimulation and, consequently, the pyramidal cells (and other

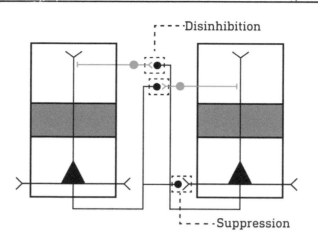

At low doses, NMDA antagonists mainly disinhibit [activate] deep pyr. cells by blocking NMDA receptors on interneurons and so reducing lateral inhibiton. At higher doses, they directly suppress pyr. cell firing by blocking NMDA receptors on the pyr. cells themselves.

types of neuron) they synapse with no longer receive as much GA-BA-mediated inhibition. That is, cortical neurons are disinhibited (16) and respond more strongly to stimulation (17). Since these interneurons are also responsible for sculpting the pattern of column activation, competition between columns is reduced and active columns can more easily activate other columns — activity tends to spread more freely across the cortex and it becomes more difficult for particular hypotheses to win out over competing ones. This is somewhat comparable to the effect of the classic psychedelics, although since ketamine doesn't directly activate the deep pyramidal cells, at low doses, visions and hallucinations are less common.

This disruption of the organisation of column activity is amplified by blockade of the NMDA receptors on the pyramidal cells themselves, essential for maintenance of synchronised alpha oscillations. Just as with the classic psychedelics, ketamine causes a dramatic reduction in alpha power as measured by EEG, a marker of disorganised cortical activity (18). When given ketamine in an experimental setting, people struggle to distinguish between different objects presented to them (19), since their world model is unable to provide the precise predictions necessary to differentiate objects with visual similarities. This is similar to the kind of object-blending that occurs with the classic psychedelics — the cortex is unable to settle on a hypothesis and objects in the world shift and switch their identity:

> "This strange incorrect image of a street that was mostly made up of what I consider archetypical for a street...started turning into a huge wall of a building and street lanterns... I saw structures and parts of buildings that in reality weren't there, or at least looked significantly different, but my brain was trying its best to make something out of the spinning moving static buzzing chaos that I vaguely could perceive, but at least I understood from all of this that I was sitting outside." (20)

As well as altering the structure of the world model, the arylcyclohexylamines also block the NMDA receptors on the superficial layer dendrites receiving the top-down predictions from the model. However, since there is no disruption of bottom-up processing, the flow of sensory information (error signals) continues unabated (21). The balance between trusting the world model and trusting sensory information is tipped towards the latter — this is the opposite of the tropane alkaloids, which allow the world model to remain uncontested despite becoming more and more divorced from the environment. As with the classic psychedelics, this shift towards upwards information flow is experienced as an increase in sensitivity to sensory information — colours become brighter, sounds are enhanced, and the world model becomes unstable and more susceptible to being updated by prediction errors (22).

At higher doses, particularly in an eyes-closed state, entirely novel patterns of cortical column activity, together with the strange worlds they encode, can emerge:

リアリティスイッチ

Sparse column activity

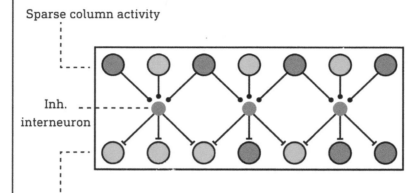

Inh.
interneuron

Column activation isn't suppressed

Clustered column activity

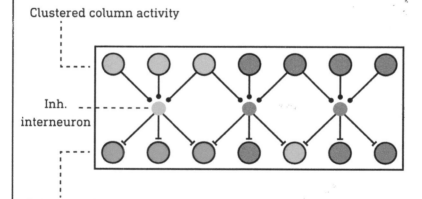

Inh.
interneuron

Column activation strongly suppressed

Compared to sparse activity, clustered column activity more effectively recruits inhibitory interneurons to suppress the activtiy of columns in competing object representations [inhibited columns in red].

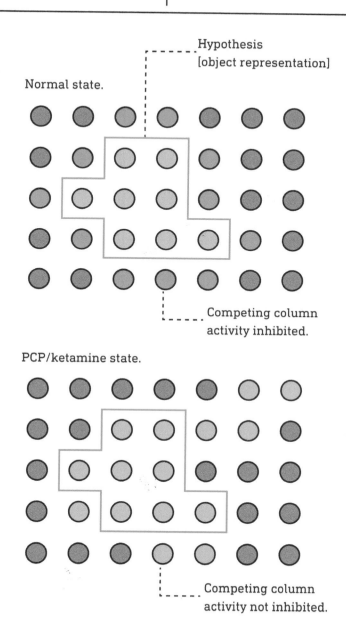

Hypothesis
[object representation]

Normal state.

Competing column
activity inhibited.

PCP/ketamine state.

Competing column
activity not inhibited.

A hypothesis built from clustered column activity can successfully recruit inhibitory interneurons and suppress competing column activity. NMDA antagonists block interneuron recruitment and reduce lateral competition between columns, allowing competing column activity to establish itself.

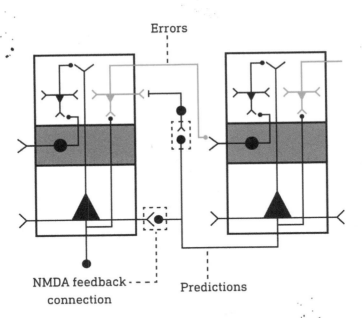

Errors

NMDA feedback
connection

Predictions

Normal state.

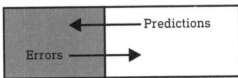

Predictions

Errors

PCP/ketamine state.

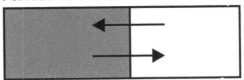

By suppressing feedback connections broadcasting model predictions,
NMDA antagonists push the prediction-error balance towards error signals,
effectively increasing the flow of sensory information into the cortex.

"I lost complete awareness of my body and went through several levels of existence before ending up on/in what I will call the hardware level since it seemed that all existence was a strange computer...a world that was fairly similar to this one, but inhabited by many strange creatures. There were trees and plants like in this world, though they didn't look quite the same. I felt like I had some kind of power, though I am not sure what it was. I could see a city on a hill in the distance, with shiny buildings, perhaps glass reflecting sunlight." (23)

"I was in a completely different place. New rules applied here. I felt like a higher force was controlling everything. And that I was just an observer. I had no control in this place. I didn't need to be in control. Something was taking care of me. Everything felt very organic in a very alien way. The creatures appeared once more. This time closer, but still too far away. " (24)

The other well-known member of the arylcyclohexylamine family, PCP, was also developed as an effective anaesthetic but without the risk of cardiorespiratory depression seen with other general anaesthetics. It found its way onto the streets of San Francisco in the 1960s, usually sold in a tablet known as a PeaCe Pill, or in powder form as *angel dust*, as an alternative to LSD in the burgeoning hippie culture with a growing appetite for altered states of consciousness. However, as a psychedelic, its reputation turned sour as its less desirable effects soon became apparent.

Like ketamine, PCP is a dissociative psychedelic, with its primary action as an antagonist at NMDA receptors. However, PCP also affects other neurotransmitter systems, including dopamine and serotonin (25). In a manner similar to the amphetamines, PCP blocks the removal of both dopamine and serotonin from the synaptic cleft, enhancing its effect on the postsynaptic neuron and adding to the complexity of its psychological effects.

Dopamine has a central role in the reward pathway, a hard-wired network that regulates the drive to seek activities, substances, and situations that give pleasure or satisfaction, such as food and sex. Dopamine-enhancing drugs essentially hijack this pathway — ingestion of amphetamine or cocaine, for example, not only generates an immediate feeling of pleasure but, with extended use, triggers a long-lasting urge to seek the drug in its absence. Like the amphetamines, PCP gives the user a powerful sense of well-being and heightened alertness that can often descend into agitation and rage. Coupled with PCP's dramatic effects on consciousness, the user will often develop paranoid delusions and audiovisual hallucinations that can lead to extremely violent behaviour, including a tendency towards self-mutilation (26). A particularly grotesque case involved a young PCP user who, whilst under the influence of the drug, used the glass from a broken mirror to peel off his face, including his nose and one of his eyes. He then fed the lot to his dog before the emergency services were alerted and he was rushed to hospital. Remarkably, he survived. (27).

Of course, the arylcyclohexylamines aren't known only for their psychedelic effects — they were, after all, originally developed as anaesthetics. At the low doses often employed recreationally, the psychedelic state manifests. However, this is really only a surface level effect — things become much more interesting, and much more weird, as the dose is increased. Ketamine, in particular, displays two distinct dose-dependent effect plateaus.

Ketamine can only bind to the NMDA receptor after the magnesium ion dissociates, exposing the binding site — ketamine then blocks the channel (28). So, the higher the firing rate of a neuron, the more susceptible it will be to NMDA antagonists, since it will spend more time in a depolarised state when the magnesium ion has been released from the NMDA ion channels. The inhibitory interneurons tend to fire at a constant high rate, whereas pyramidal cells are more likely to display intermittent bursts of action potentials. As such, the NMDA receptors embedded in inhibitory interneurons spend more time without their magnesium ion and so more time susceptible to the effects of NMDA antagonists.

At low doses, when the concentration of ketamine in the brain is relatively low, the molecule exerts a much stronger effect on the highly susceptible inhibitory interneurons than it does at pyramidal cells — this leads to disinhibition (and so increased excitability) of the pyramidal cells and the psychedelic effects. However, as the dose — and brain concentration — of ketamine is increased, the direct effect on pyramidal cells becomes more pronounced and, eventually, begins to dominate. Since NMDA receptors are excitatory, their widespread blockade begins to suppress pyramidal cell firing — a complete inversion of the effects at low doses. This is when the anaesthetic effects begin to manifest. But the ketamine-induced anaesthetised state is unlike the sleep-like state experienced with other general anaesthetics. The directly opposing effects of NMDA blockade — simultaneous disinhibition via inhibitory interneurons and direct suppression of pyramidal cell firing — causes a strange type of cortical network activity to emerge, in which the cortex alternates every few seconds between an active state similar to normal waking consciousness and a suppressed anaesthetised state (29).

This unusual neural activity can be monitored using EEG, which can provide a measure of the *complexity* of brain dynamics during drug-induced states. Complexity here is defined as the diversity of cortical activation patterns over time — high complexity conditions are those in which the cortex moves through a variety of distinct patterns, and the psychedelic state sits at the high end of this scale. Complexity is positively correlated with conscious awareness, and normal waking consciousness sits just below the psychedelic states (30), whereas states of unconsciousness, in which awareness is lost, lie at the bottom of the scale.

As expected, and as observed with the classic psychedelics, low sub-anaesthetic doses of ketamine cause an increase in the complexity of cortical activity, consistent with disruption of the world model by pyramidal cell disinhibition and the observed psychedelic effects at these dosages (29, 31). The general anaesthetics used during surgery induce a sustained decrease in cortical complexity associated with loss of consciousness (32). However, at anaesthet-

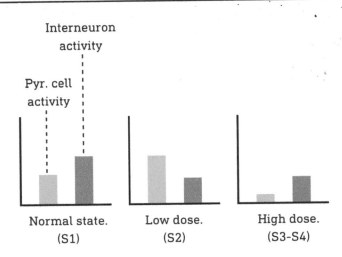

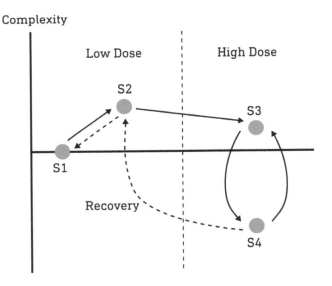

At low doses, ketamine induces a psychedelic state by suppression of feedback predictions and disinhibition of pyramidal cells. At higher doses, direct suppression of pyramidal cells begins to dominate and an unusual state of consciousness emerges, alternating between high and low complexity (anaesthetised) states.

ic doses of ketamine, cortical activity alternates between periods of high complexity and anaesthesia-associated low complexity before returning to the psychedelic high complexity state during recovery. The user's (or patient's) consciousness rapidly switches between full awareness and an unconscious state disconnected from the environment — a fragmented dream-like state unlike that elicited by any other class of psychedelic molecule.

For most users, this deep state is undesirable and likely represents the "K-hole" experience when stumbled into by accidental overdosing (the margin of error is quite narrow) (29, 33). As the drug is metabolised, brain levels drop and the more psychedelic sub-anaesthetic effects begin to return — neural complexity rises and stabilises at the high complexity psychedelic state before returning to that of normal waking consciousness as the drug is cleared from the brain. The deep anaesthetised state is often accompanied by amnesia, so it's difficult to be definitive about when the more intense visionary states are most likely to be experienced — during the deep K-hole state or once brain levels begin to decline again. However, ketamine undoubtedly has the capacity to immerse the user in entirely new worlds — distinct areas of the World Space — which are often inhabited, like the DMT Space, by communicative intelligences.

Physician and dolphin-whisperer John Lilly used ketamine extensively whilst floating in an isolation tank — he believed that the combination of the unique ketamine-induced state of consciousness lowered the threshold for receiving information from extra-terrestrial intelligences (34). Although the interpretation of these encounters will vary, it isn't unusual for high-dose ketamine users to be carried on journeys across fantastical landscapes to meet with a range of intelligent beings. This is, in many ways, comparable to the type of breakthrough state experienced with DMT, although the structure, geometry, and ambience of the ketamine space is entirely distinct. Very high doses often propel the user into a formless state of pure awareness in an infinite space field, not entirely dissimilar to the state induced by 5-MeO-DMT. However, again, the experiences remain distinct. Of course, in all cases, whether DMT-, 5-MeO-DMT-, or ketamine-induced, the state results from a restructuring of the World Space Landscape generated by cortical activity. By antagonising NMDA receptors, ketamine perturbs the cortex's complex world-building machinery, distorts the landscape, and shifts the attractor states to regions outside of the Consensus Reality Space. What's particularly striking about ketamine is how this restructuring of the landscape, and the cortex's trajectory through it, can vary dramatically depending on dosage.

At low doses, when cortical excitation predominates, ketamine flattens the World Space Landscape in a manner similar to the classic psychedelics, increasing the state repertoire by lowering the energetic gap between favoured and disfavoured states. Also, as with the classic psychedelics, the upwards flow of sensory information is increased relative to downward-flowing predictions, which actively moves the cortex around the landscape, experienced as an unstable world with frequent hypothesis shifts. However, at the higher, anaesthetic, doses, a unique trajectory through the World Space begins to emerge.

Recall that not all states within the cortical state space are also within the World Space, which comprises only those states that represent experienced phenomenal worlds. The states adopted by the cortex during deep anaesthesia don't appear to represent phenomenal worlds and dreams occasionally reported following deep anaesthesia most likely occur during the recovery phase (35). As such, these low complexity states likely exist outside the World Space — these are the no-World states. Under conditions when the cortex *is* constructing a phenomenal world — the normal waking state, the REM dream state, and the classic psychedelic state, for example — the cortex normally tends to glide across the World Space Landscape smoothly from state to state. However, the high-dose ketamine-induced trajectory is starkly different and appears to be more of a 'hopping' across the Landscape — the cortex moves across the World Space Landscape only intermittently, before hopping off the Landscape into the no-World Space before, a few seconds later, landing back on the Landscape.

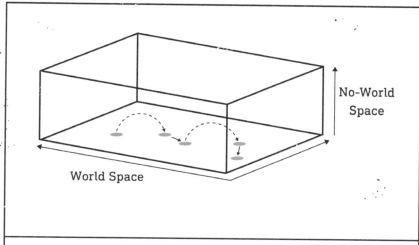

No-World Space

World Space

High-dose ketamine induces a unique hopping trajectory across the World Space Landscape unlike any other psychedelic.

As we begin to think about the development of molecular and other technologies for exploration of the World Space, ketamine hints at how we might engineer not only the geometry of the World Space Landscape but also the manner in which it might be traversed. The short-acting tryptamines, such as DMT, require a highly disorientating initial acceleration through the World Space before reaching the destination — the DMT Space. Ketamine reveals how the cortex is capable of rapidly and cleanly shifting between high-complexity World states and low-complexity No-World states. As such, we might consider whether this initial "blast off" phase is necessary, or if the cortex could be switched from an induced low-complexity — anaesthetised — state directly to states in distant regions of the World Space. Using a combination of agents, rather than being blasted through the World Space to reach unchartered regions, the explorer would be induced into an unconscious state before being rapidly "woken up" in the new domain. This would be akin to employing some kind of wormhole technology to travel through physical space, rather than relying on explosively propelled rocket ships with all the obstacles and dangers inherent in this more traditional Newtonian approach to space exploration.

236

現実制御学研究所、東京

リアリティ
スイッチ

<XXXXXX_3489_073_CX>

Chapter 13: The K-Switch

世界空間 K—スイッチ

「セカイクウカン K—スイッチ」

"Reality is for people who can't face drugs."

Tom Waits

"IT IS TOTAL MADNESS... TEARING APART THE FABRIC OF REALITY."

First words written following the very first salvinorin-A trip in a human, Daniel Siebert, June 6th 1993, approx. 2mg

Amateur mycologist, botanist, and explorer R. Gordon Wasson arrived in the small town of San Bartolomé Ayautla — in the municipality of Oaxaca in Southern Mexico — in early July 1961 with the hope of experiencing the effects of a psychoactive plant known amongst the Mazatecs as *Hojas de la Maria Pastora* — Leaves of Mary the Shepherdess. Soon to be given the Latin binomial *Salvia divinorum*, Wasson had learned of the plant a decade earlier whilst studying the sacred Psilocybe mushrooms used by the same people.

A traditional *Salvia* ceremony requires several dozen of the fresh leaves to be nibbled slowly with the incisors and then swallowed. Despite struggling with their astringent taste, Wasson managed to consume 68 leaves on the evening of July 12th, but was somewhat underwhelmed by the effects:

> "There was not the slightest doubt about the effect, but it did not go beyond the initial effects of the mushrooms — dancing colours in elaborate three-dimensional designs. Whether a larger dose would have produced a greater effect, I do not know." (1)

Although the first of the psychedelic components of *Salvia divinorum* was isolated and characterised in 1982 (2), Wasson would die before its reality-tearing properties in humans were recognised, answering in the strongest possible affirmative that indeed a larger dose most certainly has a greater effect. The salvinorins were entirely unexpected psychedelic molecules, not only in terms of their structure, but also their mechanism of action in the brain. All the known naturally-occurring psychedelics, prior to the discovery of salvinorin-A, were nitrogen-containing alkaloids. Salvinorin-A — the first of ten closely-related salvinorins (A-J) to be isolated from the *Salvia divinorum* plant — belongs to an entirely different class of natural molecules: the terpenes (3).

Whereas the alkaloids are built using amino acids as the starting material, the terpenes are derived by stitching together a simple three-carbon molecule, isoprene, to form chains that are then folded to form complex ringed structures. Salvinorin is a diterpene, a 20-carbon molecule built by joining four isoprene subunits to yield geranylgeranyldiphosphate, which then undergoes a cascade of carbon-carbon bond forming reactions to generate salvinorin's characteristic three ring skeleton (4).

Somewhat echoing Albert Hofmann's unintentional 250µg LSD power-dose almost exactly 50 years prior, American ethnobotanist and Salvia aficionado Daniel Siebert's first attempt at smoking purified salvinorin-A would turn out to be a reality-shattering overshoot (5). Unsure as to the activity of the crystalline material he'd isolated from the plant's leaves, Siebert "decided to play it safe" and smoked what he thought would be a fairly small dose — 2.5mg of what turned out to be around 80% pure salvinorin-A:

> *"Quite suddenly I found myself in a confused, fast moving state of consciousness with absolutely no idea where my body or my universe had gone." (6)*

Siebert lost all memory of his human existence and struggled desperately to find a way back to some kind of recognisable reality:

> *"I realized that I had no actual memory of ever having existed in any other state of consciousness than the disembodied one I was now in. So I decided to stop panicking and just relax. After all, there was no place to get back to. I was totally convinced that this state of existence was all there ever was."*

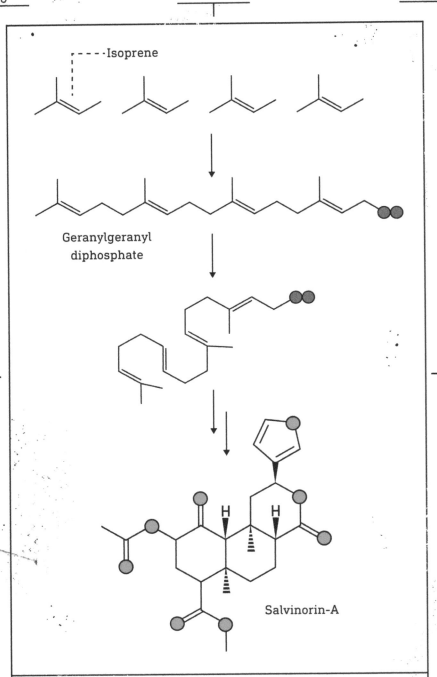

Isoprene

Geranylgeranyl
diphosphate

Salvinorin-A

The complex structure of the salvinorins is derived from a chain of four
isoprene molecules, unlike the alkaloids derived from amino acids.

Siebert's trip lasted for another 10-15 minutes, during which he was catapulted between various scenes from his past, including the living room of his long-dead grandparents, before being returned to the normal waking world "shaken to the soul" but elated at having discovered the psychedelic essence of *Salvia divinorum*.

Although salvinorin can certainly be a ferocious psychedelic, uprooting any and all fundamental assumptions about the kind of phenomenal worlds humans could or should be able to experience, its effects have a mechanistic underpinning, albeit an unusual one. When ingested at dosages above a half milligram or so, salvinorin, like the classic psychedelics, disrupts the normal waking world model and perturbs the cortical world-building machinery such that terrifically strange new worlds emerge (7). Salvinorin engenders the emergence of an entirely unprecedented, and entirely unpredicted, World Space Landscape geometry. Understanding the facility with which it achieves this will require us to think again about the construction, maintenance, and dynamics of the world model.

Whenever a world is experienced, it is a world constructed by the cortex from information — a pattern of cortical column activation, a single state of the cortex selected from a practically infinite repertoire of states within the cortical World Space. The experience of a world is the experience of the cortex gliding from state to state through this World Space. For this world model to be coherent, meaningful and, above all, useful, each state must not only be properly constructed but must also give way to the next state — there must be an orderly transition of power from state to state. Naturally, the differences between sequential states will often be subtle, since the world model isn't built anew each moment. However, no state is identical to the last, nor to any state in the past or future — you never experience the same world twice — and the cortex is always shifting seamlessly to a brand new, never before seen, state. In your phenomenal world, changes might appear to be limited to a bird flitting into your field of view, or leaves fluttering in the wind, but each moment is distinct from the last — hypotheses are updated as the features of objects and their relationships to each other change. The patterns that represent these hypotheses within the overall cortical state shift in a tightly orchestrated and sequential manner.

Or, at least, they should.

The claustrum is a relatively small sheet of highly interconnected neurons sitting beneath the cortex and connected with almost all of its areas (8). The claustrum's major function is as a regulator and orchestrator of cortical activity. The control over cortical activity maintained by the claustrum is one of general inhibition and selective amplification (9). Strong stimulation of the claustrum causes a swift and powerful inhibition of the cortex and unconsciousness (10). But, through its unique pattern of connectivity with the cortex, the claustrum is able to amplify patterns of cortical activity representing the world model whilst suppressing extraneous noisy activity that might threaten to disrupt it (11). Synchronised column activity — representing robust hypotheses — is passed to the claustrum, which then sends outputs that amplify this activity whilst suppressing weak, poorly synchronised, or noisy activity (12).

The claustrum is largely composed of excitatory principal neurons interconnected with a dense network of inhibitory interneurons (13). The deep layers of the cortex — containing the pyramidal cells that represent the world model — contain cortico-claustro neurons that connect to both the principal and inhibitory interneurons in the claustrum (14). In return, the principal claustral neurons send claustro-cortical connections to the input layer (layer 4) of the cortex, completing the loop (15). As with the cortico-claustro connections, these claustro-cortical axons connect with both excitatory and inhibitory neurons in the cortex — a pattern of connectivity that has an important role in the claustrum's function.

Whilst a single neuron might receive inputs from large numbers of presynaptic neurons, the tightness of their synchronisation will determine how likely they are to successfully induce the postsynaptic neuron to fire, since EPSPs spaced closely in time are more

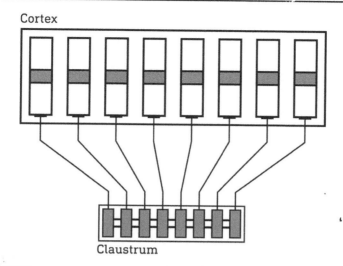

Cortex

Claustrum

Every cortical column is reciprocally connected to areas within the claustrum sitting below the cortex.

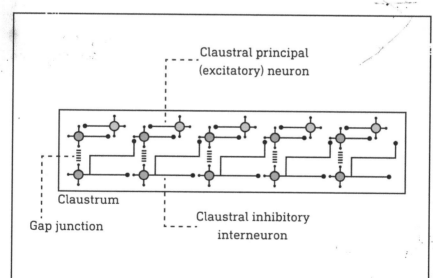

Claustral principal (excitatory) neuron

Claustrum

Gap junction

Claustral inhibitory interneuron

The claustrum contains excitatory principal neurons amongst a dense network of highly interconnected inhibitory interneurons.

likely to be summed before decaying. In many instances, a set of highly synchronised inputs is more likely to represent important information that should be processed and transmitted to other neurons. On the other hand, inputs generated randomly over time are more likely to be noise that can safely be ignored. This summation time window not only helps a neuron distinguish between signal and noise received from other neurons, but also supports the proper timing of its outputs — essential for maintaining the structure of the world model and in the broadcasting of predictions and error signals.

This time window can be made even more narrow — to further increase the required synchrony of the inputs — using a type of connectivity known as a feedforward inhibitory circuit (16). To form this circuit, a presynaptic neuron connects not only to the postsynaptic neuron it's attempting to stimulate, but also to an inhibitory interneuron, which itself also connects to the postsynaptic neuron. So, whenever the presynaptic neuron fires, it both stimulates (using a simple monosynaptic excitatory connection) and inhibits (by stimulating the inhibitory interneuron) the postsynaptic neuron. However, since the inhibition must be transmitted through two synapses, there is a delay before it affects the postsynaptic excitatory neuron. This opens a very narrow window of time during which the neuron can be stimulated, and EPSPs summed, before being inhibited. The time constraint generated by this simple circuit is much more strict than that enforced by EPSP decay alone, and presynaptic neurons must synchronise their firing with millisecond precision if they are to successfully drive the postsynaptic neuron to fire before it's overwhelmed by a powerful wave of inhibition. Overall, a feedforward inhibitory circuit makes the postsynaptic neuron highly sensitive to the timing of its presynaptic inputs.

The claustrum uses these feedforward inhibitory circuits to distinguish between tightly synchronised patterns of cortical activity, which it enhances, and unsynchronised noise, which it suppresses. When a cortical column is activated, it sends outputs to the claustrum using the cortico-claustro axons running from its deep

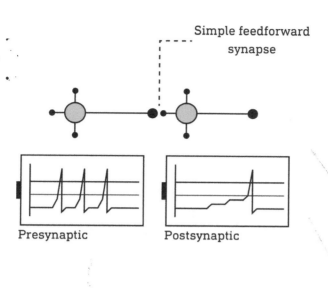

Simple feedforward
synapse

Presynaptic   Postsynaptic

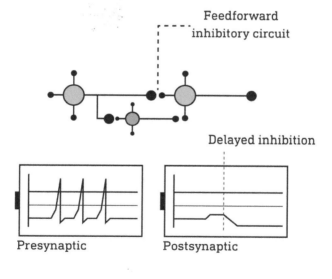

Feedforward
inhibitory circuit

Delayed inhibition

Presynaptic   Postsynaptic

With a simple feedforward connection, EPSPs generated within the time
window of their decay will be summed. However, with a FFI circuit, the
inhibitory interneuron generates powerful inhibition shortly following the
initial EPSP, narrowing the time window for their summation.

現実管理課

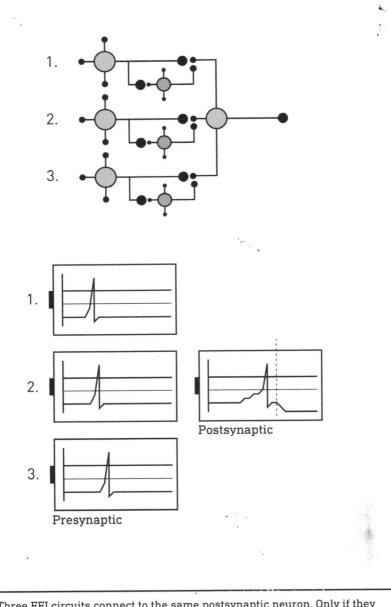

1.

2.

Postsynaptic

3.

Presynaptic

Three FFI circuits connect to the same postsynaptic neuron. Only if they can synchronise their inputs (EPSPs) within a narrow time window, before the wave of inhibition, can they successfully elicit an action potential response in the postsynaptic neuron.

layers. Because of the feedforward inhibitory circuits, this elicits a brief activation of the claustral principal cells with which the axons connect, before they're strongly inhibited by the interneurons. In the same manner, when the claustral principal neurons are activated, they deliver an initial activating impulse to the neurons in the input layer of the cortex, before they're quieted by the inhibition that quickly follows (17).

The network of interneurons within the claustrum is heavily interconnected by special electrical connections known as gap junctions. Whereas chemical synapses depend upon the release and diffusion of neurotransmitter molecules across the synaptic cleft, gap junctions allow ions to be passed between neurons using specialised channel proteins called connexins. Since sodium and potassium ions carry the electrical charge responsible for the action potential, gap junctions allow the direct transmission of action potentials from neuron to neuron. As such, compared to chemical synapses, gap junctions are extremely fast, and networks of interneurons connected using these junctions can rapidly generate highly synchronised patterns of activity when stimulated (18).

A pattern of synchronised column activity can stimulate the claustral principal neurons almost simultaneously and, before the delayed inhibition extinguishes it, implant their pattern of activity in the claustrum. Using the dense network of inhibitory interneurons, this rapidly establishes a pattern of highly synchronised and structured activity within the claustral principal neurons, which then output back to the cortex, amplifying and reinforcing the synchronised column activity. Poorly synchronised or noisy column activity will fail to generate synchronised activity in the claustrum and will receive weaker and poorly synchronised inputs in return which suppresses their activity via the feedforward inhibitory circuits. Of course, even the amplified columns will experience a wave of inhibition after a delay, which terminates their activity, making way for new patterns to establish themselves. Overall, this allows the cortex to move from state to state in a regulated sequential manner, with each state briefly amplified and then terminated (18).

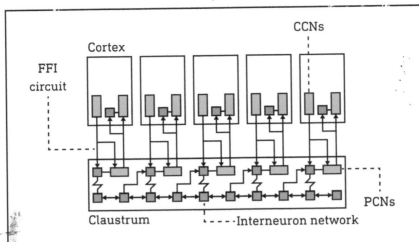

Cortico-claustral neurons (CCNs) connect to the claustrum using FFI circuits. In turn, the principal claustral neurons (PCNs) send connections back to the cortex, also using FFI circuits.

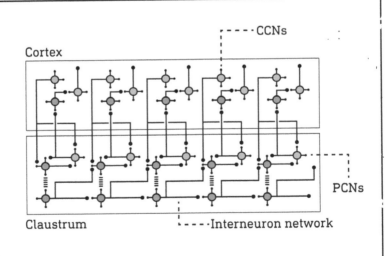

Connections between the cortex and the claustrum showing the patterns of connections between neurons.

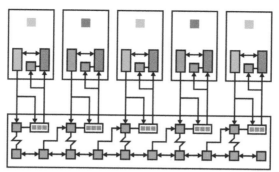

Synchronised [blue] and unsynchronised [red]
activity passed from cortex to claustrum.

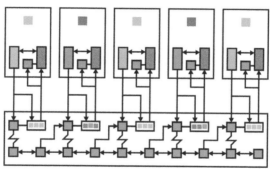

Synchronised activity established in claustrum.

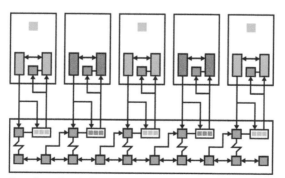

Synchronised claustral activity passed back to
cortex, reinforcing synchronised cortical activity.
Unsynchronised cortical activity is suppressed.

In a manner analogous to the conductor of an orchestra, who must control when each set of instruments should sound and when they should again be quiet, the claustrum orchestrates the activity of the cortex by amplifying patterns of column activation representing the world model, quieting noisy activity, and guiding the cortex smoothly from state to state.

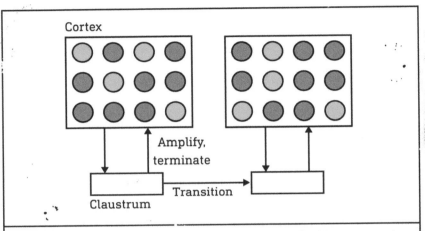

World model states are passed to the claustrum, amplified in return, and then terminated for a smooth transition to the next state.

Not only is salvinorin entirely unique in its structure and origin, but also in its mechanism of action, which specifically targets the claustrum to achieve its effects. Salvinorin binds and activates one specific member of the opioid receptor family. The term opioid derives from the morphine-related analgesic compounds, known collectively as the opiates, isolated from the seed pods of several species of poppy plant. Morphine and its semisynthetic close relative, diacetylmorphine (heroin), are the most famous members of the opiate class, and produce their analgesic and euphoric effects by activating opioid receptors. This G-protein coupled receptor family comprises four subtypes with the *delta*, *mu*, and *kappa* subtypes being the most well-understood (19). The opiate drugs primarily act as agonists at the mu-receptors in the brain and spinal cord, but it's the kappa receptors in the claustrum which are central to salvinorin's entirely unrelated psychedelic effects (20).

The claustrum contains the highest density of kappa opioid receptors in the brain (21), with large numbers embedded in the
dendrites of the excitatory claustral principal neuron in particular (22). Like the 5HT1A receptor, the kappa opioid receptor, when
activated, binds to a Gi-protein which dissociates into its alpha
subunit and beta-gamma complex (23). The free beta-gamma
complex binds to both calcium ion channels and a type of potassium ion channel called GIRK. When bound to the beta-gamma
complex, the GIRK channel is opened, allowing potassium ions to
flow out of, and thus hyperpolarise, the neuron. (24). In contrast,
calcium ion channels are deactivated as the beta-gamma complex
binds, preventing the influx of calcium essential for triggering the
release of neurotransmitters from the presynaptic terminal (25).
So, overall, kappa opioid receptor activation decreases the excitability of neurons by hyperpolarisation, as well as reducing their
ability to communicate synaptically with other neurons.

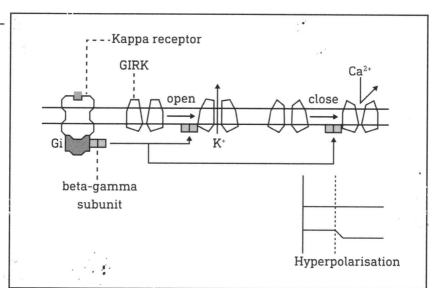

Activation of kappa opioid receptors leads to the opening of K-channels
(GIRK) and hyperpolarisation via activation of Gi. In addition, Ca-
channels are closed, inhibiting the Ca signal that triggers the release of
neurotransmitters from the presynaptic bouton.

Salvinorin's three-ring skeleton is adorned with three oxygen-bearing groups perfectly positioned to interact with the hydroxyls of three tyrosine residues in the kappa receptor ligand binding site. The additional furan ring — a 5-membered oxygen-containing ring — is an unusual feature of the salvinorin molecule, and forms a bond with a glutamine residue (20, 26). Together these interactions lock the salvinorin molecule in the ligand binding site and allow it to activate the receptor and so reduce the excitability of the neurons within which the receptor is embedded. By activating kappa opioid receptors on the claustral principal cells, salvinorin A strongly inhibits the claustrum and deactivates the claustro-cortical connections that act as the inhibitory "orchestrator" of the cortex (27).

The key amino acids in the kappa opioid receptor ligand binding site that interact with the salvinorin molecule.

We've already seen how the inhibitory interneurons nestled between excitatory neurons in the cortex are essential in maintaining control over both the level and structure of cortical activity, and how new patterns of activity can emerge when these interneurons are compromised. In a similar manner, salvinorin's inhibtion of the claustrum releases the cortex from its global inhibition. That is, the cortex is disinhibited, allowing activity that would normally be extinguished to establish itself and propagate through the cortical networks. At the same time, the activity representing the world model isn't properly amplified. So, the distinction between coherent world model activity and extraneous noisy activity is reduced. In addition to this, the claustrum fails to orchestrate the smooth transition between states: the coherent and synchronised claustral activity required to first amplify and then terminate column activation is disrupted.

Overall, the cortex loses control over its activity and the flow from state to state. This might be compared to instructing an orchestra to play a complex symphony faster and faster and then shooting the conductor. It is hardly surprising then that salvinorin has such "reality tearing" properties as described first by Siebert.

Under the influence of salvinorin, functional MRI imaging reveals, as with the classic psychedelics, a breaking down of established cortical networks and increased communication between networks, reflecting loss of control over the structure and flow of information through the cortex (28). In a manner similar to DMT, this breakdown of the world model is followed, assuming the dosage is sufficient, by the emergence of a new order, albeit an extremely bizarre one.

The time course of a typical salvinorin trip, when ingested by vapour inhalation, is also similar to that of the short-acting tryptamines. Almost immediately as the lungs are filled:

> "Salvinorin comes on with an irresistibly powerful, spiraling force which is much stronger than that felt on any other psychedelic." (29)

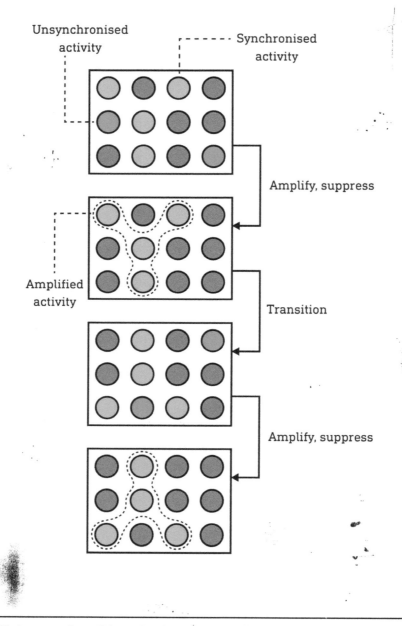

Under normal conditions, the claustrum amplifies synchronised cortical column patterns, suppresses noisy and unsynchronised activity, and then coordinates the smooth transition to the next state.

リアリティスイッチ

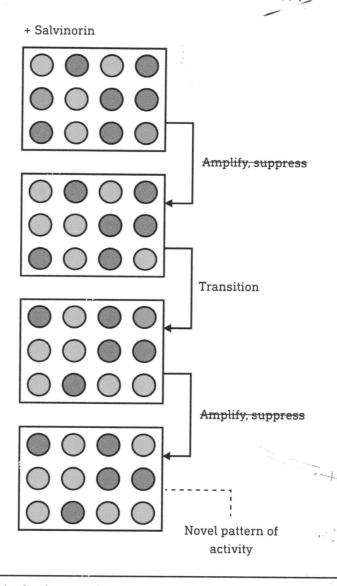

+ Salvinorin

Amplify, suppress

Transition

Amplify, suppress

Novel pattern of
activity

With salvinorin, the claustrum is suppressed by kappa receptor activation.
Synchronised activity is no longer amplified, nor noisy activity suppressed,
and there is no smooth transition between states. Entirely novel patterrns
of cortical activity can emerge and sustain themselves over time.

Whilst with DMT there is certainly a sense of being thrust into and travelling within the space, there is much more of a physical sensation of bodily and spatial distortion with salvinorin — space, time, and the structure of reality itself are twisted and torn apart, before the tripper is hurled through the fissures wrought by this irresistible process (30). Often the tripper becomes part of the distorting and reconfiguring manifold of the space. Awareness of the body is usually lost, often with the memory of ever having a body, of ever being human and, at the extreme, of the concept of human existence itself. This effect is consistent with the sudden loss of claustral control over the large areas of the cortex that maintain not only the structure of the world model, but also the positioning of the body within the world, the sense of self, and their relationship to the environment. All existential points of reference are ripped from their moorings and cast into an unfathomably strange space with no connection to the world lost.

The DMT worlds are almost universally described as "hyperdimensional", with users awestruck at the intricacy and complexity of its geometrical construction. In contrast, the Salvia space is much more likely to be experienced as a kind of manifold that twists and contorts, pulling the tripper with it. Worlds reduced to two-dimensional surfaces or membranes are also uniquely Salvia-esque:

> "I can't isolate any part of it, it was all a fuzzy bubbling gestalt with myself knotted through.... I was totally disoriented – I had no name, no conception of what tripping was or what had happened to cause this. I did have a sense of body, but not a human body. My "body" seemed to be twisting into fluid shapes and words and concepts." (31)

The experience of becoming or merging with inanimate objects is also common:

> "I was not a person, nor did I remember ever having been a person, or taken any drug. At some point

> *in my travels it seemed that I had stopped moving.*
> *I was perceiving everything as though I was an ex-*
> *terior wall of a house. I could see a yard, a street,*
> *and a village with many trees around. It could have*
> *been from my childhood. but does not bring to*
> *mind any specific memories. I soon realized that I*
> *was "glued" to this particular existence as the side*
> *of a house. I had become something inanimate and*
> *material, yet I was aware of life around me." (29)*

The Salvia space is often occupied by intelligent beings, including spritely elfin beings similar to those that typify the DMT space:

> *"I found myself in a realm filled with fairie and elf-*
> *in creatures. I enjoyed playing with these critters*
> *which had a highly distinctive visual appearance...*
> *quite different from those I've frequently encoun-*
> *tered while on DMT. They were composed of nu-*
> *merous different elements, were quite abstract,*
> *and each was uniquely intricate." (29)*

> *"They are incredibly encouraging, playful, and*
> *fairy-like trickster sprites, though their personal-*
> *ities ranged infinitely. I saw them all move up and*
> *to the left, as I was headed in that direction: home.*
> *We were going to where I know I have always been*
> *headed and can hardly wait to experience." (33)*

Perhaps the most disturbing recurring feature of the deep salvinorin trip is a point of realisation of a kind of existential absoluteness of the space — an undeniable realisation that the molecule has granted you access not merely to another reality, but to the only true reality, with your previous human existence being a mere sideshow. A sideshow that just ended:

> *"Nothing existed any longer... I no longer had a con-*
> *cept of being anything at all but some entity whose*
> *entire perception of previous life was implanted,*

was fake, was like a staged play. I knew it never really existed that way outside of our made-believe world that was implanted on us; yet I, and people, and animals, and nature, and air, and empty spaces between objects were put through our paces of fake existence, until suddenly the master decided to close down the show — that was instantaneously clear, and that unambiguous clarity was very disturbing. There was no denying or analyzing it." (34)

"On Salvia it is not a parallel reality, it is a complete substitution of reality. There is no other reality but the one Salvia gives you, and there never was any other reality." (34)

Whatever one might believe about the existential nature of the Salvia space, and whether its inhabitants are living conscious beings much like ourselves, salvinorin insists upon a confrontation with the undeniable fact that the Consensus Reality Space is but a tiny district within the almost endless terrains of the World Space:

"Whatever it was I was falling into, or becoming, or being snatched up in, it had some vague connection with humanity, but it was like humanity was one small node in its superstructure." (35)

Although the World Space Switches we have discussed so far have entirely distinct mechanistic underpinnings, they are unified in their perturbing of the complex world-building machinery of the human neocortex, altering the structure of the World Space Landscape, and causing entirely new patterns of activity, and worlds, to emerge. Whereas the classic psychedelics provide an excitatory perturbation, nudging pyramidal cells closer to their firing threshold, salvinorin employs a release mechanism, disengaging the apparatus that normally keeps cortical activity under control.

The geometry of the World Space Landscape emerges not only from the underlying connectivity of the cortical columns, but also from the activation level of both the excitatory and inhibitory neurons from which they're built. The unique mechanism of salvinorin alters the geometry of the cortex's World Space Landscape in a manner unlike any other class of psychedelic, rendering yet another region within the World Space available for exploration.

As many have wondered why the DMT molecule ought to be so ubiquitous in the natural world, scattered across countless plant species, many are shocked that molecules such as the salvinorins, with such a ferocious ability to tear apart the fabric of reality and plunge the user into terrifyingly bizarre alternate worlds, ought to have found their expression in one of the world's rarest (at least in the wild) and obscure plants — a plant that rarely even sets seed and, until its discovery and redistribution in the West, could be found only in an isolated mountainous cloud forest in Southern Mexico.

Is *Salvia divinorum* a one off? A fluke of nature? Or are there other reality-switching molecules hiding in plant species, waiting to be discovered by humans? It's estimated that at least 80,000 plant species remain to be discovered and characterised by science (36) — how many of them might bear entirely new reality-switching molecules?

Of course, we no longer need wait for new molecules to be extracted from the natural world. We now have the ability to create new molecules, perhaps based on known psychedelic molecules or, as with the arylcyclohexylamines, garnered entirely from the ingenuity and imagination of modern medicinal chemists and pharmacologists. By developing our understanding of how the known World Space Switches function and can be activated, we can begin to look towards a future when we can engineer the geometry of the World Space Landscape and explore its uncharted territories at will.

To discover and explore new worlds.

To engineer reality itself.

現実制御学研究所、東京

リアリティ
スイッチ

<XXXXXX_3489_081_QT>

Chapter 14: Engineering Reality

現実制御学

「ゲンジツセイギョガク」

"Learn to use your nervous system."

Timothy Leary

It seems nothing short of miraculous that we each carry within us a gelatinous information-generating machine capable of constructing an almost infinite array of worlds. Worlds teeming with strange intelligent creatures with whom we can learn to communicate. Worlds of impossible complexity and inexpressible beauty, terrifying hellscapes beyond even Dante's imagination, and vast formless landscapes devoid of all but the pure light of consciousness itself. And, perhaps even more miraculous, it is a machine that we can learn to operate.

Psychedelic molecules are currently the primary tools for exploring the cortical World Space. Each molecule perturbs the complex world-building machinery of the cortex in its own unique way, from the receptor level upwards through the organisational hierarchy, distorting the World Space Landscape and lowering the energy of previously unexplored terrains across its immeasurably vast plains.

Throughout the second half of the 20th century, a veritable pharmacopeia of psychedelic molecules has been procured — the majority either plucked directly from or, at least, chemically derived from the plant and fungal kingdoms. But discovering a new psychedelic molecule is only the first step in developing it as a tool for exploring the World Space. The effect of every psychedelic molecule has a mechanistic underpinning: a receptor (or set of receptors) linked to an intracellular signalling network. Understanding how psychedelic molecules interact with receptors and influence intracellular signalling is an important, but highly challenging, step in developing them as tools for World Space exploration.

Prior to this biochemical level of understanding, a more brute force approach to developing new psychedelic tools was the only one available, and one that found its most important expression in the peerless work of Alexander "Sasha" Shulgin, who began with the mescaline molecule and, from this basic phenethylamine skeleton, semi-systematically derived an additional 178 structural variants (a select clutch of which we met in chapter 8). In recent years, with a more sophisticated appreciation of drug-receptor signalling interactions, a more directed approach has become possible. X-ray crystallography can now provide atomic resolution 3-D models of a drug molecule nestled in the ligand binding site of a receptor, allowing the crucial interactions between molecule and receptor to be visualised. Combined with computational modelling techniques, we now have the tools to visualise the actual conformational changes that drive the drug-induced activation of a receptor. Crystallisation of the LSD-5HT2A receptor interaction was one of the most significant milestones in the molecular pharmacology of psychedelics, resolving long-standing questions regarding the molecule's mechanism of 5HT2A receptor activation, unique potency, and duration of action (1).

But the utility of these modern technologies is not restricted to understanding the mechanism of extant psychedelic molecules, but also in the design of new ones. Once the crucial interactions between a psychedelic molecule and a receptor are understood, it becomes possible to systematically construct entirely new agonists and antagonists. Pioneering psychedelic pharmacologist David Nichols designed a 5HT2A receptor agonist with a potency in humans rivalling that of LSD (200-800ug), but with a much longer duration of action — up to several days.

3C-Bromo-Dragonfly is a structural analogue of 2,5-dimethoxy-4-bromoamphetamine (DOB), one of Shulgin's psychedelic phenylethylamines described in his magnum opus, PIHKAL. DOB contains two methoxy (-OCH_3) groups sitting directly opposite on the phenyl ring, which computational modelling suggested are positioned to form hydrogen bonds with two serine residues in the 5HT2A ligand binding site (2). The formation of a hydrogen bond requires that the pair of electrons on the methoxy oxygen be correctly aligned with the serine hydrogen. Since each methoxy group can rotate about the single bond connecting it to the phenyl ring, a hydrogen bond can only form when the methyl group rotates into the correct orientation. Nichols surmised that converting the methoxy group to a rigid 5-membered ring — in which the oxygen is locked into the correct orientation for hydrogen bond formation — ought to generate a much higher affinity agonist. And this indeed turned out to be the case: further tweaking of each 5-membered ring by addition of a double bond (which affects the distribution of electrons around the ring) produced a molecule — 3C-Bromo-Dragonfly — with a 60-fold higher affinity for the 5HT2A receptor than DOB and a potency (in rats) almost twice that of LSD (3).

Eventually, it will become possible not only to design a molecule to selectively bind and activate a particular receptor, but also to control the conformational change induced by the molecule and thus the interactions with the intracellular signalling pathways. This will be the next step in the design of molecules to elicit a specific type of psychedelic effect or to access particular areas of the World Space Landscape. Whilst all the classic psychedelics act via the 5HT2A receptor, each perturbs the intracellular signalling pathway in its own unique way, albeit currently with little control.

Since the intracellular signalling network is a complex system, it's extremely challenging to predict, let alone control, the pattern of network activity a particular molecule will induce when it activates a receptor, especially when — as is usually the case — the psychedelic binds to more than one receptor (sub)type. However, using computational systems biology, in which the signalling molecules and their interactions are modelled using systems of coupled differential equations, such control might eventually be achieved. But, despite the potential of these emerging technologies, there is almost certainly a limit to the regions of the World Space that can be accessed using a single receptor. It's unlikely, for example, that the spaces accessible using kappa opioid agonists (such as the salvinorins) will also be reachable using classic 5HT2A agonists. However, the development of molecules highly selective for particular receptor types, tailored to activate specific signalling pathways, will create the opportunity to activate multiple receptor types simultaneously, with precise control, using molecular combinations. Exploration of the unique spaces accessible by combining two or more psychedelics is already a pastime at the more intrepid fringes of the psychonaut subculture, although the approach is largely hit and miss.

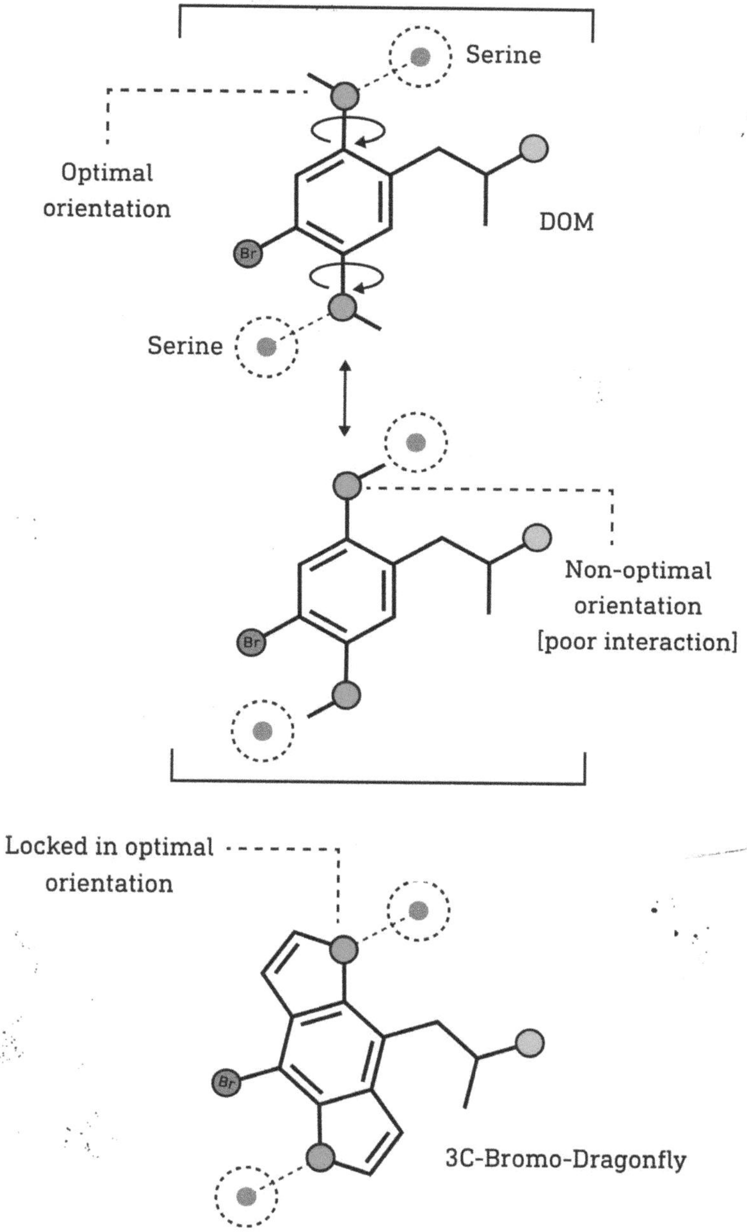

Serine

Optimal
orientation

DOM

Serine

Non-optimal
orientation
[poor interaction]

Locked in optimal
orientation

3C-Bromo-Dragonfly

現実管理課

3C-Bromo-Dragonfly locks the methoxy group oxygens in the optimal
orientation to interact with key serines in the 5HT2AR binding site.

In the near future, using a systematic exploration of receptor activation combinations, it might be possible to actually map the World Space with a coordinate system developed for the purpose. However, owing to the complexity of the human cortex, moving through the World Space is certain to be a highly non-linear, non-Euclidean affair, and techniques from higher mathematics, such as algebraic topology and hyperbolic geometry, will likely be required to direct vectors through its unusual structure. Despite these complexities, accessing a particular region of the World Space might eventually be as simple as dialling the coordinates into specially designed software, which would calculate the appropriate receptor stimulation/inhibition combination necessary to generate the vector from the Consensus Reality Space into that World Space location.

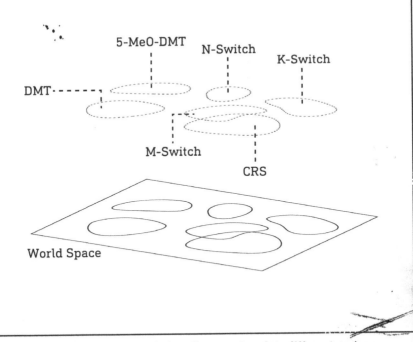

The known World Space Switches direct vectors into different regions of the World Space (by restructuring the Landscape). However, the vast majority of this landscape certainly remains to be discovered and explored.

And we needn't stop there: we can project even further into the future when humans will be able to access any region of the World Space without even the requirement of exogenous molecules. The approaches discussed so far rely entirely upon the Switch mechanisms endogenously expressed in all healthy human brains. However, since a psychedelic molecule essentially hijacks an endogenous receptor-signalling system, its activity is limited by the receptor itself — the conformations it can adopt and the signalling pathways with which it can interact.

As the name implies, Designer Receptors Exclusively Activated by Designer Drugs (DREADDs) are receptors engineered to be activated only by otherwise inert exogenous designer molecules, but unresponsive to endogenous molecules (4). The gene sequence of a receptor with the desired signalling properties — such as a 5HT2A receptor coupled to Gq — is engineered to generate a series of mutant receptor proteins which are then screened against synthetic molecules. Once a candidate receptor that binds to the molecule has been identified, the gene is implanted into a virus programmed to insert the receptor DNA into specific neuron types. For example, the DREADD hM4Di is a mutated form of the muscarinic M4 receptor which, rather than binding to acetylcholine, binds only to an otherwise pharmacologically inert molecule, clozapine-N-oxide (CNO), but retains the same intracellular signalling properties — a general inhibitory effect on neurons — as the natural receptor (5). hM4Di has been selectively expressed in glutamatergic neurons in the hippocampus (a part of the cortex important for memory formation) and used to specifically inhibit activity in this part of the brain (6).

Using these DREADDs, receptors with desired signalling properties — coupled to Gq, Gi, and other G-proteins, for example — could be designed and inserted into targeted cell types, such as cortical pyramidal cells, to control their activity in a highly selective manner using molecules that have no effect on other receptors or neurons. Different DREADDs could be embedded in different cells to create an "orchestra" of receptors that could be activated to varying degrees, each modulating its own cell type dependent on the controlled administration of its own particular activator molecule. This is true neuropharmaco-engineering — the human brain would be equipped with an array of switches which, until activated by the exogenous activator molecules, would remain silent. A cocktail of these molecules would be administered to elicit a particular pattern of receptor, and thus neuron, activation so as to generate a desired vector through the World Space.

Of course, even with such a sophisticated neuropharmacological technology, the problems inherent in relying upon exogenous molecules remain. Even if intravenous infusion is employed, avoiding issues with gastrointestinal tract absorption and first-pass metabolism by the liver, the same dose might well have different effects on different individuals, depending upon idiosyncratic variables controlling absorption into the brain, metabolic enzyme expression, and so on. Ideally, we ought to think towards dispensing with exogenous molecules entirely, and rely upon more rapid, less invasive and more precisely controllable means of activating the receptor array.

Magnetoreceptors are a relatively new — at least to science — class of receptors activated not by the binding of ligands but by the application of a magnetic field. Rather than a ligand binding site, the receptor is coupled to superparamagnetic nanobeads about the same size as a synaptic vesicle. Upon exposure to the magnetic field, the nanobeads pull the receptors into a cluster which activates them (7). Since magnetic fields are transparent to biological tissue, including bone, activation of the receptors is rapid, safe, and can be controlled remotely. The World Space Explorer, having been equipped with the receptor array using viral transfer at an earlier date, would lie down in a comfortable pod and be fitted with a helmet within which the electromagnets are arranged around the skull. Flicking the reality switch, instantaneously transporting the voyager to an alternate world, would be as simple as activating the magnets.

Of course, it will take something of a pioneering spirit for these technologies to be deployed in humans for any kind of World

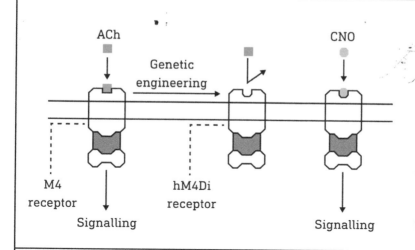

hM4Di is an engineered mutant form of the M4 receptor that's only activated by the otherwise inert molecule clozapine-N-oxide (CNO). hM4Di can be inserted into, and used to selectively activate, specific neuron types.

Space exploration project. But we needn't wait for these new technologies to be developed before we can begin such expeditions. The molecules we already have at hand, especially DMT, are likely to keep us busy for quite some time yet, and efforts should also be directed towards developing these simple and readily available molecules as World Space exploration technologies.

DMT, in particular, is unique in possessing a number of pharmacological peculiarities that make it an ideal candidate for this kind of endeavour, including its extremely rapid onset and the brevity of its effects: following intravenous injection of the drug, the effects begin almost instantaneously and full breakthrough into the DMT space occurs within 60 seconds. The voyager then remains in this space for around five minutes before being jolted back into the consensus world with only residual effects. 20-30 minutes later the effects are fully resolved (8). Many are frustrated by this brevity, complaining of being dragged back from hyperspace just when the maelstrom was beginning the stabilise and the intelligences beginning to speak, although, for most, five minutes is quite long enough. But, for those wanting to return to the DMT worlds in short order, DMT has an additional unique characteristic: lack of subjective tolerance. Again, unlike the other classic psychedelics, which display diminishing effects with closely spaced doses, DMT can be injected repeatedly without any loss of subjective potency (9). Entry and exit from the DMT Space is clean and rapid and, as soon as the tripper returns, re-entry is as simple as injecting a repeat dose.

For World Space exploration, a technology for attaining and maintaining a precisely controlled brain DMT concentration over time is required. Developed for the regulated delivery of anaesthetic drugs to the brain during surgery, target-controlled intravenous infusion (TCIV) represents the pinnacle of modern drug administration technologies: a continuous but variable infusion of a drug into the bloodstream, delivered by a programmable infusion device, allows a specific target concentration of drug within the brain to be reached and maintained (10). Remarkably, the pharmacological characteristics required of anaesthetic drugs delivered using this infusion technology — short duration of action, rapid and clean metabolism, and lack of tolerance — are precisely those possessed by DMT. However, this doesn't mean that repurposing TCIV for use with DMT is a straightforward affair.

As soon as a drug is introduced into the body by intravenous injection, it is rapidly diluted and distributed by the blood. Although it reaches the effect site — the brain — within seconds, it also equilibrates to varying degrees with muscles, fats, and other soft tissues. The elimination of the drug from the body also begins immediately, by a combination of enzymatic transformation, and excretion through the kidneys and biliary system. A mathematical model that takes into account all of these factors must be developed to regulate the infusion (11). The initial infusion rate must be high to overcome the brisk dilution and distribution of the drug in the circulatory system and tissues, allowing the brain DMT concentration to surpass the threshold for breakthrough into the DMT space. However, this initially high rate must then be gradually reduced to maintain a stable brain DMT concentration. If such a high initial rate is maintained, the concentration of DMT in the brain will continue to rise to extreme levels and, eventually, the user will reach a blackout state, beyond which all memory of the experience is lost. Conversely, if the rate is reduced too far or too quickly, brain DMT levels will fall below the threshold, resulting in an early exit from the space. To enter and maintain a stable state within the space, brain DMT levels must be held within this narrow concentration window at all times. This is a difficult task requiring a deep and detailed understanding of human pharmacokinetics, drug metabolism, and drug distribution, as well as idiosyncratic factors that can affect the behaviour of DMT inside the circulatory system and brain. However, a target-controlled intravenous infusion model for DMT has already been developed (12), and will provide the basis for more advanced models ready to deploy in human studies in the near future.

A well-coordinated World Space Exploration team will require more than just the willing and well-trained explorer, but a team of specialists from various fields of the arts and sciences: physicians, neuroscientists, pharmacologists, mathematicians, anthropologists, psychologists, linguists, artists, and others will all find their individual expertise being drawn upon during these expeditions, which could, in theory, last days or longer. The explorer would, obviously, require an extensive period of training before taking part in DMT Space expeditions beyond their usual several minute duration. It would be the responsibility of the explorer to orient themselves within the DMT Space, before attempting to communicate with any intelligences encountered, perform experiments and, importantly, deliver information back to the team waiting on the other side. The standard "trip report" approach, and that employed by Rick Strassman in his pioneering DMT study in the early 1990s (13), is to ask the explorer to describe their experience, either verbally or in writing, in as much detail as possible immediately after exiting the DMT space. However, for more extended expeditions, during which sophisticated experiments could be performed and prolonged communication with intelligences attempted, techniques for real time communication from within the DMT Space would be required.

Despite being maligned by some, Harvard psychologist and psychedelic guru Timothy Leary was, in many ways, well ahead of his time in this regard. Although he is certainly most famous for his promotion of LSD and Psilocybe mushrooms, Leary was an extensive user of DMT and even developed a tool — the Experiential Typewriter — for communicating with a team in real time during a breakthrough DMT trip. The Typewriter consisted of two keyboards (one for each hand) connected to a recording device (14). Each keyboard contained ten keys, each allocated to communicate a particular aspect or feature of the experience. Obviously, a much more sophisticated device, with a control panel designed by specialist members of the exploration team, would be used in modern expeditions, but the principle would be similar. The World Space Explorer would be trained to control the device with precision during even the deepest and most turbulent of journeys, providing the team with a real-time flow of information about the structure and content of the space, and the nature of any intelligences resident therein.

Since there is no theoretical limit on the duration of the expeditions using this extended-state technology, World Space Explorers could remain within the DMT Space for as long as is necessary to gather and communicate detailed and sophisticated information, to perform experiments, and to establish communication with any contacted intelligent entities. In fact, extended sojourns lasting weeks or longer aren't completely out of the question. However, naturally, the amount of preparation required (and potential risks) will increase with the length of the expedition. Once journeys beyond a single day are undertaken, meeting the nutritive requirements of the human body, as well as the removal of waste, will need to be taken care of. Fortunately, intravenous feeding systems and apparatus for the collection of urinary and faecal wastes are already well-developed for medical intensive care settings, and their incorporation as part of a unified extended-state journeying system is likely to be relatively straightforward. However, aside from these basic physiological needs, the neurological and psychological impacts of longer expeditions must be carefully considered.

As the cortex would be constructing entirely distinct world models over days and weeks, there is the potential for remoulding of neural connectivity. Whilst the cortex clearly demonstrates a remarkable ability to switch between world models by rapidly shifting between disjoint patterns of emergent column activity (hence the facility with which one can enter and exit the DMT Space), it's plausible that restructuring of the underlying structural synaptic connections may occur over time. This might make exit from an extended journey itself a somewhat extended affair, perhaps requiring days (or even weeks) of gradual "retuning" to the Consensus Reality Space and the functional environment model. It's also difficult to gauge the potential psychological impacts of immersion in an entirely novel reality for long periods of time. Even with the standard 5-minute trip, it's not uncommon for DMT users to lose touch with their human identity, the concept of Earthly existence in a bodily form in its entirety, as well as the usual sense of spatial awareness and the passage of time. It seems reasonable to assume that these kinds of effects are likely to be amplified during extended sojourns, and returning to the Consensus Reality Space might well be as shocking and disorientating as the initial breakthrough into the DMT Space.

Of course, nobody promised that the pioneering of World Space exploration technologies would be easy and hazard free. But, given its particular pharmacological suitability for extended expeditions, DMT offers a perfect opportunity to understand how the human brain (and mind) deals with unusual trajectories through the World Space over time, and how we might deal with the challenges that will certainly present themselves. Once perfected, similar techniques could be deployed for other molecular and "post-molecular" technologies, opening up much broader terrains across the World Space Landscape for exploration and, ultimately, mapping. This will amount to nothing less than a complete paradigm shift for the human species, as we transcend the constraints of the Consensus Reality Space and become engineers of our reality, both individually and as a collective. Indeed, these technologies will eventually reach outside of the more formal academic research settings, to anyone who wishes to use them.

Whether in pursuit of answers to deeply-held personal questions about the nature of existence and our place within it, or to explore and probe at the limits of human experience, or simply for the sheer joy of dancing amongst the most marvellous of creatures in the most miraculous of worlds, the World Space will be ours to enjoy. A space to explore and to play and to be confronted with the immensity of our own existence — and the existence of others.

Children at play in the endless landscapes of the mind. Worlds without end.

Whatever our motives might be, as individuals and as a society, for making these journeys to these strange strange lands, there can be no doubt that the World Space of the human brain is a wondrous thing and ought to be explored with as much vigour and ambition as with which we reach with our rocket ships to the stars.

So, ahoy shipmates! Ahoy!

Off to the magical fractal shores beyond the veil!
Off to the crystal cities and electric oceans!
Off to the twisted worlds anew! Ahoy! Ahoy!

And fear not, for your friends will be waiting, here on the other side...

Where did you go? What did you see? Who did you meet?

Well...
        I met a little alien in a strange neighbourhood.
        And this is what he told me
        Or, at least,
        Was what I understood...

諸事万端は本物です

現実
管理

APPENDIX:

Organic molecules possess a carbon and hydrogen skeleton, with most psychoactive molecules also including oxygen and/or nitrogen, as well other atom types in some cases.

Carbon forms 4 covalent bonds; nitrogen 3; oxygen 2; hydrogen 1. In addition to single covalent bonds, carbon often forms double (and occasionally triple) bonds between carbon atoms (shown as a double line in the skeletal diagram).

For clarity, the carbon and hydrogen atoms are usually omitted from chemical structure diagrams, unless they are particularly salient (e.g. hydrogens on chiral carbons -- see later).

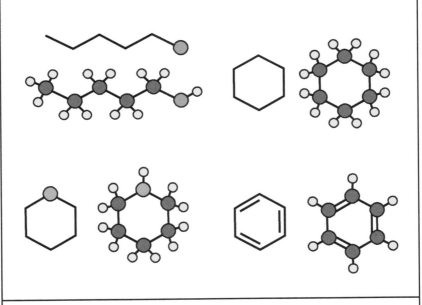

The structure of some organic molecules. The full structure and simplified molecular diagram omitting carbon and hydrogen are shown [carbon - grey; hydrogen - yellow; nitrogen - blue; oxygen - red].

A basic carbon skeleton can be decorated with sets of atoms known as functional groups, which are often important in the binding of a psychoactive molecule to a receptor and thus its psychoactive effects.

Below are some of the most important functional groups attached to a 6-membered cyclohexane ring:

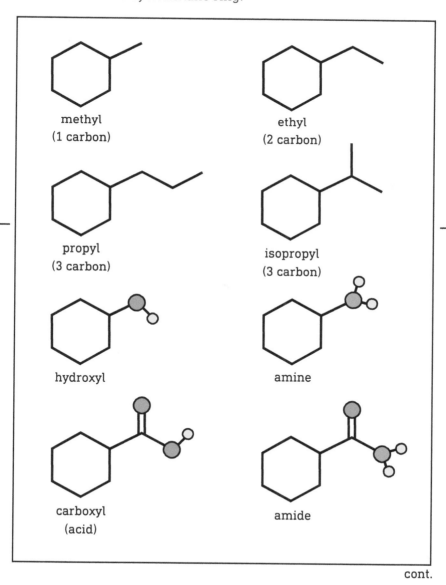

methyl
(1 carbon)

ethyl
(2 carbon)

propyl
(3 carbon)

isopropyl
(3 carbon)

hydroxyl

amine

carboxyl
(acid)

amide

cont.

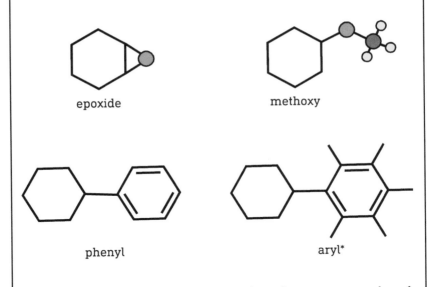

epoxide

methoxy

phenyl

aryl*

*If any of the hydrogens around a phenyl group are replaced
with a different atom, the group is known as an aryl group.

The indole and phenethylamine skeletons are the basis of
many important psychedelic molecules. The atoms around
the ring to which functional groups can be added (replacing
hydrogen atoms) are numbered as below:

indole

phenethylamine

If a single carbon atom in a molecule is bonded to four different atoms/groups, the carbon is chiral and the molecule
can exist in two non-superimposable mirror image isomers
known as enantiomers (each given the prefix R or S).

A solution of each enantiomer will rotate polarised light in opposite directions and, as such, they are also known as optical
isomers. A 50:50 mixture of both isomers doesn't rotate light
and is known as a racemic mixture.

mirror plane

Optical isomers (enantiomers).

If a molecule contains more than one chiral carbon, there are 2^n
possible stereoisomers (where n=number of chiral carbons). However, only pairs of stereoisomers in which all the chiral carbons
have opposite chirality are mirror images and thus optical isomers.

Since amino acids also contain chiral carbon atoms, one stereoisomer might bind and activate a particular receptor more effectively than the other. In some cases, only one stereoisomer is
active at all. For example, of the 4 possible stereoisomers of LSD
(which has 2 chiral carbons), only (5R,8R)-LSD is active.

References and Further Reading.

Chapter 1.

1. Schultes, R.E., Hofmann, A., Ratsch, C. (2001). Plants of the Gods: Their Sacred, Healing, and Hallucinogenic Powers, 2nd Ed. Healing Arts Press

2. McKenna 1998; McKenna, D., & Riba, J. (2015). New World Tryptamine Hallucinogens and the Neuroscience of Ayahuasca. Current topics in behavioral neurosciences, Advance online publication; McKenna D. J. (2005). Ayahuasca and human destiny. Journal of psychoactive drugs, 37(2), 231–234; Frenopoulo, C. (2005). The ritual use of ayahuasca. J. Psychoactive Drugs 37, 237–239

3. Sessa, B., (2019). The Psychedelic Renaissance: Reassessing the Role of Psychedelic Drugs in 21st Century Psychiatry and Society. Aeon Academic; Johnson, M. W., & Griffiths, R. R. (2017). Potential Therapeutic Effects of Psilocybin. Neurotherapeutics : the journal of the American Society for Experimental NeuroTherapeutics, 14(3), 734–740; Griffiths, R. R., Johnson, M. W., Carducci, M. A., Umbricht, A., Richards, W. A., Richards, B. D., Cosimano, M. P., & Klinedinst, M. A. (2016). Psilocybin produces substantial and sustained decreases in depression and anxiety in patients with life-threatening cancer: A randomized double-blind trial. Journal of psychopharmacology (Oxford, England), 30(12), 1181–1197; Goldberg, S. B., Pace, B. T., Nicholas, C. R., Raison, C. L., & Hutson, P. R. (2020). The experimental effects of psilocybin on symptoms of anxiety and depression: A meta-analysis. Psychiatry research, 284, 112749; Carhart-Harris, R. L., Bolstridge, M., Day, C., Rucker, J., Watts, R., Erritzoe, D. E., Kaelen, M., Giribaldi, B., Bloomfield, M., Pilling, S., Rickard, J. A., Forbes, B., Feilding, A., Taylor, D., Curran, H. V., & Nutt, D. J. (2018). Psilocybin with psychological support for treatment-resistant depression: six-month follow-up. Psychopharmacology, 235(2), 399–408

4. Luke, D.L. (2019). Otherworlds: Psychedelics and Exceptional Human Experience. Aeon Academic

5. Prisinzano T. E. (2005). Psychopharmacology of the hallucinogenic sage Salvia divinorum. Life sciences, 78(5), 527–531

Chapter 2.

1. Kant, I. (1999). Critique of Pure Reason. Cambridge University Press

2. Metzinger, T. (2009). The Ego Tunnel. Basic Books

3. Goekoop, R., & Looijestijn, J. (2011). A Network Model of Hallucinations. In Hallucinations: Research and Practice by J. D. D. Blom, & I. E. C. Sommer, New York: Springer

4. Nestler, E.J., Hyman, S.E., and Malenka R.J. (2001). Molecular Neuropharmacology: Foundation for Clinical Neuroscience. New York: McGraw Hill

5. Raghavan, M., Fee, D., & Barkhaus, P. E. (2019). Generation and propagation of the action potential. Handbook of clinical neurology, 160, 3–22; Barnett, M. W., & Larkman, P. M. (2007). The action potential. Practical neurology, 7(3), 192–197; Kang, J., Huguenard, J. R., & Prince, D. A. (2000). Voltage-gated potassium channels activated during action potentials in layer V neocortical pyramidal neurons. Journal of neurophysiology, 83(1), 70–80. https://doi.org/10.1152/jn.2000.83.1.70

6. deCharms, R. C., & Zador, A. (2000). Neural representation and the cortical code. Annual review of neuroscience, 23, 613–647; Eggermont J. J. (1998). Is there a neural code?. Neuroscience and biobehavioral reviews, 22(2), 355–370; Shamir M. (2014). Emerging principles of population coding: in search for the neural code. Current opinion in neurobiology, 25, 140–148

7. Sporns, O. (2011). Networks of the Brain. MIT Press

8. Hyman S. E. (2005). Neurotransmitters. Current biology : CB, 15(5), R154–R158

9. Greger, I. H., Watson, J. F., & Cull-Candy, S. G. (2017). Structural and Functional Architecture of AMPA-Type Glutamate Receptors and Their Auxiliary Proteins. Neuron, 94(4), 713–730; Gouaux E. (2004). Structure and function of AMPA receptors. The Journal of physiology, 554(Pt 2), 249–253

10. Bettler, B., Kaupmann, K., Mosbacher, J., & Gassmann, M. (2004). Molecular structure and physiological functions of GABA(B) receptors. Physiological reviews, 84(3), 835–867; Michels, G., & Moss, S. J. (2007). GABAA receptors: properties and traffick-

ing. Critical reviews in biochemistry and molecular biology, 42(1), 3–14

11. Koch, C. 1999, Biophysics of Computation. Information Processing in Single Neurons, New York: Oxford Univ. Press, p87

12. Gallimore, A.R., Kim, T., Tanaka-Yamamoto, K. & De Schutter, E. (2018). Cell Reports, 22, 722-733.

13. Edelman, G. M. (2000). A Universe of Consciousness: How Matter Becomes Imagination. Basic Books; Tononi, G., & Edelman, G. M. (2000; Schizophrenia and the mechanisms of conscious integration. Brain research. Brain research reviews, 31(2-3), 391–400

14. Hubel, D. H., & Wiesel, T. N. (1974). Uniformity of monkey striate cortex: a parallel relationship between field size, scatter, and magnification factor. The Journal of comparative neurology, 158(3), 295–305; Ts'o, D. Y., Zarella, M., & Burkitt, G. (2009). Whither the hypercolumn?. The Journal of physiology, 587(Pt 12), 2791–2805

15. Tsunoda, K., Yamane, Y., Nishizaki, M., & Tanifuji, M. (2001). Complex objects are represented in macaque inferotemporal cortex by the combination of feature columns. Nature neuroscience, 4(8), 832–838

Chapter 3.

1. Edelman, G. M. (1993). Neural Darwinism: Selection and re-entrant signalling in higher brain function. Neuron, 10, 115–125

2. Llinás, R. R., & Paré, D. (1991). Of dreaming and wakefulness. Neuroscience, 44(3), 521–535; Bayne, T., Seth, A. K., & Massimini, M. (2020). Are There Islands of Awareness?. Trends in neurosciences, 43(1), 6–16

3. Schredl, R., & Hofmann, F. (2003). Continuity between waking activities and dream activities. Consciousness and Cognition, 12, 298–308

4. Sporns, O. (2011). Networks of the Brain. MIT Press; Tononi, G., Edelman, G. M. and Sporns, O. (1998) 'Complexity and coherency: integrating information in the brain', Trends in Cognitive Sciences, 2(12), 474-484

5. Sherman, S. M., & Guillery, R. W. (2002). The role of the thal-

amus in the flow of information to the cortex. Philosophical transactions of the Royal Society of London. Series B, Biological sciences, 357(1428), 1695–1708

6. Mumford D. (1991). On the computational architecture of the neocortex. I. The role of the thalamo-cortical loop. Biological cybernetics, 65(2), 135–145

7. Ward L. M. (2011). The thalamic dynamic core theory of conscious experience. Consciousness and cognition, 20(2), 464–486; Llinás, R., Ribary, U., Contreras, D., & Pedroarena, C. (1998). The neuronal basis for consciousness. Philosophical transactions of the Royal Society of London. Series B, Biological sciences, 353(1377), 1841–1849

8. Snowden, R., Thompson, P., & Troscianko, T. (2006). Basic Vision: An Introduction to Visual Perception. Oxford University Press

9. Antolík, J., & Bednar, J. A. (2011). Development of maps of simple and complex cells in the primary visual cortex. Frontiers in computational neuroscience, 5, 17

10. Hubel, D. H., & Wiesel, T. N. (1974). Sequence regularity and geometry of orientation columns in the monkey striate cortex. The Journal of comparative neurology, 158(3), 267–293; Dow B. M. (2002). Orientation and color columns in monkey visual cortex. Cerebral cortex (New York, N.Y. : 1991), 12(10), 1005–1015; Yacoub, E., Harel, N., & Ugurbil, K. (2008). High-field fMRI unveils orientation columns in humans. Proceedings of the National Academy of Sciences of the United States of America, 105(30), 10607–10612

11. Antolík 2011; Quiroga, R. Q., Reddy, L., Kreiman, G., Koch, C., & Fried, I. (2005). Invariant visual representation by single neurons in the human brain. Nature, 435(7045), 1102–1107

12. Blakemore, C., & Cooper, G. F. (1970). Development of the brain depends on the visual environment. Nature, 228(5270), 477–478

13. Llinas, R., Pare, D. (1991). Of dreaming and wakefulness.Neuroscience, 44(3), 521-535

Chapter 4.

1. Lineweaver, C., Davies, P., & Ruse, M. (2013). What is complex-

ity? Is it increasing? In Complexity and the Arrow of Time (pp. 3-16).Cambridge University Press

2. Johnston, J. 2010, The Allure of Machinic Life, MIT Press

3. Friston, K. 2010, The free-energy principle: a unified brain theory?. Nat Rev Neurosci 11, 127–138; Hohwy, J. 2013, The Predictive Mind, Oxford University Press

4. Rao, R., Ballard, D., 1999, Predictive coding in the visual cortex: a functional interpretation of some extra-classical receptive-field effects. Nat Neurosci 2, 79–87

5. DiCarlo, J.J., Cox, D.D., 2007, Untangling invariant object recognition, Trends in Cognitive Sciences, 11(8), 333-341

6. Hollow face illusion modified from User:Empetrisor, Wikimedia Commons, under the Creative Commons Attribution-Share Alike 4.0 International (CC BY-SA 4.0) license.

Chapter 5.

1. Kanai, R., Komura, Y., Shipp, S., & Friston, K. (2015). Cerebral hierarchies: predictive processing, precision and the pulvinar. Philosophical transactions of the Royal Society of London. Series B, Biological sciences, 370(1668), 20140169

2. Adesnik, H., & Naka, A. (2018). Cracking the Function of Layers in the Sensory Cortex. Neuron, 100(5), 1028–1043; Eyal, G., Verhoog, M. B., Testa-Silva, G., Deitcher, Y., Benavides-Piccione, R., DeFelipe, J., de Kock, C., Mansvelder, H. D., & Segev, I. (2018). Human Cortical Pyramidal Neurons: From Spines to Spikes via Models. Frontiers in cellular neuroscience, 12, 181

3. Gilbert, C. D., & Li, W. (2013). Top-down influences on visual processing. Nature reviews. Neuroscience, 14(5), 350–363; Bastos, A. M., Usrey, W. M., Adams, R. A., Mangun, G. R., Fries, P., & Friston, K. J. (2012). Canonical microcircuits for predictive coding. Neuron, 76(4), 695–711; Keller, G. B., & Mrsic-Flogel, T. D. (2018). Predictive Processing: A Canonical Cortical Computation. Neuron, 100(2), 424–435

4. Bastos, A. M., Vezoli, J., Bosman, C. A., Schoffelen, J. M., Oostenveld, R., Dowdall, J. R., De Weerd, P., Kennedy, H., & Fries, P. (2015). Visual areas exert feedforward and feedback influences through distinct frequency channels. Neuron, 85(2), 390–401

5. Friston K. (2002). Functional integration and inference in the brain. Progress in neurobiology, 68(2), 113–143

6. Cornford, J. H., Mercier, M. S., Leite, M., Magloire, V., Häusser, M., & Kullmann, D. M. (2019). Dendritic NMDA receptors in parvalbumin neurons enable strong and stable neuronal assemblies. eLife, 8, e49872

7. Friston K. (2002). Functional integration and inference in the brain. Progress in neurobiology, 68(2), 113–143

8. Buzsaki, G. Rhythms of the Brain, Oxford University Press, Oxford, 2006; Cardin, J. A., Carlén, M., Meletis, K., Knoblich, U., Zhang, F., Deisseroth, K., Tsai, L. H., & Moore, C. I. (2009). Driving fast-spiking cells induces gamma rhythm and controls sensory responses. Nature, 459(7247), 663–667; Klimesch, W., Sauseng, P., & Hanslmayr, S. (2007). EEG alpha oscillations: the inhibition-timing hypothesis. Brain research reviews, 53(1), 63–88

9. van Kerkoerle, T., Self, M. W., Dagnino, B., Gariel-Mathis, M. A., Poort, J., van der Togt, C., & Roelfsema, P. R. (2014). Alpha and gamma oscillations characterize feedback and feedforward processing in monkey visual cortex. Proceedings of the National Academy of Sciences of the United States of America, 111(40), 14332–14341; Silva, L. R., Amitai, Y., & Connors, B. W. (1991). Intrinsic oscillations of neocortex generated by layer 5 pyramidal neurons. Science (New York, N.Y.), 251(4992), 432–435

10. Auksztulewicz, R., Friston, K. J., & Nobre, A. C. (2017). Task relevance modulates the behavioural and neural effects of sensory predictions. PLoS biology, 15(12), e2003143

11. Roopun, A. K., Kramer, M. A., Carracedo, L. M., Kaiser, M., Davies, C. H., Traub, R. D., Kopell, N. J., & Whittington, M. A. (2008). Period concatenation underlies interactions between gamma and beta rhythms in neocortex. Frontiers in cellular neuroscience, 2, 1;Palva, S., & Palva, J. M. (2007). New vistas for alpha-frequency band oscillations. Trends in neurosciences, 30(4), 150–158. https://doi.org/10.1016/j.tins.2007.02.001; Womelsdorf, T., Schoffelen, J. M., Oostenveld, R., Singer, W., Desimone, R., Engel, A. K., & Fries, P. (2007). Modulation of neuronal interactions through neuronal synchronization. Science (New York, N.Y.), 316(5831), 1609–1612

12. Alamia, A., & VanRullen, R. (2019). Alpha oscillations and

traveling waves: Signatures of predictive coding?. PLoS biology, 17(10), e3000487; Friston K. J. (2019). Waves of prediction. PLoS biology, 17(10), e3000426; Mayer, A., Schwiedrzik, C. M., Wibral, M., Singer, W., & Melloni, L. (2016). Expecting to See a Letter: Alpha Oscillations as Carriers of Top-Down Sensory Predictions. Cerebral cortex (New York, N.Y. : 1991), 26(7), 3146–3160

13. Michalareas, G., Vezoli, J., van Pelt, S., Schoffelen, J. M., Kennedy, H., & Fries, P. (2016). Alpha-Beta and Gamma Rhythms Subserve Feedback and Feedforward Influences among Human Visual Cortical Areas. Neuron, 89(2), 384–397

14. Cardin, J. A., Carlén, M., Meletis, K., Knoblich, U., Zhang, F., Deisseroth, K., Tsai, L. H., & Moore, C. I. (2009). Driving fast-spiking cells induces gamma rhythm and controls sensory responses. Nature, 459(7247), 663–667; Traub, R. D., Contreras, D., Cunningham, M. O., Murray, H., LeBeau, F. E., Roopun, A., Bibbig, A., Wilent, W. B., Higley, M. J., & Whittington, M. A. (2005). Single-column thalamocortical network model exhibiting gamma oscillations, sleep spindles, and epileptogenic bursts. Journal of neurophysiology, 93(4), 2194–2232

15. Auksztulewicz 2017; Auksztulewicz, R., & Friston, K. (2016). Repetition suppression and its contextual determinants in predictive coding. Cortex; a journal devoted to the study of the nervous system and behavior, 80, 125–140

Chapter 6.

1. St. John 2016, https://chacruna.net/terence-mckenna-first-smoked-dmt/

2. Thurner, S., Hanel,R., Klimek, P. (2018). Introduction to the Theory of Complex Systems, Oxford University Press, Oxford.

3. Hopfield J. J. (1982). Neural networks and physical systems with emergent collective computational abilities. Proceedings of the National Academy of Sciences of the United States of America, 79(8), 2554–2558

4. Deco, G., & Jirsa, V. K. (2012). Ongoing cortical activity at rest: criticality, multistability, and ghost attractors. The Journal of neuroscience : the official journal of the Society for Neuroscience, 32(10), 3366–3375; Gu, S., Cieslak, M., Baird, B., Muldoon, S.

F., Grafton, S. T., Pasqualetti, F., & Bassett, D. S. (2018). The Energy Landscape of Neurophysiological Activity Implicit in Brain Network Structure. Scientific reports, 8(1), 2507

5. Kenet, T., Bibitchkov, D., Tsodyks, M., Grinvald, A., & Arieli, A. (2003). Spontaneously emerging cortical representations of visual attributes. Nature, 425(6961), 954–956

Chapter 7.

1. Miner, L. H., Schroeter, S., Blakely, R. D., & Sesack, S. R. (2000). Ultrastructural localization of the serotonin transporter in superficial and deep layers of the rat prelimbic prefrontal cortex and its spatial relationship to dopamine terminals. The Journal of comparative neurology, 427(2), 220–234

2. McCorvy, J. D., & Roth, B. L. (2015). Structure and function of serotonin G protein-coupled receptors. Pharmacology & therapeutics, 150, 129–142

3. Araneda, R., & Andrade, R. (1991). 5-Hydroxytryptamine2 and 5-hydroxytryptamine 1A receptors mediate opposing responses on membrane excitability in rat association cortex. Neuroscience, 40(2), 399–412

4. Leff, P., Scaramellini, C., Law, C., & McKechnie, K. (1997). A three-state receptor model of agonist action. Trends in pharmacological sciences, 18(10), 355–362

5. De la Fuente, I. M., Cortes, J. M., Pelta, D. A., & Veguillas, J. (2013). Attractor metabolic networks. PloS one, 8(3), e58284

6. Gallimore, A. R., Kim, T., Tanaka-Yamamoto, K., & De Schutter, E. (2018). Switching On Depression and Potentiation in the Cerebellum. Cell reports, 22(3), 722–733

7. Bhalla, U. S., & Iyengar, R. (1999). Emergent properties of networks of biological signaling pathways. Science (New York, N.Y.), 283(5400), 381–387

Chapter 8.

1. Nichols D. E. (2020). Psilocybin: from ancient magic to modern medicine. The Journal of antibiotics, 73(10), 679–686; Hofmann, A., Troxler, F. (1959). Identifizierung von Psilocin (Identification

of psilocin). Experientia, 15(3), 101–102; Hofmann, A., Frey, A., Ott, H., Petr Zilka, T., Troxler, F. (1958). Konstitutionsaufklärung und Synthese von Psilocybin (Elucidation of the structure and the synthesis of psilocybin). Experientia, 14(11), 397–399

2. Lyttle, T., Goldstein, D., & Gartz, J. (1996). Bufo toads and bufotenine: fact and fiction surrounding an alleged psychedelic. Journal of psychoactive drugs, 28(3), 267–290

3. Bufo alvarius) (Weil, A. T., & Davis, W. (1994). Bufo alvarius: a potent hallucinogen of animal origin. Journal of ethnopharmacology, 41(1-2), 1–8

4. Shulgin, A. & Shulgin A. (1997). TIHKAL: The Continuation, Transform Press

5. Schardl, C. L., Panaccione, D. G., & Tudzynski, P. (2006). Ergot alkaloids--biology and molecular biology. The Alkaloids. Chemistry and biology, 63, 45–86

6. Carod-Artal F. J. (2015). Hallucinogenic drugs in pre-Columbian Mesoamerican cultures. Neurologia (Barcelona, Spain), 30(1), 42–49

7. Amici, A. M., Minghetti, A., Scotti, T., Spalla, C., & Tognoli, L. (1966). Production of ergotamine by a strain of Claviceps purpurea (Fr.) Tul. Experientia, 22(6), 415–416; Bassett, R. A., Chain, E. B., & Corbett, K. (1973). Biosynthesis of ergotamine by Claviceps purpurea (Fr.) Tul. The Biochemical journal, 134(1), 1–10

8. Hofmann A. (1979). How LSD originated. Journal of psychedelic drugs, 11(1-2), 53–60

9. Shulgin A. T. (1973). Mescaline: the chemistry and pharmacology of its analogs. Lloydia, 36(1), 46–58; Kapadia, G. J., & Fayez, M. B. (1973). The chemistry of peyote alkaloids. Lloydia, 36(1), 9–35

10. Shulgin, A. & Shulgin A. (1991). PiHKAL: A Chemical Love Story, Transform Press

11. Nichols D. E. (2016). Psychedelics. Pharmacological reviews, 68(2), 264–355; Glennon, R. A., Titeler, M., & McKenney, J. D. (1984). Evidence for 5-HT2 involvement in the mechanism of action of hallucinogenic agents. Life sciences, 35(25), 2505–2511; Vollenweider, F. X., Vollenweider-Scherpenhuyzen, M. F., Bäbler, A., Vogel, H., & Hell, D. (1998). Psilocybin induces schizophrenia-like psychosis in humans via a serotonin-2 agonist action. Neuroreport, 9(17), 3897–3902

12. Almaula, N., Ebersole, B. J., Zhang, D., Weinstein, H., & Seal-fon, S. C. (1996). Mapping the binding site pocket of the serotonin 5-Hydroxytryptamine2A receptor. Ser3.36(159) provides a second interaction site for the protonated amine of serotonin but not of lysergic acid diethylamide or bufotenin. The Journal of biological chemistry, 271(25), 14672–14675; Kristiansen, K., Kroeze, W. K., Willins, D. L., Gelber, E. I., Savage, J. E., Glennon, R. A., & Roth, B. L. (2000). A highly conserved aspartic acid (Asp-155) anchors the terminal amine moiety of tryptamines and is involved in membrane targeting of the 5-HT(2A) serotonin receptor but does not participate in activation via a "salt-bridge disruption" mechanism. The Journal of pharmacology and experimental therapeutics, 293(3), 735–746

13. Braden, M. R., & Nichols, D. E. (2007). Assessment of the roles of serines 5.43(239) and 5.46(242) for binding and potency of agonist ligands at the human serotonin 5-HT2A receptor. Molecular pharmacology, 72(5), 1200–1209; Yap, B. K., Buckle, M. J., & Doughty, S. W. (2012). Homology modeling of the human 5-HT1A, 5-HT 2A, D1, and D2 receptors: model refinement with molecular dynamics simulations and docking evaluation. Journal of molecular modeling, 18(8), 3639–3655

14. Kim, K., Che, T., Panova, O., DiBerto, J. F., Lyu, J., Krumm, B. E., Wacker, D., Robertson, M. J., Seven, A. B., Nichols, D. E., Shoichet, B. K., Skiniotis, G., & Roth, B. L. (2020). Structure of a Hallucinogen-Activated Gq-Coupled 5-HT2A Serotonin Receptor. Cell, 182(6), 1574–1588

15. Roth, B. L., Shoham, M., Choudhary, M. S., & Khan, N. (1997). Identification of conserved aromatic residues essential for agonist binding and second messenger production at 5-hydroxytryptamine2A receptors. Molecular pharmacology, 52(2), 259–266

16. Ebersole, B. J., Visiers, I., Weinstein, H., & Sealfon, S. C. (2003). Molecular basis of partial agonism: orientation of indoleamine ligands in the binding pocket of the human serotonin 5-HT2A receptor determines relative efficacy. Molecular pharmacology, 63(1), 36–43

17. McLean, T. H., Chambers, J. J., Parrish, J. C., Braden, M. R., Marona-Lewicka, D., Kurrasch-Orbaugh, D., & Nichols, D. E. (2006). C-(4,5,6-trimethoxyindan-1-yl)methanamine: a mescaline ana-

logue designed using a homology model of the 5-HT2A receptor. Journal of medicinal chemistry, 49(14), 4269–4274

18. Shulgin, A. T., Sargent, T., & Naranjo, C. (1966). Role of 3,4-dimethoxyphenethylamine in schizophrenia. Nature, 212(5070), 1606–1607; Shulgin, A. T., Sargent, T., & Naranjo, C. (1967). The chemistry and psychopharmacology of nutmeg and of several related phenylisopropylamines. Psychopharmacology bulletin, 4(3), 13; Wesson D. R. (2011). Psychedelic drugs, hippie counterculture, speed and phenobarbital treatment of sedative-hypnotic dependence: a journey to the Haight Ashbury in the Sixties. Journal of psychoactive drugs, 43(2), 153–164

19. Brecher, E.M. (1973), The Consumers Union Report on Licit and Illicit Drugs, Little Brown & Co.

20. Nichols D. E. (2017). Chemistry and Structure-Activity Relationships of Psychedelics. Current topics in behavioral neurosciences, 36, 1–43

21. Ray T. S. (2010). Psychedelics and the human receptorome. PloS one, 5(2), e9019

22. Chambers, J. J., & Nichols, D. E. (2002). A homology-based model of the human 5-HT2A receptor derived from an in silico activated G-protein coupled receptor. Journal of computer-aided molecular design, 16(7), 511–520

23. Perez-Aguilar, J. M., Shan, J., LeVine, M. V., Khelashvili, G., & Weinstein, H. (2014). A functional selectivity mechanism at the serotonin-2A GPCR involves ligand-dependent conformations of intracellular loop 2. Journal of the American Chemical Society, 136(45), 16044–16054

24. Nichols D. E. (2018). Chemistry and Structure-Activity Relationships of Psychedelics. Current topics in behavioral neurosciences, 36, 1–43

25. De Lean, A., Stadel, J. M., & Lefkowitz, R. J. (1980). A ternary complex model explains the agonist-specific binding properties of the adenylate cyclase-coupled beta-adrenergic receptor. The Journal of biological chemistry, 255(15), 7108–7117; Kenakin T. (2001). Inverse, protean, and ligand-selective agonism: matters of receptor conformation. FASEB journal : official publication of the Federation of American Societies for Experimental Biology, 15(3), 598–611; Leff, P., Scaramellini, C., Law, C., & McKechnie, K. (1997).

A three-state receptor model of agonist action. Trends in pharmacological sciences, 18(10), 355–362

26. Chang, C. W., Poteet, E., Schetz, J. A., Gümüş, Z. H., & Weinstein, H. (2009). Towards a quantitative representation of the cell signaling mechanisms of hallucinogens: measurement and mathematical modeling of 5-HT1A and 5-HT2A receptor-mediated ERK1/2 activation. Neuropharmacology, 56 Suppl 1(Suppl 1), 213–225

27. Roberson, E. D., English, J. D., Adams, J. P., Selcher, J. C., Kondratick, C., & Sweatt, J. D. (1999). The mitogen-activated protein kinase cascade couples PKA and PKC to cAMP response element binding protein phosphorylation in area CA1 of hippocampus. The Journal of neuroscience : the official journal of the Society for Neuroscience, 19(11), 4337–4348

28. Yuan, L. L., Adams, J. P., Swank, M., Sweatt, J. D., & Johnston, D. (2002). Protein kinase modulation of dendritic K+ channels in hippocampus involves a mitogen-activated protein kinase pathway. The Journal of neuroscience : the official journal of the Society for Neuroscience, 22(12), 4860–4868

29. Smart T. G. (1997). Regulation of excitatory and inhibitory neurotransmitter-gated ion channels by protein phosphorylation. Current opinion in neurobiology, 7(3), 358–367

30. Zhong, P., Yuen, E. Y., & Yan, Z. (2008). Modulation of neuronal excitability by serotonin-NMDA interactions in prefrontal cortex. Molecular and cellular neurosciences, 38(2), 290–299; Schrader, L. A., Birnbaum, S. G., Nadin, B. M., Ren, Y., Bui, D., Anderson, A. E., & Sweatt, J. D. (2006). ERK/MAPK regulates the Kv4.2 potassium channel by direct phosphorylation of the pore-forming subunit. American journal of physiology. Cell physiology, 290(3), C852–C861

31. Rahman, S., & Neuman, R. S. (1993). Activation of 5-HT2 receptors facilitates depolarization of neocortical neurons by N-methyl-D-aspartate. European journal of pharmacology, 231(3), 347–354; Zhang, G., & Stackman, R. W., Jr (2015). The role of serotonin 5-HT2A receptors in memory and cognition. Frontiers in pharmacology, 6, 225

32. Villalobos, C., Beique, J. C., Gingrich, J. A., & Andrade, R. (2005). Serotonergic regulation of calcium-activated potassium currents

in rodent prefrontal cortex. The European journal of neuroscience, 22(5), 1120–1126

33. Andrade, R., Foehring, R. C., & Tzingounis, A. V. (2012). The calcium-activated slow AHP: cutting through the Gordian knot. Frontiers in cellular neuroscience, 6, 47

34. Zhong, P., Yuen, E. Y., & Yan, Z. (2008). Modulation of neuronal excitability by serotonin-NMDA interactions in prefrontal cortex. Molecular and cellular neurosciences, 38(2), 290–299

35. Seroussi, Y., Brosh, I., & Barkai, E. (2002). Learning-induced reduction in post-burst after-hyperpolarization (AHP) is mediated by activation of PKC. The European journal of neuroscience, 16(5), 965–969; Zhang, Z. W., & Arsenault, D. (2005). Gain modulation by serotonin in pyramidal neurones of the rat prefrontal cortex. The Journal of physiology, 566(Pt 2), 379–394

36. Hibino, H., Inanobe, A., Furutani, K., Murakami, S., Findlay, I., & Kurachi, Y. (2010). Inwardly rectifying potassium channels: their structure, function, and physiological roles. Physiological reviews, 90(1), 291–366; Polter, A. M., & Li, X. (2010). 5-HT1A receptor-regulated signal transduction pathways in brain. Cellular signalling, 22(10), 1406–1412; Andrade, R., Malenka, R. C., & Nicoll, R. A. (1986). A G protein couples serotonin and GABAB receptors to the same channels in hippocampus. Science (New York, N.Y.), 234(4781), 1261–1265

37. Davies, M. F., Deisz, R. A., Prince, D. A., & Peroutka, S. J. (1987). Two distinct effects of 5-hydroxytryptamine on single cortical neurons. Brain research, 423(1-2), 347–352; Tanaka, E., & North, R. A. (1993). Actions of 5-hydroxytryptamine on neurons of the rat cingulate cortex. Journal of neurophysiology, 69(5), 1749–1757; Araneda, R., & Andrade, R. (1991). 5-Hydroxytryptamine2 and 5-hydroxytryptamine 1A receptors mediate opposing responses on membrane excitability in rat association cortex. Neuroscience, 40(2), 399–412

38. Egan, C. T., Herrick-Davis, K., Miller, K., Glennon, R. A., & Teitler, M. (1998). Agonist activity of LSD and lisuride at cloned 5HT2A and 5HT2C receptors. Psychopharmacology, 136(4), 409–414). Lisuride, however, has no psychedelic effects (White, F. J., & Appel, J. B. (1982). Lysergic acid diethylamide (LSD) and lisuride: differentiation of their neuropharmacological actions. Science

(New York, N.Y.), 216(4545), 535–537

39. Crespo, P., Xu, N., Simonds, W. F., & Gutkind, J. S. (1994). Ras-dependent activation of MAP kinase pathway mediated by G-protein beta gamma subunits. Nature, 369(6479), 418–420; Gutkind J. S. (2000). Regulation of mitogen-activated protein kinase signaling networks by G protein-coupled receptors. Science's STKE : signal transduction knowledge environment, 2000(40), re1; Quinn, J. C., Johnson-Farley, N. N., Yoon, J., & Cowen, D. S. (2002). Activation of extracellular-regulated kinase by 5-hydroxytryptamine(2A) receptors in PC12 cells is protein kinase C-independent and requires calmodulin and tyrosine kinases. The Journal of pharmacology and experimental therapeutics, 303(2), 746–752

40. González-Maeso, J., Weisstaub, N. V., Zhou, M., Chan, P., Ivic, L., Ang, R., Lira, A., Bradley-Moore, M., Ge, Y., Zhou, Q., Sealfon, S. C., & Gingrich, J. A. (2007). Hallucinogens recruit specific cortical 5-HT(2A) receptor-mediated signaling pathways to affect behavior. Neuron, 53(3), 439–452

41. Dutar, P., Petrozzino, J. J., Vu, H. M., Schmidt, M. F., & Perkel, D. J. (2000). Slow synaptic inhibition mediated by metabotropic glutamate receptor activation of GIRK channels. Journal of neurophysiology, 84(5), 2284–2290; Reiner, A., & Levitz, J. (2018). Glutamatergic Signaling in the Central Nervous System: Ionotropic and Metabotropic Receptors in Concert. Neuron, 98(6), 1080–1098

42. González-Maeso, J., Ang, R. L., Yuen, T., Chan, P., Weisstaub, N. V., López-Giménez, J. F., Zhou, M., Okawa, Y., Callado, L. F., Milligan, G., Gingrich, J. A., Filizola, M., Meana, J. J., & Sealfon, S. C. (2008). Identification of a serotonin/glutamate receptor complex implicated in psychosis. Nature, 452(7183), 93–97

43. Fribourg, M., Moreno, J. L., Holloway, T., Provasi, D., Baki, L., Mahajan, R., Park, G., Adney, S. K., Hatcher, C., Eltit, J. M., Ruta, J. D., Albizu, L., Li, Z., Umali, A., Shim, J., Fabiato, A., MacKerell, A. D., Jr, Brezina, V., Sealfon, S. C., Filizola, M., ... Logothetis, D. E. (2011). Decoding the signaling of a GPCR heteromeric complex reveals a unifying mechanism of action of antipsychotic drugs. Cell, 147(5), 1011–1023

44. Moreno, J. L., Miranda-Azpiazu, P., García-Bea, A., Younkin, J., Cui, M., Kozlenkov, A., Ben-Ezra, A., Voloudakis, G., Fakira, A.

K., Baki, L., Ge, Y., Georgakopoulos, A., Morón, J. A., Milligan, G., López-Giménez, J. F., Robakis, N. K., Logothetis, D. E., Meana, J. J., & González-Maeso, J. (2016). Allosteric signaling through an mGlu2 and 5-HT2A heteromeric receptor complex and its potential contribution to schizophrenia. Science signaling, 9(410), ra5; Moreno, J. L., Muguruza, C., Umali, A., Mortillo, S., Holloway, T., Pilar-Cuéllar, F., Mocci, G., Seto, J., Callado, L. F., Neve, R. L., Milligan, G., Sealfon, S. C., López-Giménez, J. F., Meana, J. J., Benson, D. L., & González-Maeso, J. (2012). Identification of three residues essential for 5-hydroxytryptamine 2A-metabotropic glutamate 2 (5-HT2A·mGlu2) receptor heteromerization and its psychoactive behavioral function. The Journal of biological chemistry, 287(53), 44301–44319

Chapter 9.

1. Santana, N., Bortolozzi, A., Serrats, J., Mengod, G., & Artigas, F. (2004). Expression of serotonin1A and serotonin2A receptors in pyramidal and GABAergic neurons of the rat prefrontal cortex. Cerebral cortex (New York, N.Y. : 1991), 14(10), 1100–1109
2. Aghajanian G. K. (2009). Modeling "psychosis" in vitro by inducing disordered neuronal network activity in cortical brain slices. Psychopharmacology, 206(4), 575–585; Carhart-Harris, R. L., Muthukumaraswamy, S., Roseman, L., Kaelen, M., Droog, W., Murphy, K., Tagliazucchi, E., Schenberg, E. E., Nest, T., Orban, C., Leech, R., Williams, L. T., Williams, T. M., Bolstridge, M., Sessa, B., McGonigle, J., Sereno, M. I., Nichols, D., Hellyer, P. J., Hobden, P., … Nutt, D. J. (2016). Neural correlates of the LSD experience revealed by multimodal neuroimaging. Proceedings of the National Academy of Sciences of the United States of America, 113(17), 4853–4858; Schartner, M. M., Carhart-Harris, R. L., Barrett, A. B., Seth, A. K., & Muthukumaraswamy, S. D. (2017). Increased spontaneous MEG signal diversity for psychoactive doses of ketamine, LSD and psilocybin. Scientific reports, 7, 46421; Carhart-Harris, R. L., Leech, R., Hellyer, P. J., Shanahan, M., Feilding, A., Tagliazucchi, E., Chialvo, D. R., & Nutt, D. (2014). The entropic brain: a theory of conscious states informed by neuroimaging research with psychedelic drugs. Frontiers in human neuroscience, 8, 20;

Carhart-Harris R. L. (2018). The entropic brain - revisited. Neuropharmacology, 142, 167–178; Preller, K. H., Razi, A., Zeidman, P., Stämpfli, P., Friston, K. J., & Vollenweider, F. X. (2019). Effective connectivity changes in LSD-induced altered states of consciousness in humans. Proceedings of the National Academy of Sciences of the United States of America, 116(7), 2743–2748

3. Lord, L. D., Expert, P., Atasoy, S., Roseman, L., Rapuano, K., Lambiotte, R., Nutt, D. J., Deco, G., Carhart-Harris, R. L., Kringelbach, M. L., & Cabral, J. (2019). Dynamical exploration of the repertoire of brain networks at rest is modulated by psilocybin. NeuroImage, 199, 127–142

4. Jones, S. R., Pinto, D. J., Kaper, T. J., & Kopell, N. (2000). Alpha-frequency rhythms desynchronize over long cortical distances: a modeling study. Journal of computational neuroscience, 9(3), 271–291; Moreau, A. W., Amar, M., Le Roux, N., Morel, N., & Fossier, P. (2010). Serotoninergic fine-tuning of the excitation-inhibition balance in rat visual cortical networks. Cerebral cortex (New York, N.Y. : 1991), 20(2), 456–467

5. Santana, N., Bortolozzi, A., Serrats, J., Mengod, G., & Artigas, F. (2004). Expression of serotonin1A and serotonin2A receptors in pyramidal and GABAergic neurons of the rat prefrontal cortex. Cerebral cortex (New York, N.Y. : 1991), 14(10), 1100–1109

6. Carhart-Harris, R. L., Erritzoe, D., Williams, T., Stone, J. M., Reed, L. J., Colasanti, A., Tyacke, R. J., Leech, R., Malizia, A. L., Murphy, K., Hobden, P., Evans, J., Feilding, A., Wise, R. G., & Nutt, D. J. (2012). Neural correlates of the psychedelic state as determined by fMRI studies with psilocybin. Proceedings of the National Academy of Sciences of the United States of America, 109(6), 2138–2143; Celada, P., Puig, M. V., Díaz-Mataix, L., & Artigas, F. (2008). The hallucinogen DOI reduces low-frequency oscillations in rat prefrontal cortex: reversal by antipsychotic drugs. Biological psychiatry, 64(5), 392–400; Carhart-Harris, R. L., Erritzoe, D., Williams, T., Stone, J. M., Reed, L. J., Colasanti, A., Tyacke, R. J., Leech, R., Malizia, A. L., Murphy, K., Hobden, P., Evans, J., Feilding, A., Wise, R. G., & Nutt, D. J. (2012). Neural correlates of the psychedelic state as determined by fMRI studies with psilocybin. Proceedings of the National Academy of Sciences of the United States of America, 109(6), 2138–2143; Muthukumaras-

wamy, S. D., Carhart-Harris, R. L., Moran, R. J., Brookes, M. J., Williams, T. M., Errtizoe, D., Sessa, B., Papadopoulos, A., Bolstridge, M., Singh, K. D., Feilding, A., Friston, K. J., & Nutt, D. J. (2013). Broadband cortical desynchronization underlies the human psychedelic state. The Journal of neuroscience : the official journal of the Society for Neuroscience, 33(38), 15171–15183

7. Kometer, M., Schmidt, A., Jäncke, L., & Vollenweider, F. X. (2013). Activation of serotonin 2A receptors underlies the psilocybin-induced effects on ⏃ oscillations, N170 visual-evoked potentials, and visual hallucinations. The Journal of neuroscience : the official journal of the Society for Neuroscience, 33(25), 10544–10551

8. Carhart-Harris, R. L., & Friston, K. J. (2019). REBUS and the Anarchic Brain: Toward a Unified Model of the Brain Action of Psychedelics. Pharmacological reviews, 71(3), 316–344

9. Huxely, A. (2004). The Doors of Perception: And Heaven and Hell, Vintage Classics.

10. Shulgin, A., Shulgin, A. (1991), PIHKAL: A Chemical Love Story. Transform Press.

11. Hickok, G., & Poeppel, D. (2007). The cortical organization of speech processing. Nature reviews. Neuroscience, 8(5), 393–402

12. Qin, P. M., and Northoff, G. (2011). How is our self related to midline regions and the default-mode network? Neuroimage 57, 1221–1233. doi: 10.1016/j.neuroimage.2011.05.028

13. Fox, M. D., Snyder, A. Z., Vincent, J. L., Corbetta, M., Van Essen, D. C., & Raichle, M. E. (2005). The human brain is intrinsically organized into dynamic, anticorrelated functional networks. Proceedings of the National Academy of Sciences of the United States of America, 102(27), 9673–9678

14. Rizzolatti, G., Semi, A. A., & Fabbri-Destro, M. (2014). Linking psychoanalysis with neuroscience: the concept of ego. Neuropsychologia, 55, 143–148; Di Plinio, S., Perrucci, M. G., Aleman, A., & Ebisch, S. (2020). I am Me: Brain systems integrate and segregate to establish a multidimensional sense of self. NeuroImage, 205, 116284; Smigielski, L., Scheidegger, M., Kometer, M., & Vollenweider, F. X. (2019). Psilocybin-assisted mindfulness training modulates self-consciousness and brain default mode network connectivity with lasting effects. NeuroImage, 196, 207–215

15. Letheby, C., & Gerrans, P. (2017). Self unbound: ego dissolution in psychedelic experience. Neuroscience of consciousness, 2017(1), nix016; Tagliazucchi, E., Roseman, L., Kaelen, M., Orban, C., Muthukumaraswamy, S. D., Murphy, K., Laufs, H., Leech, R., McGonigle, J., Crossley, N., Bullmore, E., Williams, T., Bolstridge, M., Feilding, A., Nutt, D. J., & Carhart-Harris, R. (2016). Increased Global Functional Connectivity Correlates with LSD-Induced Ego Dissolution. Current biology : CB, 26(8), 1043–1050; Lebedev, A. V., Lövdén, M., Rosenthal, G., Feilding, A., Nutt, D. J., & Carhart-Harris, R. L. (2015). Finding the self by losing the self: Neural correlates of ego-dissolution under psilocybin. Human brain mapping, 36(8), 3137–3153
16. Preller, K. H., & Vollenweider, F. X. (2018). Phenomenology, Structure, and Dynamic of Psychedelic States. Current topics in behavioral neurosciences, 36, 221–256

Chapter 10.

1. Szára S. (1957). The comparison of the psychotic effect of tryptamine derivatives with the effects of mescaline and LSD-25 in self-experiments. In Psychotropic Drugs. Ed. by S. Garattini & V. Ghetti. Elsevier; Szara, S. (1989). The social chemistry of discovery – the DMT story. Social Pharmacology 3, 237-248; Szára S. (2007). DMT at fifty. Neuropsychopharmacologia Hungarica : a Magyar Pszichofarmakologiai Egyesulet lapja = official journal of the Hungarian Association of Psychopharmacology, 9(4), 201–205
2. Gallimore, A.R., Luke, D.P. (2015). DMT Research from 1956 to the Edge of Time. Neurotransmissions – An Anthology of Essays on Psychedelics from Breaking Convention. Strange Attractor Press
3. Sai-Halasz, A., Brunecker, G., Szara, S. (1958). Dimethyltryptamine: a new psycho-active drug. Psychiatria et neurologia, 135(4-5), 285–301
4. Leary, T. (1966). Programmed Communication During Experiences With DMT. Psychedelic Review, 8
5. St. John, G. (2016). When Terence McKenna First Smoked DMT, https://chacruna.net/terence-mckenna-first-smoked-dmt/
6. Schultes 1954; Agurell, S., Holmstedt, B., Lindgren, J. E., &

Schultes, R. E. (1969). Alkaloids in certain species of Virola and other South American plants of ethnopharmacologic interest. Acta chemica Scandinavica, 23(3), 903–916

7. Rätsch, C. (1998). The Encyclopedia of Psychoactive Plants: Ethnopharmacology and Its Applications. Park Street Press; Buchanan, M. S., Carroll, A. R., Pass, D., & Quinn, R. J. (2007). NMR spectral assignments of a new chlorotryptamine alkaloid and its analogues from Acacia confusa. Magnetic resonance in chemistry : MRC, 45(4), 359–361

8. Davis, A. K., Barsuglia, J. P., Lancelotta, R., Grant, R. M., & Renn, E. (2018). The epidemiology of 5-methoxy- N, N-dimethyltryptamine (5-MeO-DMT) use: Benefits, consequences, patterns of use, subjective effects, and reasons for consumption. Journal of psychopharmacology (Oxford, England), 32(7), 779–792; Uthaug, M. V., Lancelotta, R., van Oorsouw, K., Kuypers, K., Mason, N., Rak, J., Šuláková, A., Jurok, R., Maryška, M., Kuchař, M., Páleníček, T., Riba, J., & Ramaekers, J. G. (2019). A single inhalation of vapor from dried toad secretion containing 5-methoxy-N,N-dimethyltryptamine (5-MeO-DMT) in a naturalistic setting is related to sustained enhancement of satisfaction with life, mindfulness-related capacities, and a decrement of psychopathological symptoms. Psychopharmacology, 236(9), 2653–2666

9. Halberstadt, A. L., & Geyer, M. A. (2011). Multiple receptors contribute to the behavioral effects of indoleamine hallucinogens. Neuropharmacology, 61(3), 364–381; Smith, R. L., Canton, H., Barrett, R. J., & Sanders-Bush, E. (1998). Agonist properties of N,N-dimethyltryptamine at serotonin 5-HT2A and 5-HT2C receptors. Pharmacology, biochemistry, and behavior, 61(3), 323–330

10. Deliganis, A. V., Pierce, P. A., & Peroutka, S. J. (1991). Differential interactions of dimethyltryptamine (DMT) with 5-HT1A and 5-HT2 receptors. Biochemical pharmacology, 41(11), 1739–1744

11. Gallimore, A. R. (2013). Building alien worlds - the neuropsychological and evolutionary implications of the Astonishing Psychoactive Effects of N,N- Dimethyltryptamine (DMT). J. Sci. Explor. 27, 455–503; Luke, D. (2011). Discarnate entities and dimethyltryptamine (DMT): Psychopharmacology, phenomenology and ontology. J. Soc. Psychical Res. 75, 26–42; Strassman, R. (2001). DMT - The Spirit Molecule. Vermont, VT: Park Street Press

12. Meyer, P. (1997). Apparent Communication with Discarnate Entities Induced by Dimethyltryptamine (DMT). http://www.serendipity.li/dmt/dmtart00.html; Meyer, P., Pup (2005). 340 DMT Trip Reports. http://www.serendipity.li/dmt/340_dmt_trip_reports.htm

13. Shulgin, A., Shulgin, A. (2002). TIHKAL: The Continuation. Transform Press.

14. Luppi, A. I., Carhart-Harris, R. L., Roseman, L., Pappas, I., Menon, D. K., & Stamatakis, E. A. (2021). LSD alters dynamic integration and segregation in the human brain. NeuroImage, 227, 117653

15. Tagliazucchi, E., Carhart-Harris, R., Leech, R., Nutt, D., & Chialvo, D. R. (2014). Enhanced repertoire of brain dynamical states during the psychedelic experience. Human brain mapping, 35(11), 5442–5456

16. Lioni, A., & Deneubourg, J. L. (2004). Collective decision through self-assembling. Die Naturwissenschaften, 91(5), 237–241

17. Ichimura, T., Uemoto, T., Hara, A., & Mackin, K. J. (2014). Emergence of altruism behavior in army ant-based social evolutionary system. SpringerPlus, 3, 712

18. Akrami, A., Russo, E., & Treves, A. (2012). Lateral thinking, from the Hopfield model to cortical dynamics. Brain research, 1434, 4–16; Tang, H., Li, H., & Yan, R. (2010). Memory dynamics in attractor networks with saliency weights. Neural computation, 22(7), 1899–1926; Yang, X. S., & Huang, Y. (2006). Complex dynamics in simple Hopfield neural networks. Chaos (Woodbury, N.Y.), 16(3), 033114

19. Urban, J. D., Clarke, W. P., von Zastrow, M., Nichols, D. E., Kobilka, B., Weinstein, H., Javitch, J. A., Roth, B. L., Christopoulos, A., Sexton, P. M., Miller, K. J., Spedding, M., & Mailman, R. B. (2007). Functional selectivity and classical concepts of quantitative pharmacology. The Journal of pharmacology and experimental therapeutics, 320(1), 1–13; Backstrom, J. R., Chang, M. S., Chu, H., Niswender, C. M., & Sanders-Bush, E. (1999). Agonist-directed signaling of serotonin 5-HT2C receptors: differences between serotonin and lysergic acid diethylamide (LSD). Neuropsychopharmacology : official publication of the American College of

Neuropsychopharmacology, 21(2 Suppl), 77S–81S; Schmid, C. L., Raehal, K. M., & Bohn, L. M. (2008). Agonist-directed signaling of the serotonin 2A receptor depends on beta-arrestin-2 interactions in vivo. Proceedings of the National Academy of Sciences of the United States of America, 105(3), 1079–1084

20. Martin, D. A., & Nichols, C. D. (2016). Psychedelics Recruit Multiple Cellular Types and Produce Complex Transcriptional Responses Within the Brain. EBioMedicine, 11, 262–277

21. Pallavicini, C., Vilas, M. G., Villarreal, M., Zamberlan, F., Muthukumaraswamy, S., Nutt, D., Carhart-Harris, R., & Tagliazucchi, E. (2019). Spectral signatures of serotonergic psychedelics and glutamatergic dissociatives. NeuroImage, 200, 281–291

22. Alamia, A., Timmermann, C., Nutt, D. J., VanRullen, R., & Carhart-Harris, R. L. (2020). DMT alters cortical travelling waves. eLife, 9, e59784

23. Bressloff, P. C., Cowan, J. D., Golubitsky, M., Thomas, P. J., & Wiener, M. C. (2002). What geometric visual hallucinations tell us about the visual cortex. Neural computation, 14(3), 473–491

24. Carhart-Harris, R., & Nutt, D. (2014). Was it a vision or a waking dream?. Frontiers in psychology, 5, 255

Chapter 11.

1. Fodor, G., & Dharanipragada, R. (1991). Tropane alkaloids. Natural product reports, 8(6), 603–612

2. Smulyan H. (2018). The Beat Goes On: The Story of Five Ageless Cardiac Drugs. The American journal of the medical sciences, 356(5), 441–450

3. Pearn, J., & Thearle, J. (1982). The history of hyoscine. Histoire des sciences medicales, 17(Spec 2), 257–261; Kohnen-Johannsen, K. L., & Kayser, O. (2019). Tropane Alkaloids: Chemistry, Pharmacology, Biosynthesis and Production. Molecules (Basel, Switzerland), 24(4), 796

4. Müller J. L. (1998). Love potions and the ointment of witches: historical aspects of the nightshade alkaloids. Journal of toxicology. Clinical toxicology, 36(6), 617–627

5. Schultes, 1992, Plants of the Gods

6. Lakstygal, A. M., Kolesnikova, T. O., Khatsko, S. L., Zabegalov, K.

N., Volgin, A. D., Demin, K. A., Shevyrin, V. A., Wappler-Guzzetta, E. A., & Kalueff, A. V. (2019). DARK Classics in Chemical Neuroscience: Atropine, Scopolamine, and Other Anticholinergic Deliriant Hallucinogens. ACS chemical neuroscience, 10(5), 2144–2159

7. Müller, J., & Wanke, K. (1998). Intoxikationspsychosen durch Atropin und Skopolamin (Toxic psychoses from atropine and scopolamine). Fortschritte der Neurologie-Psychiatrie, 66(7), 289–295

8. Erowid, Tropane Alkaloids and Phantom Smoking: An unusual reported effect of Datura, Brugmansia, and Belladonna, v1.0 - Nov 27, 2008

9. Neri P. (2010). How inherently noisy is human sensory processing?. Psychonomic bulletin & review, 17(6), 802–808

10. Faisal, A. A., Selen, L. P., & Wolpert, D. M. (2008). Noise in the nervous system. Nature reviews. Neuroscience, 9(4), 292–303

11. Kanai, R., Komura, Y., Shipp, S., & Friston, K. (2015). Cerebral hierarchies: predictive processing, precision and the pulvinar. Philosophical transactions of the Royal Society of London. Series B, Biological sciences, 370(1668), 20140169

12. Feldman, H., & Friston, K. J. (2010). Attention, uncertainty, and free-energy. Frontiers in human neuroscience, 4, 215

13. Friston K. (2009). The free-energy principle: a rough guide to the brain?. Trends in cognitive sciences, 13(7), 293–301; Hohwy J. (2012). Attention and conscious perception in the hypothesis testing brain. Frontiers in psychology, 3, 96

14. Wohleb, E. S., Gerhard, D., Thomas, A., & Duman, R. S. (2017). Molecular and Cellular Mechanisms of Rapid-Acting Antidepressants Ketamine and Scopolamine. Current neuropharmacology, 15(1), 11–20

15. Ishii, M., & Kurachi, Y. (2006). Muscarinic acetylcholine receptors. Current pharmaceutical design, 12(28), 3573–3581

16. Langmead, C. J., Watson, J., & Reavill, C. (2008). Muscarinic acetylcholine receptors as CNS drug targets. Pharmacology & therapeutics, 117(2), 232–243

17. Brown D. A. (2018). Regulation of neural ion channels by muscarinic receptors. Neuropharmacology, 136(Pt C), 383–400

18. Chemin, J., Patel, A. J., Duprat, F., Lauritzen, I., Lazdunski, M., & Honoré, E. (2005). A phospholipid sensor controls mechanogat-

ing of the K+ channel TREK-1. The EMBO journal, 24(1), 44–53

19. Bista, P., Pawlowski, M., Cerina, M., Ehling, P., Leist, M., Meuth, P., Aissaoui, A., Borsotto, M., Heurteaux, C., Decher, N., Pape, H. C., Oliver, D., Meuth, S. G., & Budde, T. (2015). Differential phospholipase C-dependent modulation of TASK and TREK two-pore domain K+ channels in rat thalamocortical relay neurons. The Journal of physiology, 593(1), 127–144; Rivas-Ramírez, P., Cadaveira-Mosquera, A., Lamas, J. A., & Reboreda, A. (2015). Muscarinic modulation of TREK currents in mouse sympathetic superior cervical ganglion neurons. The European journal of neuroscience, 42(2), 1797–1807

20. Brown, D. A., & Adams, P. R. (1980). Muscarinic suppression of a novel voltage-sensitive K+ current in a vertebrate neurone. Nature, 283(5748), 673–676; Wang, Z., & McCormick, D. A. (1993). Control of firing mode of corticotectal and corticopontine layer V burst-generating neurons by norepinephrine, acetylcholine, and 1S,3R-ACPD. The Journal of neuroscience : the official journal of the Society for Neuroscience, 13(5), 2199–2216

21. Ballinger, E. C., Ananth, M., Talmage, D. A., & Role, L. W. (2016). Basal Forebrain Cholinergic Circuits and Signaling in Cognition and Cognitive Decline. Neuron, 91(6), 1199–1218; Vazquez, J., & Baghdoyan, H. A. (2001). Basal forebrain acetylcholine release during REM sleep is significantly greater than during waking. American journal of physiology. Regulatory, integrative and comparative physiology, 280(2), R598–R601

22. Moran, R. J., Campo, P., Symmonds, M., Stephan, K. E., Dolan, R. J., & Friston, K. J. (2013). Free energy, precision and learning: the role of cholinergic neuromodulation. The Journal of neuroscience : the official journal of the Society for Neuroscience, 33(19), 8227–8236; Gu 2003; Groleau 2015

23. Hasselmo, M. E., & McGaughy, J. (2004). High acetylcholine levels set circuit dynamics for attention and encoding and low acetylcholine levels set dynamics for consolidation. Progress in brain research, 145, 207–231; Yu, A. J., & Dayan, P. (2002). Acetylcholine in cortical inference. Neural networks : the official journal of the International Neural Network Society, 15(4-6), 719–730; Groleau, M., Kang, J. I., Huppé-Gourgues, F., & Vaucher, E. (2015). Distribution and effects of the muscarinic receptor subtypes in

the primary visual cortex. Frontiers in synaptic neuroscience, 7, 10

24. Börgers, C., Epstein, S., & Kopell, N. J. (2005). Background gamma rhythmicity and attention in cortical local circuits: a computational study. Proceedings of the National Academy of Sciences of the United States of America, 102(19), 7002–7007; Fisahn, A., Pike, F. G., Buhl, E. H., & Paulsen, O. (1998). Cholinergic induction of network oscillations at 40 Hz in the hippocampus in vitro. Nature, 394(6689), 186–189; Fisahn, A., Pike, F. G., Buhl, E. H., & Paulsen, O. (1998). Cholinergic induction of network oscillations at 40 Hz in the hippocampus in vitro. Nature, 394(6689), 186–189

25. Behrends, J. C., & ten Bruggencate, G. (1993). Cholinergic modulation of synaptic inhibition in the guinea pig hippocampus in vitro: excitation of GABAergic interneurons and inhibition of GABA-release. Journal of neurophysiology, 69(2), 626–629; Hasselmo 2004; Pitler, T. A., & Alger, B. E. (1992). Cholinergic excitation of GABAergic interneurons in the rat hippocampal slice. The Journal of physiology, 450, 127–142

26. Cheng, K., Khurana, S., Chen, Y., Kennedy, R. H., Zimniak, P., & Raufman, J. P. (2002). Lithocholylcholine, a bile acid/acetylcholine hybrid, is a muscarinic receptor antagonist. The Journal of pharmacology and experimental therapeutics, 303(1), 29–35

27. Fletcher, P. C., & Frith, C. D. (2009). Perceiving is believing: a Bayesian approach to explaining the positive symptoms of schizophrenia. Nature reviews. Neuroscience, 10(1), 48–58; Perry, E. K., & Perry, R. H. (1995). Acetylcholine and hallucinations: disease-related compared to drug-induced alterations in human consciousness. Brain and cognition, 28(3), 240–258

28. Erowid Experience Vaults, Exp. 93015, https://erowid.org/experiences/exp.php?ID=93015

29. Erowid Experience Vaults, Exp. 67153, https://erowid.org/experiences/exp.php?ID=67153

30. Erowid Experience Vaults, Exp. 88479, https://erowid.org/experiences/exp.php?ID=88479

31. Erowid Experience Vaults, Exp. 16996, https://erowid.org/experiences/exp.php?ID=16996

32. Kanamaru, T., Fujii, H., & Aihara, K. (2013). Deformation of

attractor landscape via cholinergic presynaptic modulations: a computational study using a phase neuron model. PloS one, 8(1), e53854

Chapter 12.

1. Maddox V. H. (1980). The discovery of phencyclidine. Psychopharmacology bulletin, 16(4), 53–54; Maddox, V. H., Godefroi, E. F., & Parcell, R. F. (1965). The Synthesis Of Phencyclidine And Other 1-Arylcyclohexylamines. Journal of medicinal chemistry, 8, 230–235

2. Domino E. F. (2010). Taming the ketamine tiger. 1965. Anesthesiology, 113(3), 678–684; Meyer J.S., Greifenstein F., Devault M. (1959). A new drug causing symptoms of sensory deprivation. J Nervous & Mental Disorders, 129, 54–61

3. Johnstone, M., Evans, V., & Baigel, S. (1959). Sernyl (CI-395) in clinical anaesthesia. British journal of anaesthesia, 31, 433–439

4. Domino, E. F., & Luby, E. D. (2012). Phencyclidine/schizophrenia: one view toward the past, the other to the future. Schizophrenia bulletin, 38(5), 914–919

5. Krystal, J. H., Karper, L. P., Seibyl, J. P., Freeman, G. K., Delaney, R., Bremner, J. D., Heninger, G. R., Bowers, M. B., Jr, & Charney, D. S. (1994). Subanesthetic effects of the noncompetitive NMDA antagonist, ketamine, in humans. Psychotomimetic, perceptual, cognitive, and neuroendocrine responses. Archives of general psychiatry, 51(3), 199–214; Gouzoulis-Mayfrank, E., Heekeren, K., Neukirch, A., Stoll, M., Stock, C., Obradovic, M., & Kovar, K. A. (2005). Psychological effects of (S)-ketamine and N,N-dimethyltryptamine (DMT): a double-blind, cross-over study in healthy volunteers. Pharmacopsychiatry, 38(6), 301–311

6. Seeman, P., Ko, F., & Tallerico, T. (2005). Dopamine receptor contribution to the action of PCP, LSD and ketamine psychotomimetics. Molecular psychiatry, 10(9), 877–883

7. Johnson, J. W., & Ascher, P. (1990). Voltage-dependent block by intracellular Mg2+ of N-methyl-D-aspartate-activated channels. Biophysical journal, 57(5), 1085–1090

8. Self, M. W., Kooijmans, R. N., Supèr, H., Lamme, V. A., & Roelfsema, P. R. (2012). Different glutamate receptors convey feedforward and recurrent processing in macaque V1. Proceedings of

the National Academy of Sciences of the United States of America, 109(27), 11031–11036

9. Daw, N. W., Stein, P. S., & Fox, K. (1993). The role of NMDA receptors in information processing. Annual review of neuroscience, 16, 207–222

10. Khorsand, P., Moore, T., & Soltani, A. (2015). Combined contributions of feedforward and feedback inputs to bottom-up attention. Frontiers in psychology, 6, 155; Le Roux, N., Cabezas, C., Böhm, U. L., & Poncer, J. C. (2013). Input-specific learning rules at excitatory synapses onto hippocampal parvalbumin-expressing interneurons. The Journal of physiology, 591(7), 1809–1822; Garrido, M. I., Kilner, J. M., Kiebel, S. J., & Friston, K. J. (2007). Evoked brain responses are generated by feedback loops. Proceedings of the National Academy of Sciences of the United States of America, 104(52), 20961–20966; Salin, P. A., & Bullier, J. (1995). Corticocortical connections in the visual system: structure and function. Physiological reviews, 75(1), 107–154). NMDA receptors embedded in superficial layer dendrites receive these predictions from the deep pyramidal cells in the cortical level above (Larkum, M. E., Nevian, T., Sandler, M., Polsky, A., & Schiller, J. (2009). Synaptic integration in tuft dendrites of layer 5 pyramidal neurons: a new unifying principle. Science (New York, N.Y.), 325(5941), 756–760

11. Rotaru, D. C., Yoshino, H., Lewis, D. A., Ermentrout, G. B., & Gonzalez-Burgos, G. (2011). Glutamate receptor subtypes mediating synaptic activation of prefrontal cortex neurons: relevance for schizophrenia. The Journal of neuroscience : the official journal of the Society for Neuroscience, 31(1), 142–156

12. Silva, L. R., Amitai, Y., & Connors, B. W. (1991). Intrinsic oscillations of neocortex generated by layer 5 pyramidal neurons. Science (New York, N.Y.), 251(4992), 432–435

13. Eyal, G., Verhoog, M. B., Testa-Silva, G., Deitcher, Y., Benavides-Piccione, R., DeFelipe, J., de Kock, C., Mansvelder, H. D., & Segev, I. (2018). Human Cortical Pyramidal Neurons: From Spines to Spikes via Models. Frontiers in cellular neuroscience, 12, 181

14. Cornford JH, Mercier MS, Leite M, Magloire V, Häusser M, Kullmann DM. Dendritic NMDA receptors in parvalbumin neu-

rons enable strong and stable neuronal assemblies. Elife. 2019 Oct 28;8:e49872

15. Anis, N. A., Berry, S. C., Burton, N. R., & Lodge, D. (1983). The dissociative anaesthetics, ketamine and phencyclidine, selectively reduce excitation of central mammalian neurones by N-methyl-aspartate. British journal of pharmacology, 79(2), 565–575; Martin, D., & Lodge, D. (1985). Ketamine acts as a non-competitive N-methyl-D-aspartate antagonist on frog spinal cord in vitro. Neuropharmacology, 24(10), 999–1003; Lodge, D., & Johnson, K. M. (1990). Noncompetitive excitatory amino acid receptor antagonists. Trends in pharmacological sciences, 11(2), 81–86

16. Homayoun, H., & Moghaddam, B. (2007). NMDA receptor hypofunction produces opposite effects on prefrontal cortex interneurons and pyramidal neurons. The Journal of neuroscience : the official journal of the Society for Neuroscience, 27(43), 11496–11500

17. Di Lazzaro, V., Oliviero, A., Profice, P., Pennisi, M. A., Pilato, F., Zito, G., Dileone, M., Nicoletti, R., Pasqualetti, P., & Tonali, P. A. (2003). Ketamine increases human motor cortex excitability to transcranial magnetic stimulation. The Journal of physiology, 547(Pt 2), 485–496

18. McMillan, R., & Muthukumaraswamy, S. D. (2020). The neurophysiology of ketamine: an integrative review. Reviews in the neurosciences, 31(5), 457–503

19. van Loon, A. M., Fahrenfort, J. J., van der Velde, B., Lirk, P. B., Vulink, N. C., Hollmann, M. W., Scholte, H. S., & Lamme, V. A. (2016). NMDA Receptor Antagonist Ketamine Distorts Object Recognition by Reducing Feedback to Early Visual Cortex. Cerebral cortex (New York, N.Y. : 1991), 26(5), 1986–1996

20. Erowid Experience Vaults, Exp. 99510, https://erowid.org/experiences/exp.php?ID=99510

21. Schroeder, K. E., Irwin, Z. T., Gaidica, M., Nicole Bentley, J., Patil, P. G., Mashour, G. A., & Chestek, C. A. (2016). Disruption of corticocortical information transfer during ketamine anesthesia in the primate brain. NeuroImage, 134, 459–465; McMillan, R., & Muthukumaraswamy, S. D. (2020). The neurophysiology of ketamine: an integrative review. Reviews in the neurosciences, 31(5), 457–503

22. Pomarol-Clotet, E., Honey, G. D., Murray, G. K., Corlett, P. R., Absalom, A. R., Lee, M., McKenna, P. J., Bullmore, E. T., & Fletcher, P. C. (2006). Psychological effects of ketamine in healthy volunteers. Phenomenological study. The British journal of psychiatry : the journal of mental science, 189, 173–179; Powers, A. R., 3rd, Gancsos, M. G., Finn, E. S., Morgan, P. T., & Corlett, P. R. (2015). Ketamine-Induced Hallucinations. Psychopathology, 48(6), 376–385; Sumner, R. L., McMillan, R., Spriggs, M. J., Campbell, D., Malpas, G., Maxwell, E., Deng, C., Hay, J., Ponton, R., Sundram, F., & Muthukumaraswamy, S. D. (2020). Ketamine improves short-term plasticity in depression by enhancing sensitivity to prediction errors. European neuropsychopharmacology : the journal of the European College of Neuropsychopharmacology, 38, 73–85; Corlett, P. R., Frith, C. D., & Fletcher, P. C. (2009). From drugs to deprivation: a Bayesian framework for understanding models of psychosis. Psychopharmacology, 206(4), 515–530; Sterzer, P., Adams, R. A., Fletcher, P., Frith, C., Lawrie, S. M., Muckli, L., Petrovic, P., Uhlhaas, P., Voss, M., & Corlett, P. R. (2018). The Predictive Coding Account of Psychosis. Biological psychiatry, 84(9), 634–643; Bonhomme, V., Vanhaudenhuyse, A., Demertzi, A., Bruno, M. A., Jaquet, O., Bahri, M. A., Plenevaux, A., Boly, M., Boveroux, P., Soddu, A., Brichant, J. F., Maquet, P., & Laureys, S. (2016). Resting-state Network-specific Breakdown of Functional Connectivity during Ketamine Alteration of Consciousness in Volunteers. Anesthesiology, 125(5), 873–888

23. Erowid Experience Vaults, Exp. 78894, https://erowid.org/experiences/exp.php?ID=78894

24. Erowid Experience Vaults, Exp. 67104, https://erowid.org/experiences/exp.php?ID=67104

25. Johnson, K. M., & Jones, S. M. (1990). Neuropharmacology of phencyclidine: basic mechanisms and therapeutic potential. Annual review of pharmacology and toxicology, 30, 707–750

26. Bey, T., & Patel, A. (2007). Phencyclidine intoxication and adverse effects: a clinical and pharmacological review of an illicit drug. The California journal of emergency medicine, 8(1), 9–14

27. Geberth, Vernon J. Practical Homicide Investigation: Tactics, Procedures, and Forensic Techniques 4th Edition, 2006 Boca Raton, FL CRC Press, LLC, Taylor & Francis

28. Huettner, J. E., & Bean, B. P. (1988). Block of N-methyl-D-aspartate-activated current by the anticonvulsant MK-801: selective binding to open channels. Proceedings of the National Academy of Sciences of the United States of America, 85(4), 1307–1311; Lodge, D., & Johnson, K. M. (1990). Noncompetitive excitatory amino acid receptor antagonists. Trends in pharmacological sciences, 11(2), 81–86

29. Li, D., & Mashour, G. A. (2019). Cortical dynamics during psychedelic and anesthetized states induced by ketamine. NeuroImage, 196, 32–40; Akeju, O., Song, A. H., Hamilos, A. E., Pavone, K. J., Flores, F. J., Brown, E. N., & Purdon, P. L. (2016). Electroencephalogram signatures of ketamine anesthesia-induced unconsciousness. Clinical neurophysiology : official journal of the International Federation of Clinical Neurophysiology, 127(6), 2414–2422; Sarasso, S., Boly, M., Napolitani, M., Gosseries, O., Charland-Verville, V., Casarotto, S., Rosanova, M., Casali, A. G., Brichant, J. F., Boveroux, P., Rex, S., Tononi, G., Laureys, S., & Massimini, M. (2015). Consciousness and Complexity during Unresponsiveness Induced by Propofol, Xenon, and Ketamine. Current biology : CB, 25(23), 3099–3105

30. Schartner, M. M., Carhart-Harris, R. L., Barrett, A. B., Seth, A. K., & Muthukumaraswamy, S. D. (2017). Increased spontaneous MEG signal diversity for psychoactive doses of ketamine, LSD and psilocybin. Scientific reports, 7, 46421

31. Schartner, M. M., Carhart-Harris, R. L., Barrett, A. B., Seth, A. K., & Muthukumaraswamy, S. D. (2017). Increased spontaneous MEG signal diversity for psychoactive doses of ketamine, LSD and psilocybin. Scientific reports, 7, 46421

32. Schartner, M., Seth, A., Noirhomme, Q., Boly, M., Bruno, M. A., Laureys, S., & Barrett, A. (2015). Complexity of Multi-Dimensional Spontaneous EEG Decreases during Propofol Induced General Anaesthesia. PloS one, 10(8), e0133532

33. Nicol, A. U., & Morton, A. J. (2020). Characteristic patterns of EEG oscillations in sheep (Ovis aries) induced by ketamine may explain the psychotropic effects seen in humans. Scientific reports, 10(1), 9440

34. Lilly, J.C. (1996). The Scientist: A Metaphysical Autobiography. Ronin Publishing.

35. Leslie, K., Skrzypek, H., Paech, M. J., Kurowski, I., & Whybrow, T. (2007). Dreaming during anesthesia and anesthetic depth in elective surgery patients: a prospective cohort study. Anesthesiology, 106(1), 33–42

Chapter 13.

1. Wasson, R. (1962). A New Mexican Psychotropic Drug From The Mint Family. Botanical Museum Leaflets, Harvard University, 20(3), 77-84

2. Ortega, A., Blount, J.F., Manchand, P.S., (1982). Salvinorin, a new trans-neoclerodane diterpene from Salvia divinorum(Labiatae), J. Chem. Soc., Perkin Trans. 1, 2505-2508; Valdes, L.J., Butler, W.M., Hatfield, G.M., Paul, A.G., Koreeda, M. (1984). Divinorin A, a psychotropic terpenoid, and divinorin B from the hallucinogenic Mexican mint, Salvia divinorum, The Journal of Organic Chemistry, 49(24), 4716-4720

3. Valdés L. J., 3rd (1994). Salvia divinorum and the unique diterpene hallucinogen, Salvinorin (divinorin) A. Journal of psychoactive drugs, 26(3), 277–283

4. Pelot, K. A., Mitchell, R., Kwon, M., Hagelthorn, L. M., Wardman, J. F., Chiang, A., Bohlmann, J., Ro, D. K., & Zerbe, P. (2017). Biosynthesis of the psychotropic plant diterpene salvinorin A: Discovery and characterization of the Salvia divinorum clerodienyl diphosphate synthase. The Plant journal : for cell and molecular biology, 89(5), 885–897; Kutrzeba, L., Dayan, F. E., Howell, J., Feng, J., Giner, J. L., & Zjawiony, J. K. (2007). Biosynthesis of salvinorin A proceeds via the deoxyxylulose phosphate pathway. Phytochemistry, 68(14), 1872–1881

5. Siebert D. J. (1994). Salvia divinorum and salvinorin A: new pharmacologic findings. Journal of ethnopharmacology, 43(1), 53–56

6. Siebert, D.J. (1993). Salvinorin A: The Breakthrough. www.sagewisdom.org/salvexpe.html

7. Baggott, M. J., Erowid, E., Erowid, F., Galloway, G. P., & Mendelson, J. (2010). Use patterns and self-reported effects of Salvia divinorum: an internet-based survey. Drug and alcohol dependence, 111(3), 250–256

8. Brown, S. P., Mathur, B. N., Olsen, S. R., Luppi, P. H., Bickford, M. E., & Citri, A. (2017). New Breakthroughs in Understanding the Role of Functional Interactions between the Neocortex and the Claustrum. The Journal of neuroscience : the official journal of the Society for Neuroscience, 37(45), 10877–10881

9. Jackson, J., Karnani, M. M., Zemelman, B. V., Burdakov, D., & Lee, A. K. (2018). Inhibitory Control of Prefrontal Cortex by the Claustrum. Neuron, 99(5), 1029–1039.e4

10. Koubeissi, M. Z., Bartolomei, F., Beltagy, A., & Picard, F. (2014). Electrical stimulation of a small brain area reversibly disrupts consciousness. Epilepsy & behavior : E&B, 37, 32–35

11. Mathur B. N. (2014). The claustrum in review. Frontiers in systems neuroscience, 8, 48

12. Smythies, J., Edelstein, L., & Ramachandran, V. (2012). Hypotheses relating to the function of the claustrum. Frontiers in integrative neuroscience, 6, 53

13. Gómez-Urquijo, S. M., Gutiérrez-Ibarluzea, I., Bueno-López, J. L., & Reblet, C. (2000). Percentage incidence of gamma-aminobutyric acid neurons in the claustrum of the rabbit and comparison with the cortex and putamen. Neuroscience letters, 282(3), 177–180

14. Smith, J. B., & Alloway, K. D. (2010). Functional specificity of claustrum connections in the rat: interhemispheric communication between specific parts of motor cortex. The Journal of neuroscience : the official journal of the Society for Neuroscience, 30(50), 16832–16844; Smith, J. B., & Alloway, K. D. (2014). Interhemispheric claustral circuits coordinate sensory and motor cortical areas that regulate exploratory behaviors. Frontiers in systems neuroscience, 8, 93; Dillingham CM, Jankowski MM, Chandra R, Frost BE, O'Mara SM. The claustrum: Considerations regarding its anatomy, functions and a programme for research. Brain Neurosci Adv. 2017 Jul 13;1:2398212817718962

15. Kim, J., Matney, C. J., Roth, R. H., & Brown, S. P. (2016). Synaptic Organization of the Neuronal Circuits of the Claustrum. The Journal of neuroscience : the official journal of the Society for Neuroscience, 36(3), 773–784

16. Bruno R. M. (2011). Synchrony in sensation. Current opinion in neurobiology, 21(5), 701–708; Milo, R., Shen-Orr, S., Itzkovitz,

S., Kashtan, N., Chklovskii, D., & Alon, U. (2002). Network motifs: simple building blocks of complex networks. Science (New York, N.Y.), 298(5594), 824–827

17. Tsumoto, T., & Suda, K. (1982). Effects of stimulation of the dorsocaudal claustrum on activities of striate cortex neurons in the cat. Brain research, 240(2), 345–349; LeVay S. (1986). Synaptic organization of claustral and geniculate afferents to the visual cortex of the cat. The Journal of neuroscience : the official journal of the Society for Neuroscience, 6(12), 3564–3575; Narikiyo, K., Mizuguchi, R., Ajima, A., Shiozaki, M., Hamanaka, H., Johansen, J. P., Mori, K., & Yoshihara, Y. (2020). The claustrum coordinates cortical slow-wave activity. Nature neuroscience, 23(6), 741–753

18. Vervaeke, K., Lorincz, A., Gleeson, P., Farinella, M., Nusser, Z., & Silver, R. A. (2010). Rapid desynchronization of an electrically coupled interneuron network with sparse excitatory synaptic input. Neuron, 67(3), 435–451;Vidyasagar, T. R., & Levichkina, E. (2019). An Integrated Neuronal Model of Claustral Function in Timing the Synchrony Between Cortical Areas. Frontiers in neural circuits, 13, 3

19. Al-Hasani, R., & Bruchas, M. R. (2011). Molecular mechanisms of opioid receptor-dependent signaling and behavior. Anesthesiology, 115(6), 1363–1381

20. Roth, B. L., Baner, K., Westkaemper, R., Siebert, D., Rice, K. C., Steinberg, S., Ernsberger, P., & Rothman, R. B. (2002). Salvinorin A: a potent naturally occurring nonnitrogenous kappa opioid selective agonist. Proceedings of the National Academy of Sciences of the United States of America, 99(18), 11934–11939; Sheffler, D. J., & Roth, B. L. (2003). Salvinorin A: the "magic mint" hallucinogen finds a molecular target in the kappa opioid receptor. Trends in pharmacological sciences, 24(3), 107–109; Chavkin, C., Sud, S., Jin, W., Stewart, J., Zjawiony, J. K., Siebert, D. J., Toth, B. A., Hufeisen, S. J., & Roth, B. L. (2004). Salvinorin A, an active component of the hallucinogenic sage salvia divinorum is a highly efficacious kappa-opioid receptor agonist: structural and functional considerations. The Journal of pharmacology and experimental therapeutics, 308(3), 1197–1203

21. Peckys, D., & Landwehrmeyer, G. B. (1999). Expression of mu, kappa, and delta opioid receptor messenger RNA in the human

CNS: a 33P in situ hybridisation study. Neuroscience, 88(4), 1093–1135

22. Borroto-Escuela, D. O., & Fuxe, K. (2020). On the G Protein-Coupled Receptor Neuromodulation of the Claustrum. Neurochemical research, 45(1), 5–15

23. Lawrence, D. M., & Bidlack, J. M. (1993). The kappa opioid receptor expressed on the mouse R1.1 thymoma cell line is coupled to adenylyl cyclase through a pertussis toxin-sensitive guanine nucleotide-binding regulatory protein. The Journal of pharmacology and experimental therapeutics, 266(3), 1678–1683

24. Henry, D. J., Grandy, D. K., Lester, H. A., Davidson, N., & Chavkin, C. (1995). Kappa-opioid receptors couple to inwardly rectifying potassium channels when coexpressed by Xenopus oocytes. Molecular pharmacology, 47(3), 551–557; Vivaudou, M., Chan, K. W., Sui, J. L., Jan, L. Y., Reuveny, E., & Logothetis, D. E. (1997). Probing the G-protein regulation of GIRK1 and GIRK4, the two subunits of the KACh channel, using functional homomeric mutants. The Journal of biological chemistry, 272(50), 31553–31560; Hibino, H., Inanobe, A., Furutani, K., Murakami, S., Findlay, I., & Kurachi, Y. (2010). Inwardly rectifying potassium channels: their structure, function, and physiological roles. Physiological reviews, 90(1), 291–366

25. Ikeda S. R. (1996). Voltage-dependent modulation of N-type calcium channels by G-protein beta gamma subunits. Nature, 380(6571), 255–258; Law PY, Wong YH, Loh HH. Molecular mechanisms and regulation of opioid receptor signaling. Annu Rev Pharmacol Toxicol. 2000;40:389–430

26. Cunningham, C. W., Rothman, R. B., & Prisinzano, T. E. (2011). Neuropharmacology of the naturally occurring kappa-opioid hallucinogen salvinorin A. Pharmacological reviews, 63(2), 316–347; Che, T., Majumdar, S., Zaidi, S. A., Ondachi, P., McCorvy, J. D., Wang, S., Mosier, P. D., Uprety, R., Vardy, E., Krumm, B. E., Han, G. W., Lee, M. Y., Pardon, E., Steyaert, J., Huang, X. P., Strachan, R. T., Tribo, A. R., Pasternak, G. W., Carroll, F. I., Stevens, R. C., … Roth, B. L. (2018). Structure of the Nanobody-Stabilized Active State of the Kappa Opioid Receptor. Cell, 172(1-2), 55–67

27. Stiefel, K. M., Merrifield, A., & Holcombe, A. O. (2014). The claustrum's proposed role in consciousness is supported by the

effect and target localization of Salvia divinorum. Frontiers in integrative neuroscience, 8, 20

28. Doss, M. K., May, D. G., Johnson, M. W., Clifton, J. M., Hedrick, S. L., Prisinzano, T. E., Griffiths, R. R., & Barrett, F. S. (2020). The Acute Effects of the Atypical Dissociative Hallucinogen Salvinorin A on Functional Connectivity in the Human Brain. Scientific reports, 10(1), 16392

29. Turner, D.M. (1996). Salvinorin: The Psychedelic Essence of Salvia Divinorum, Panther Press.

30. Johnson, M. W., MacLean, K. A., Reissig, C. J., Prisinzano, T. E., & Griffiths, R. R. (2011). Human psychopharmacology and dose-effects of salvinorin A, a kappa opioid agonist hallucinogen present in the plant Salvia divinorum. Drug and alcohol dependence, 115(1-2), 150–155; Maqueda, A. E., Valle, M., Addy, P. H., Antonijoan, R. M., Puntes, M., Coimbra, J., Ballester, M. R., Garrido, M., González, M., Claramunt, J., Barker, S., Johnson, M. W., Griffiths, R. R., & Riba, J. (2015). Salvinorin-A Induces Intense Dissociative Effects, Blocking External Sensory Perception and Modulating Interoception and Sense of Body Ownership in Humans. The international journal of neuropsychopharmacology, 18(12), pyv065

31. Erowid Experience Vaults, Exp. 42505, https://erowid.org/experiences/exp.php?ID=42505

32. Erowid Experience Vaults, Exp. 45012, https://erowid.org/experiences/exp.php?ID=45012

33. MacLean, K. A., Johnson, M. W., Reissig, C. J., Prisinzano, T. E., & Griffiths, R. R. (2013). Dose-related effects of salvinorin A in humans: dissociative, hallucinogenic, and memory effects. Psychopharmacology, 226(2), 381–392

34. Sasha (1993). The Universe Had Ceased To Exist. http://www.sagewisdom.org/ceasedtoexist.html

35. Erowid Experience Vaults, Exp. 42505, https://erowid.org/experiences/exp.php?ID=42505

36. Arthur D Chapman. (2009). Numbers of Living Species in Australia and the World. 2nd edition. Australian Government, Department of the Environment, Water, Heritage and the Arts. Canberra, Australia

Chapter 14.

1. Wacker, D., Wang, S., McCorvy, J. D., Betz, R. M., Venkatakr-ishnan, A. J., Levit, A., Lansu, K., Schools, Z. L., Che, T., Nichols, D. E., Shoichet, B. K., Dror, R. O., & Roth, B. L. (2017). Crystal Structure of an LSD-Bound Human Serotonin Receptor. Cell, 168(3), 377–389

2. Westkaemper, R. B., & Glennon, R. A. (1994). Molecular modeling of the interaction of LSD and other hallucinogens with 5-HT2 receptors. NIDA research monograph, 146, 263–283

3. Monte, A. P., Marona-Lewicka, D., Parker, M. A., Wainscott, D. B., Nelson, D. L., & Nichols, D. E. (1996). Dihydrobenzofuran analogues of hallucinogens. 3. Models of 4-substituted (2,5-di-methoxyphenyl)alkylamine derivatives with rigidified methoxy groups. Journal of medicinal chemistry, 39(15), 2953–2961; Parker, M. A., Marona-Lewicka, D., Lucaites, V. L., Nelson, D. L., & Nichols, D. E. (1998). A novel (benzodifuranyl)aminoalkane with extremely potent activity at the 5-HT2A receptor. Journal of medicinal chemistry, 41(26), 5148–5149

4. Roth B. L. (2016). DREADDs for Neuroscientists. Neuron, 89(4), 683–694

5. Zhu, H., Aryal, D. K., Olsen, R. H., Urban, D. J., Swearingen, A., Forbes, S., Roth, B. L., & Hochgeschwender, U. (2016). Cre-dependent DREADD (Designer Receptors Exclusively Activated by Designer Drugs) mice. Genesis (New York, N.Y. : 2000), 54(8), 439–446

6. Zhu, H., Pleil, K. E., Urban, D. J., Moy, S. S., Kash, T. L., & Roth, B. L. (2014). Chemogenetic inactivation of ventral hippocampal glutamatergic neurons disrupts consolidation of contextual fear memory. Neuropsychopharmacology : official publication of the American College of Neuropsychopharmacology, 39(8), 1880–1892

7. Mannix, R. J., Kumar, S., Cassiola, F., Montoya-Zavala, M., Feinstein, E., Prentiss, M., & Ingber, D. E. (2008). Nanomagnetic actuation of receptor-mediated signal transduction. Nature nanotechnology, 3(1), 36–40; Long, X., Ye, J., Zhao, D., & Zhang, S. J. (2015). Magnetogenetics: remote non-invasive magnetic activation of neuronal activity with a magnetoreceptor. Science bulletin, 60, 2107–2119

8. Strassman R. J. (1996). Human psychopharmacology of N,N-dimethyltryptamine. Behavioural brain research, 73(1-2), 121–124; Strassman, R. J., & Qualls, C. R. (1994). Dose-response study of N,N-dimethyltryptamine in humans. I. Neuroendocrine, autonomic, and cardiovascular effects. Archives of general psychiatry, 51(2), 85–97; Callaway, J. C., McKenna, D. J., Grob, C. S., Brito, G. S., Raymon, L. P., Poland, R. E., et al. (1999). Pharmacokinetics of Hoasca alkaloids in healthy humans. J. Ethnopharmacol. 65, 243–256

9. Strassman, R. J., Qualls, C. R., & Berg, L. M. (1996). Differential tolerance to biological and subjective effects of four closely spaced doses of N,N-dimethyltryptamine in humans. Biological psychiatry, 39(9), 784–795

10. Kenny, G. N. C., and White, M. (1990). A portable computerized infusion system for propofol. Anaesthesia 45, 692–693; Absalom, A. R., Glen, J. B., Zwart, G. J. C., Schnider, T. W., and Struys, M. (2016). Target-controlled infusion: a mature technology. Anesth. Analg. 122, 70–78; Coetzee, J. F. (2012). Principles of intravenous drug infusion. Anaesth. Intensive Care Med. 13, 243–246

11. Bailey, J. M., and Shafer, S. L. (1991). A simple analytical solution to the 3-compartment pharmacokinetic model suitable for computer-controlled infusion pumps. IEEE Trans. Biomed. Eng. 38, 522–525; Gambus, P. L., and Troconiz, I. F. (2015). Pharmacokinetic-pharmacodynamic modelling in anaesthesia. Br. J. Clin. Pharmacol. 79, 72–84

12. Gallimore, A. R., & Strassman, R. J. (2016). A Model for the Application of Target-Controlled Intravenous Infusion for a Prolonged Immersive DMT Psychedelic Experience. Frontiers in pharmacology, 7, 211

13. Strassman, R. (2001). DMT - The Spirit Molecule. Vermont, VT: Park Street Press

14. Leary, T. (1966). Programmed Communication During Experiences With DMT. Psychedelic Review, 8

Ingram Content Group UK Ltd.
Milton Keynes UK
UKHW021536230623
423924UK00011B/115